RIG SHIP for ULTRA QUIET

Living and working on a nuclear submarine at the end of the Cold War

ANDREW KARAM Ph.D.

Published in Australia by
Temple House Pty Ltd,
T/A Sid Harta Publishers
ACN 092 197 192
Hartwell, Victoria

Telephone: 61 3 9560 9920
Facsimile: 61 3 9545 1742
E-mail: author@sidharta.com.au

First published in Australia May 2002
Copyright © Andrew Karam, 2002
Cover design, typesetting: Alias Design
Printed by Shannon Books Melbourne

ISBN: 0 9578709 7 3

Reviews

'Andrew Karam's mission may be fictionalized but life on his submarine is very real and well worth the trip.'
Sherry Sontag, co-author of *Blind Man's Bluff*

'An intense and realistic look into the heart of nuclear submarine operations, superbly written with the clarity of a submariner who has lived through the dangers and challenges deep beneath the seas.'
Roger C. Dunham, M.D., author of *Spy Sub*

'An accurate and entertaining story which provides a real insight into life beneath the waves.'
Kerry B. Collison – author of *Indonesian Gold*

'Karam...writes absorbingly ...the book is most interesting for its insight into the submerged life of 150 men in a steel tube just 85 metres long.'
Michael O'Connor – *Defender*
(National Journal of the Australia Defence Association)

'Andrew Karam, in *Rig Ship for Ultra Quiet*, puts flesh on the bones of the book *Blind Man's Bluff*, in which non-submariners told, for the first time, some of the great tales of Cold War US covert submarine operations. Karam lived the story, and tells of his tours aboard USS Plunger (SSN595), one of the oldest nuclear attack submarines in the US Navy. Karam tells the story from the standpoint of a senior enlisted nuclear specialist, and, as a result, can give the full flavor and complexity of actual SSN operations, as well as the human dimension. The fact that he later became a civilian nuclear specialist and academic in the field gave him the perspective to re-examine his time aboard SSNs. *Rig Ship for Ultra Quiet* covers the gamut of SSN operations during the period 1986-1989, and details how the vessel conducted special operations against the USSR. But Karam's human touch makes the book valuable and enjoyable for professional and non-naval reader alike. If anything, reading *Rig Ship for Ultra Quiet* will make a reading of such books as *Blind Man's Bluff* more valuable, because it sets out a comprehensible frame of reference for those who have only experienced the "skimmer" (surface) navy or have not gone to sea at all. Frankly, with all of its detail on day-to- day operations, crew procedures and other matters, this book is also a valuable reference for the officers of all those developing navies contemplating a submarine arm. *Rig Ship for Ultra Quiet* is a great read, and a bold move for an Australian publishing house to produce for a US and worldwide market. Sid Harta Publishers has best been known for its works on Indonesian politics.'

Greg Copley
Editor-in-chief, Defense and Foreign Affairs Group

'*Rig Ship for Ultra Quiet* provides a real look at life aboard an American nuclear attack submarine just as the Cold War under the oceans was ending. Real means surprisingly tense, but with little excitement. Karam, who spent eight years in the Navy, and weeks at a time on missions on the USS Plunger, captures the essence of life aboard — dull food, dull routines, irritating fellow crewmembers, and the constant desire for uninterrupted sleep. Unlike books by writers who spend at most a few hours on a ship, and rely on interviews to find out what life below is like, *Rig Ship* is a truly first-hand report, written by an intelligent man who does a good job, but does not like the military. A useful antidote to the techno-thriller view of modern warfare.'

Jonathan D. Beard
Science Writer

About the Author

 Andy Karam joined the US Navy in 1981, enlisting for submarine duty in the Naval Nuclear Power Program. An honor graduate from Machinists' Mate school in Great Lakes, Illinois, Andy reported to duty for Naval Nuclear Power School in Orlando, Florida and then to a land-based reactor prototype unit near Saratoga Springs, NY. Andy attended further training, specializing in radiological controls and radiochemistry controls. He reported to the *USS Plunger* (SSN 595) in early 1986, where he was to spend the rest of his enlistment.

Flying to Japan to meet the San Diego-based fast attack submarine, Andy immediately went to sea for a 70 day "special operation" off the coast of the Soviet Union.

In addition to his duties in the engineering spaces, Andy served as the ship's periscope photographer and battle stations periscope assistant for nearly three years, for three spec ops.

Leaving the Navy in 1989, Andy attended college, completing his bachelor's, master's and doctoral degrees and becoming board-certified in radiation safety while working full-time in this field. He has continued working in this profession since leaving the Navy, writing over 30 scientific and technical papers. Andy is currently the Radiation Safety Officer and adjunct member of the faculty at the University of Rochester and an officer of the Health Physics Society."

These experiences have given Andy a unique perspective on submarine life and operations, which he shares through his writing.

Dedication

This book is dedicated to the memories of

Harvey A. Karam, MD, who brought me into the world
Adib Karam, MD, who taught me of the excitement it can hold
Benjamin Auburn, who left us much too soon

And, always, to Alexander and Benjamin
Who may finally be spared listening to stories they can now read.

Acknowledgements

As is the case for any author, I owe thanks and appreciation to many people for their assistance and encouragement during the process of writing this book. I would particularly like to thank my very good friend, Kerry Collison for the enormous part he played in bringing this account to print. Kerry encouraged me to write of my experiences, helped me through the editing process, gave me a few pointed reminders of impending deadlines, and much more. Without Kerry's help there is no doubt that this book would still be nothing more than a lot of illegible scrawling in several notebooks.

I would like to acknowledge my mentors, Mark Auburn, Walter Carey, Gunter Faure, and Audeen Fentiman (in no order other than alphabetical). Anyone would be fortunate to find a single person in a lifetime capable of providing the encouragement, intellectual excitement, guidance, support, and interest each of them have given me for many years. They have been my intellectual parents, my professors, and my friends. I also owe more than I can ever express to my parents, Susan and Phil; my sister, Rebecca, and my other relatives and friends, all of whom have never ceased to amaze me with their support. I am similarly grateful to Vice Admiral N. Ronald Thunman, whose help and support have meant much more to me than I can adequately express.

I decided to write this after giving a lunchtime Brownbag Seminar to the University of Rochester's Biochemistry and Biophysics Department. The genuine interest shown by all attendees gave me the final impetus to sit down and start writing and I am grateful to them all (especially Mr. Brownbag himself, D'Pesh Risal) for listening to my accounts of life underwater with such fascination.

I would also like to thank my family for their patience and good humor during the writing process (well, for that matter, at all times). They have borne well the many nights that I would disappear to clack away at the computer until crawling into bed after 1 in the morning. They have also suffered through with good grace my sea stories, still managing to sound enthralled after the tenth re-telling. In addition, my Navy friends and former roommates Jason Poyer and Tom Simpson have made special efforts to stay in touch over the years, giving me the opportunity to keep these memories fresh through the telling of stories. Finally, I would like to thank the people who read this in draft form. In particular, Tara Narcross and her father (whose name I never have learned), my father Phil and my Evil Step-Mother Ann are to be commended for their literary fortitude. Craig Wheeler, Kathy Jung, Brian Rees, Kinko Ito, and other friends were also kind enough to read early drafts and offer helpful suggestions. Others who have encouraged my writing include Genevieve Roessler, Neil Schlager, Ken Miller, and Rupprecht Maushart, all editors in one capacity or another.

In many respects, I started writing this in February, 1986 when I first reported to the Plunger. Knowing that I would someday want to be able to tell my future children (and to remind myself) what submarine life was like, I began keeping a journal from my first day onboard. All of the characters in this book are based on my shipmates. Some of them I liked, some I didn't. But they taught me how to be a submariner when I first came on board, a favor I tried to repay when I became more senior. Deserving particular mention are my former fellow ELTs, Scott Bolt and Joe St. Martin and my former roommates, Sonar Technicians Don Houck and Scott Olson, who taught me much about sonar. Also deserving special mention are Greg Peterman, our "Bull Nuke"; Bob Wise, Brian Belcher, and Booth Higgins, my former division officer and photo officers, respectively; and Matt Rensch, one of our fire control technicians and veteran of more than a few mutual adventures. Finally, but certainly not least, I would like to thank my Plunger skippers, Gary Gradisnik and Bill Large; XO, Fred Byus; and the Engineer, Dave Burkhard. They never failed to encourage and support me during my time in Plunger, even after realizing that I was a bit atypical, even for a submariner. I did not always enjoy my time onboard, but primarily because I am not, at heart, cut out for the military life. There is no doubt that my time onboard would have been far worse had I served under less capable officers.

One last note: in retrospect, I feel much different about my time in the Navy than I did while I was in. Naval Nuclear Power was a demanding program that expected near-perfection and settled for nothing less. The hours were long, and, after I reported to the Plunger, we spent a lot of time at sea. My personality is not particularly well-suited to the military life, and there were things about military life and the Navy that I did not like. However, from the perspective of more than a decade of post-Navy life, I can say with all honesty and sincerity that I would do it all again, even knowing what I now know. While still in my mid-twenties, I was standing watch supervising the operation of a nuclear reactor and propulsion plant on a fast attack submarine. I had received over a quarter million dollars' worth of training in a program in which over half the candidates were washed out, and I knew many aspects of our plant, and the submarine backwards and forwards. After leaving the Navy,

I have no doubt that I owe whatever professional and academic success I have enjoyed to having been in Naval nuclear power. In fact, in my field of radiation protection, I continually run into ex-Navy nukes, many of whom are succeeding in positions of great responsibility. And, I have to say that I am proud of what I did. There are not many people who have served on submarines, and fewer who helped operate submarine nuclear reactor plants. I am convinced that the work we did helped the US to win the Cold War. We didn't do it alone, but we certainly helped. Finally, I am convinced that my life would be less full, less interesting, and less fulfilling had I not spent those eight years in the Navy. From that perspective, I think that my time in this program, although difficult and frustrating at times, was an investment in the rest of my life, and it was a good one.

Naval Hymn

"Lord God, our power ever more, Whose arm doth reach the ocean floor,
Divine with our men beneath the sea; traverse the depths protectively.
O hear us when we pray, and keep them safe from peril in the deep.

Lord, guard and guide the men who man the submarines that guard our land.
Be with them always night and day, in quiet depths or roaring spray.
O hear us when we cry to Thee, for those in peril on the sea.

Bless those who serve beneath the deep, through lonely hours their vigil keep.
May peace their mission ever be! Protect each one, we ask of Thee.
Bless those at home who wait and pray for their return by night and day."

(Excerpt from "Eternal Father" — the Navy Hymn)

Author's Note

SUBMARINES HELPED THE ALLIES to win the War in the Pacific during World War Two. The submarine force had fewer people, sunk more ships, and had a higher loss rate than any other part of the Navy. During the Cold War, submarines continued this tradition of high return, high-risk missions. About five percent of personnel in the Navy serve on submarines, yet submarines made up nearly half of our warships. Submarines operate alone for the most part, often right at the edge of territorial waters (although the Plunger never crossed into the territorial waters of any unfriendly nation during my time onboard). Many of our missions took us as close to wartime conditions as we were likely to get without being shot at, and anyone who's served on a fast attack submarine is likely to have a Naval Expeditionary Award, given to those who serve at or near the front lines.

This book is, of necessity, a mixture of fact and fiction. Most of the materials relating to life on board a nuclear submarine really happened, although incidents from many different underway periods have been gathered together into this narrative to give a more complete picture of submarine life. Many of the details of my life and my time in the Navy are autobiographical, or nearly so. On the other hand, submarine operations are highly classified, as are the design parameters and operating characteristics of the nuclear power plant, propulsion plant, electronics, and the submarine itself. Because of this, I have provided only that information about submarine capabilities and equipment as can be found in unclassified documents or that was witnessed by family and friends during the four dependents' cruises I participated in. Nowhere in here do I give information regarding the actual design specifications or capabilities of any submarine in the US Navy.

Similarly, our missions were highly classified and, until I know that they have been declassified, I cannot discuss them in print or elsewhere. The incidents I relate are not unlike incidents that occurred during my duty on the USS Plunger, but they did not actually take place as described or at the time of this underway period. However, based on recent books (*Blind*

Man's Bluff, Submarine, The Silent War, and others) it should be apparent that the mission I describe and the incidents in it are not only plausible, but likely to have happened to some submarine at some time. And, in all cases, the actions of the crew, captain, and submarine are not only plausible, but reflect actual training and (to the best of this enlisted man's understanding) tactics.

Finally, a brief note about language. The expression "swear like a sailor" is a well-deserved cliché. However, I have chosen to omit most of the "sailorisms" from this book. I'm not trying to be politically correct or to avoid offense, but let's face it, it gets boring listening to continual swearing and reading it is even worse. So I have limited the swearing in this narrative to occasions that really called for it. For those of you who want the full naval experience, simply make a list of your favorite curse words and foul expressions and insert them after every third word of dialogue with a short string at the beginning and end of each sentence. Punctuate with various other bodily noises and you'll have the full naval conversational experience.

I think this book adds to the existing literature an enlisted man's view of submarine life during one of the most trying types of operations at the tail end of the Cold War. Other outstanding books on submarines and seafaring have been written and some of those are listed in the back of this book. Much has been written about the technical capabilities of our submarines and their missions, but nobody has yet put down on paper what it's like to live on a submarine, what you think when you hear a Soviet submarine pinging you with sonar, how you rig a boat for Ultra Quiet, where 150 men eat in a small steel tube, how to flush a submarine toilet, or any of the other realities of submarine life. I hope this book helps to address these issues and helps the reader better appreciate what takes place in the life of a submariner.

Contents

Author's Note		xv
Introduction:	A Brief Tour of the Boat	3
Chapter 1.	Mission's Start	9
Chapter 2.	Reactor Start-up	19
Chapter 3.	Leaving Port	31
Chapter 4.	At Sea	39
Chapter 5.	Racks and Sleeping	45
Chapter 6.	Working Underway	51
Chapter 7.	Angles and Dangles	59
Chapter 8.	Casualties	69
Chapter 9.	On Station	81
Chapter 10.	Holidays at Sea	91
Chapter 11.	Exercises	97
Chapter 12.	Appendicitis	105
Chapter 13.	ASW Games	111
Chapter 14.	Food and Hygiene	127
Chapter 15.	Halfway Night and other Entertainment	135
Images of USS Plunger and Crew		147
Chapter 16.	Fire	163
Chapter 17.	Officers, Chiefs, and Enlisted Men	177
Chapter 18.	Qualifications	187
Chapter 19.	Bagging the Akula	197
Chapter 20.	Ship's Photographer	203
Chapter 21.	Standing Watch	217
Chapter 22.	Rub-a-dub-dub; Clean Up the Sub (ORSE Preparation)	225
Chapter 23.	ORSE	239
Chapter 24.	Pearl	257
Chapter 25.	The Trip Home - Trim Party!	263
Chapter 26.	Epilogue	271
Appendix A:	A Detailed Tour of the 'Plunger'	283
	Diagram of the 'Plunger'	285
Appendix B:	Glossary of Terms and Abbreviations	297
Appendix C:	Working around Radiation and Nuclear Reactors	301
Appendix D:	History of Ships Named 'Plunger'	305
Appendix E:	A Mother's View of a Dependents' Cruise	307
Appendix F:	Recommended Reading	312

Introduction: a brief tour of the boat

A diagram of the USS Plunger can be found on page 285.

I should probably preface all of this by saying that most fighting vessels in the Navy are called ships. My understanding is that, technically, a ship is any vessel more than 350 feet long and anything shorter is a boat. However, all submarines, regardless of length are called boats. On the other hand, among submariners, we use the terms ship and boat almost interchangeably. This could lead to some acrimony when talking to surface sailors (or, as we called them, skimmers), who tended to take such things seriously. Inadvertently asking a skimmer what boat they were on would, at the least, be answered with a frosty look and words to the effect "My SHIP is the *Neversail*." But we submariners thought skimmers took things much too seriously in general. In this account, I tend to use the terms ship and boat as interchangeably as we did onboard the mighty *Plunger* and, in general, I try to use the same phrasing, figures of speech, and terminology I became accustomed to in my time in the Navy.

I will be talking a lot about what happens in a variety of places on the submarine I was assigned to. In addition, there are a number of terms and abbreviations used in this account. The glossary contains a brief description and explanation of these terms and abbreviations. And now, before we get into our story, I'd like to take the opportunity to briefly show you the submarine in which I served, the *USS Plunger* (SSN 595). A more detailed description of each space is found in the first Appendix.

To start with, the term "*plunger*" dates back to the late 1800s. At that time, it referred to someone with a taste for danger or risk. In fact, Webster's Dictionary carries the definition "1) a person who plunges, or dives, 2) a person who acts hastily or recklessly, especially a rash gambler or speculator." I have recently discovered, too, that the French word, plongier means "diver", and the name of the boat may share this lineage as well. The first submarine named *Plunger* was also the first submarine ordered by the Navy and my guess is that they felt it an appropriate name for such a ship. That *Plunger* failed its acceptance testing, so the first submarine purchased by the Navy was the Holland with another *Plunger* as the second. Teddy Roosevelt rode that *Plunger,* enjoying himself thoroughly, and Ensign Chester Nimitz was one of the skippers of that *Plunger.* The second submarine named *Plunger* made one of the first wartime penetrations into the Sea of Japan, earning thirteen battle stars by war's end. A more detailed description of the former *Plunger*s is found at the end of this volume. The *Plunger* on which I served was the third boat in the Thresher (later Permit) class of submarines. These were the first to take advantage of a hydrodynamic hull, integrated sonar and fire control systems, and to have a modern combat center (called Control) that is still in use in the latest submarines today. In actuality, this was the first class of ships built that were designed to be faster and more effective submerged than on the surface.

All in all, the Mighty *Plunger* was 278 feet long, 30 feet in diameter, and weighs about 4400 tons. Or, to put it another way, it's shorter than a football field and would barely squeeze through the goal posts and weighs nearly ten million pounds fully loaded. Of that space, half is devoted to the reactor and engines. Of the rest, half is taken up with electronics, weapons, air regeneration equipment, storage, tanks for water and diesel fuel, battery, and the like. The remaining quarter of the boat is where the people live, sleep, eat, shower, read, daydream, pray, cook, gripe, and do all the other things that you do at home. For, when we're not in port, this is our office, our gym, our cinema, our church, and our home. And, if anything goes drastically wrong, as happened with the Thresher, the Scorpion, and so many WW II boats, it will be our tomb.

From the pier, you see a low, black shape, rounded, sitting about four feet out of the water. At the forward end rises a small tower, the sail. It is slender, about 12 feet tall, and has large wings, the fairwater planes, sticking out of the sides. Looking aft, the hull shows welding scars, cleats, mooring lines, and other things sticking out of the hull or bolted to it. All the way aft, the hull tapers into the waters of San Diego Harbor, only to have the rudder suddenly rise again to a height of about 5 or 6 feet at the very end of the boat.

The main entry is the weapons' shipping hatch, just aft of the sail. The ladder beneath the hatch ends up in the upper level of the operations compartment (Ops Upper Level). Looking forward you see the Control room just past the ladder down to Ops Lower Level. Immediately to the right when facing forward (the starboard side) is the Nucleonics Laboratory and to the left is the electronic equipment space. Turning around and looking aft are the doors to Sonar and Supply (also on the starboard side, now to your left) while Radio and the Fan Room are on the right (the port side when facing aft). At the end of the passageway is a heavy steel door leading to the engineering spaces.

Once onboard, the first thing that strikes you is the relative lack of color. The passageway in Ops Upper Level is covered with simulated woodgrained paneling, but everywhere else you see white, gray, black, and dull red in the bilges. The only exception to this are the piping systems, which are color-coded for easy identification. So, looking up into the welter of pipes running across the ceiling (or overhead, as we call it), we see white frames, white-painted cable runs, and then a yellow pipe of fuel oil, a blue pipe carrying fresh water for cooling our electronics, or a silver pipe carrying hydraulic fluid. Valve handwheels are similarly colored, but everything else is a symphony of black, white, or gray.

Something else you notice upon entering the submarine is the smell. It's not that bad when we're in port, and even at its worst it's not as bad as diesel boats on a good day. But it's there, and it permeates and saturates clothing, skin, and everything else on board. Even now, more than a dozen years later, I can still catch a whiff of it in my memory. One guy on board was forced to put his clothes in a plastic bag before his wife would let him into the car, and she made him wash everything twice. I kept my civilian clothes in plastic bags while at sea, to try to keep them from smelling too much. It was not a pungent odor, but it was pervasive, and it cannot be described to anyone who has not smelled it.

The next level is a bit longer. From the bow of the boat and going aft we have the Bow Compartment, which contains berthing areas on this level. The Forward 9-Man berthing area is all the way forward along the centerline of the boat. On the port side of the Forward 9-Man is the Bow Compartment berthing and to the starboard is the Chiefs' Quarters, also called the Goat Locker. Set into the deck are hatches leading to the Sonar Equipment Space (forward) and the Diesel Compartment (aft). A watertight door separates the Bow Compartment from the Ops Compartment.

In Ops Middle Level, starting at the watertight door and moving aft, we have the crew's head on the port side of the centerline passageway and the After 9-Man berthing area to starboard. The galley is immediately aft of the After 9-Man with the scullery (for washing dishes and shooting trash overboard) just aft of the galley. This is adjacent to the Crew's Mess, also known as the messdecks. A short passageway running across the boat from the scullery ends in the door to the wardroom, officer's country. Just forward of this passageway (abutting the head) is the ship's office.

Inside the wardroom is a short passageway with the officer's head and two staterooms forward and three staterooms aft. Just past the staterooms is the eating area with a table and the Captain's chair at its head. On surface ships, Officer's Country is pretty much off-limits to enlisted men, without a good reason for entering. Things weren't quite as strict on submarines, and we didn't hesitate to stop by a stateroom when we had to, but we didn't spend any more time in the "O-Zone" that we needed to.

The officer's staterooms are nothing to write home about. One, for the junior-most officers, is barely large enough for the bunks, and the residents had to open the door to dress. Two other staterooms were slightly larger, with enough room for two desks, a wash basin, and small closets for the officers. The Captain and Executive Officer (CO and XO) had more luxurious accommodations - they both had private rooms, each with a desk and sink, and about as much floor space as two telephone booths put together.

Ops Lower Level is reached by descending a ladder just inboard of the crew's head, back up by the watertight door and the After 9-Man. This leads down to the 21-Man berthing area. Aft of the 21-Man is the Torpedo Room, the largest single space on the boat with the exception of the Engineroom. At the after end of the Torpedo Room is Air Regen, containing our atmosphere controls equipment. Immediately behind Air Regen is the Reactor Compartment, not accessible on this level.

The only way into the engineering spaces is through the watertight door on Ops Upper Level. Going through the door takes us into the Reactor Compartment tunnel, a short, heavily shielded passageway that is brightly lit and not at all tunnel-like. It takes us past the entry door to the Reactor Compartment (or RC) and into the Auxiliary Machinery Space (AMS) Upper Level through yet another watertight door. This houses most of the electrical and electronic gear, including many of the reactor monitoring and control equipment. Below is, of course, AMS Lower Level, where more electrical equipment is housed but, more importantly, much equipment for tending to the reactor and steam plants. This is where I stood a great many watches.

Just aft of the AMS is the Engineroom. Entered through a watertight door in AMS Upper Level, the Engineroom houses our air conditioning equipment, propulsion turbines, turbine generators, and propulsion train. To the left (or starboard, since we're facing aft) is Maneuvering, the control room for the reactor, steam, and electrical plants. To port is the lithium bromide air conditioning plant, a temperamental beast that I never was able to master. At the extreme end of the engineroom is Shaft Alley, where the shaft leaves the boat through the hull and shaft seals. The engineroom head (a single toilet in a tiny stainless steel room) is in Shaft Alley on the starboard side of the boat.

Beneath is Engineroom Lower Level, divided into several bays. From forward to aft, they are the main seawater bay, the condensate bay, the lube oil bay, the auxiliary seawater (ASW) bay to starboard, and the lube oil purifier bay to port. This brings us to the very end of the "people tank" on the lowest level of the boat and is as good a place as any to stop.

CHAPTER

1

Mission's Start

GREG HAD APPENDICITIS. This normally would have entailed a trip to the emergency room, a routine surgery, and some follow-up visits to the doctor. The only problem was that we were about 6 days from the nearest hospital, just off the coast of the Soviet Union (in international waters, to be sure, but a fine point that we doubted the Soviets would appreciate fully if they found us), at a depth of over 400 feet, no doctor on board, and most of the Soviet Navy looking for us. And we weren't allowed to pull off station without permission from Pearl Harbor. I was glad I wasn't Greg. We had no doubt he'd live, but we also had no doubt he wasn't going to be very happy for the next month or so until we could pull in. Of course, none of us were doctors or corpsmen – I noticed our sole medical person reading his appendectomy procedure and counting his bottles of antibiotics with a very concerned look. I was glad I wasn't Greg.

This mission had seemed cursed from the start. In the waning days of the Cold War there was no let-up in submarine intelligence operations. We'd been using subs to keep tabs on the Soviets for decades and, until they turned their warheads into reactors, there was no sign of that changing. So, once a year, each fast attack boat would spend up to two and a half months somewhere near the Soviet Union, keeping tabs on the Russians. Our turn this year came over Christmas, New Year's, and (worst of all) Super Bowl Sunday. So the timing of the underway period was the first strike. And then there was our late departure, the equipment problems, the surprise Soviet anti-submarine warfare exercise, and the engineering inspection and audit waiting for us at the end of the trip. But more on all of those later. I should probably introduce myself first, and then explain how we all got to this point.

My name is Andrew Karam and I'm originally from Ohio. Like most Navy Nukes, I went to college for a few years before enlisting, then decided to join the Navy. At the time of this mission, I was 27 years old, in charge of a five-man division that took care of radiation safety and water chemistry controls on our reactor and steam plants. I was designated a first-class machinists mate, qualified in submarines. This was abbreviated MM1/SS and was a relatively senior position. In a crew of 140, a dozen officers, a dozen chief petty officers, and a handful of other "firsts" were senior to me.

This was to be my last mission. I had spent nearly eight years in the Navy, starting with two years of training in nuclear power. This included six months in Orlando, Florida at Naval Nuclear Power School, where we were taught the theory that underlies nuclear reactor operations. After that, I spent another six months at a land-based nuclear reactor, learning to operate a specific power plant that had been built for testing and training. It was a challenging training program, the hardest in the Navy and one of the most difficult in any branch of the service. At the same time, the challenge made completing it that much more rewarding. Following graduation, I was offered a position as an instructor at the prototype plant, spending the next two years teaching students what I had recently learned. Hopefully I won't come across as too full of myself when I say that the top 2% or so of each graduating class were asked to stay on as "staff pickup" instructors. Then, having reenlisted for two additional years, I spent six weeks in a specialty school to learn chemical and radiological controls, and finally headed out to the *Plunger.*

When I reported to *Plunger,* I had been in the Navy for four and a half years and was an MM2, without the "SS" since I had never been to sea before. In my first year on board, I qualified in submarines and passed the exam to become a first class petty officer. A year later, the senior-most person in our division, called the Leading Engineering Technician (or LELT) left, putting me in charge. For the next few years, not much more changed. We went out to sea, did our job, and pulled back into port. Sometimes we played with our fleet in war games, sometimes we went out for our own training, and sometimes we went out to play with the Soviet Navy. And that pretty much takes us to this underway.

When the underway started, we were late leaving port for the first time in four years. Our submarine was old; one of the oldest nuclear submarines in the world at that time. And, on old boats, things break. Electrical fires happen in old wiring. Old compressed air systems spring leaks after years of holding back high pressure. The fresh water plant, seemingly run by voodoo to begin with, would develop a mind of its own. It was a point of pride that the *Plunger* always pulled out on time. On this underway, however, we got a late start because one of our auxiliary machinists mates blew up an air line during a high pressure air charge the day before we were to pull out.

Submarines use compressed air for a lot of things. Pneumatic valves, air supplied to masks worn during fires, firing torpedoes, blowing water out of the ballast tanks for an emergency blow to the surface, and a dozen other uses. As the air was used, we would deplete the air banks (large gas cylinders kept in the main ballast tanks) and, eventually, we'd need to run our air compressor to charge them back up again. For that, we used the on-board high pressure air compressor, also called the HIPAC (pronounced high-pac). There were some potential problems. The HIPAC was noisy, something not desired on a boat trying to be quiet. Sometimes at sea, we'd have to really stretch an air charge until we could make that much noise. In addition, the HIPAC was lubricated with oil. This was seemingly not much of a problem, until you remember that pressurizing air heats it up significantly. If you were doing an air charge and pressurized a section of pipe too quickly, the increase in temperature could ignite residual lube oil present in the air, creating a little single-cylinder, one-shot diesel engine in that pipe. Which is exactly what happened to Lumpy, the Auxiliaryman of the Watch that day.

Lumpy (so named because he was a big, happy, round guy) opened a valve out of sequence and looked down in time to see the pipe start to glow red and split open. He ran for the door into the torpedo room and was picked up by the burst of air from the split pipe and carried another five feet, landing on his belly. The HIPAC ran on, so Lumpy picked himself up, ran back to turn it off, and, because air at that pressure can be deadly, called in the emergency. This was the evening, so the majority of the crew was home, leaving the duty section to clean up the mess, call the Engineer, and start to order new parts. The first most of us heard about it was the next day when we came in. Reactions were mixed, ranging from "What a bonehead" to "Cool! Maybe I can spend Christmas with my kids! Thank you, Lumpy!" My reaction was closer to the first. The submarine currently in our upcoming op area was due to be relieved so they could spend Christmas at home. They'd probably been out for nearly two months already and they'd be running short of food, toilet paper, reading materials, topics of conversation, and patience. Not only would they suffer if we weren't there on time to relieve them, but the crew would never let us hear the end of it when we returned. That'd be embarrassing for the crew, and even more so for the CO. So I had no doubt we'd been granted, at most, a slight reprieve.

In some respects, the timing couldn't have been worse for the single, unattached guys (among whom I counted myself). Two months or so was too long to just leave a car in the parking lot, so I had already taken my car to the storage yard I used where they had put it up on blocks, disconnected the battery, and covered it up. Married guys just went home and guys with girlfriends had either left their cars with their honeys or could call for a ride. I was stuck on base. Plus, I was ready to go. I'd drawn my advance pay, paid all my bills a few months in advance, said my goodbyes to family and friends, updated my will, packed for the trip, and started to distance myself from land. I didn't want to be stuck in the final days before a long underway indefinitely. It was enough to make me wish for rapid repairs.

Thanks to heroic efforts on the part of A-gang (the non-nuclear machinists mates comprise Auxiliary Division, or A-Gang, and are called "A-gangers") we were ready to go. Well, actually, we were ready to go because the Old Man was breathing down the neck of the Engineer, who passed this attention (and a lot of profanity) on to the Damage Control Assistant (the officer in charge of A-Gang), who leaned on the division Chief Petty Officer, who swore and then yelled at the Leading Petty Officer, who yelled back and then screamed at the junior guys who were doing the dirty work. Everyone blamed one of the officers, usually the least popular one above them; in this case, the DCA. And the work went on for nearly 48 hours straight.

While repairs were being made, we were getting everything else ready for a prolonged time at sea. My division took care of water chemistry for the reactor and steam plants as well as doing radiological controls. We stocked up on all the chemicals, reagents, glassware, and analytical equipment needed for two months of radiochemistry at sea, made sure that at least half the expiration dates fell after our anticipated return, and then arranged and rearranged the storage in our nucleonics laboratory to make room for as much personal gear as possible. So we pulled out with two thirds of our storage space filled with pH probes, spare conductivity meters, radioactively-contaminated gauges, chemicals, stainless steel tubing, dosimeters, geiger counters, and the requisite references. The other third was split five ways for civilian clothing, books, tapes, soda, cookies, candy bars, and anything else that would help to make a submarine home for a few months. Meanwhile, the store keepers were doing last-minute stocking of spare parts, the engineering divisions were ordering (or stealing) more tools and other parts from the submarine tender, the more experienced submariners were finding room for their own toilet paper, and the cooks were trying to stack and re-stack 90 days' worth of food for 150 people as efficiently as they could. And, those who were stuck sharing a bunk (called a rack) negotiated storage space and sleeping schedules with their rackmates.

I had bought the books, food, and soda I planned to take out with us. As I had done in the past, I debated the merits of bringing my own toilet paper. The down side was that it took up a lot of space. On the other hand, Navy toilet paper was pretty harsh. I used to joke that we'd never develop hemorrhoids because the toilet paper would just sand them off as they formed. Anyhow, I decided to continue punishing myself, putting the extra space to use for food and books.

I spent some of this time putting the little personal touches on my rack that would make it seem more like home for the next few months. I had a rack-sized quilt and some Snoopy sheets that I used, rather than the standard Navy blankets and sheets. Then there was the small loop of wire that I attached to the wall at the head of the rack to hold my glasses while I slept, rather than risk rolling over on them in my sleep. I stocked my outboard locker with books, a cribbage board, and a few other odds and ends, all organized so I could find them easily, although the locker was nearly impossible to get into without getting out of bed first. And, lastly, I put Pellinore at the head of the bed, just next to my pillow.

Pellinore was a stuffed penguin that had been a gift from a friend several years earlier. I've collected penguins since before joining the Navy; a friend, knowing this, had given me Pellinore as a gift a year before I reported to the *Plunger.* In that time, he had made two WestPacs with me and this would be his second Surge Op. A bit odd? Not really. Many of the guys onboard had something similar, whether given to them by their kids, a girlfriend, or selected themselves.

The most interesting was Garth Miles, a cabbage-patch doll that belonged to our Chief Torpedoman. In his spare time, he'd make clothes for Garth. By now, Garth had a full set of Navy uniforms, including a very good set of the dress blue "crackerjacks" made during the last spec op we'd been on. Plus the dungaree working uniform, a sea bag, and even a Garth-sized copy of Playboy, made of small photos inside a miniature cover. My favorite Garth Miles story was the previous year when we were at the Navy base in Yokosuka, Japan. The Chief was carrying Garth across the base, both in their uniforms, when they passed a Marine Captain. The Chief gave a snappy salute, which the Marine returned. Then, he reached down and put Garth's hand into a salute. The Marine stopped and stared. The Chief waited a second, then snapped "This sailor just saluted you, Sir. Are you going to return his salute?" The Marine saluted, then walked off, shaking his head sadly while the Chief walked away chuckling.

One of the things that always struck me anew each time I packed for an extended underway was just how cramped our living spaces were. Not only did we have a small rack and a minuscule amount of personal storage space, but the berthing areas were tiny, and racks were crammed in everywhere possible. This was all before the recent efforts to integrate women into warships as well as onto auxiliary vessels, so we didn't devote much thought to the prospects of sharing our ship with female sailors. Looking at matters from this perspective, however, makes me wonder how the Navy will eventually achieve this goal. First, I need to point out that I am not against women in the military, in combat roles, as commanding officers, or anything else. One of my first commanding officers was a female admiral, which was enough to strike any such thoughts from my mind. That was at the Navy Training Center in Orlando. Orlando was also where all Navy women went through Boot Camp, so I knew first-hand how touchy the Navy was about propriety in relations between men and women. This included separate berthing areas and separate heads so that men and women could sleep, change clothes, shower, and go to the restroom in single-sex areas. The berthing areas could be managed, but there was no way that the *Plunger* had enough room for a women's head, and trying to establish usage hours for the showers and toilets would not go over well. In other words, the practical difficulties of integrating women onto the *Plunger* would have been great, and I imagine that (with the possible exception of the Trident-class boomers) just about any fast attack boat would have similar problems. Which is too bad, having spent some time on a Reserves frigate, I would definitely prefer to be on a submarine in wartime.

We ended up with some new people during this time, too. Just their luck; had we pulled out on time, they would have had a two month vacation before flying to Hawaii to meet the boat. Now, they had only a few days to get their families settled in (the married ones), pack, and leave for two months. The older guys were walking around with peeved expressions while the younger guys didn't know enough to realize their bad luck. They were excited to finally be going out to sea. They didn't stop to think that there's always lots of sea time to go around; it's the shore time that's important to take.

I ran into one of the new guys walking down the pier. He made some comment about the fact that seagulls seemed to love perching atop the raised masts and scopes. I gave him a conspiratorial look.

"Actually, those aren't really gulls," I said. "They're really decoys."

"What do you mean, decoys?"

"We spend a lot of time near the Soviet Union, just like in this mission coming up. If we stick a scope or radio mast up, we don't want it to be seen because that'll give away our position and we could end up being depth-charged. So what we do is to put a fake gull at the top of the masts. That way, if anyone looks our way, they'll just see a seagull and they won't think twice about it."

"Wow! That's a great idea!" He looked at the masts with new-found respect. "Wait a minute – that one just flew off!"

I started laughing. "OK, so I lied. How convincing do you think it'd be to have the Soviets look over and see a gull sitting ten feet in the air, moving across the water at five knots with its wings folded? It might give us away."

He looked chagrined, then started to laugh along with me. "I guess that would be pretty stupid, wouldn't it?"

A few days later, I ran into the same guy (I hadn't learned his name yet; he was a coner and we were too busy for all the niceties). This time he was apparently looking for something and having trouble finding it. "What's wrong?" I asked.

"I'm trying to learn my way around the boat. I was told that this piece of equipment would be on the port side of the boat, but I can't remember which side that is."

On all ships, port is the left side of the ship or boat as you're facing forward and starboard is the right side. This avoids confusion. If you tell someone that something's to their right, you have to know which way they're facing but if you tell them it's on the starboard side, it doesn't matter. As long as they remember which way is forward. The usual way to remember the difference is that port and left both have four letters. But that was too easy. "OK, first you have to face forward. Do you know which was is forward?"

"Yeah – it's this way." He pointed forward.

"Right – forward is towards the round end of the boat. Aft is the pointy end. Just the opposite of skimmers. Now, remember that port and starboard refer to your left and right as you're facing forward on the boat. So, if you're facing aft, you have to reverse the side of your body they're on. And the way I always remember is that port and left both have the letter T and starboard and right both have the letter R in them. OK?"

"That makes sense. Thanks!" He started to walk away, obviously reviewing this new information in his mind. I watched him carefully. Eight steps and he slowly came to a stop, then turned around with a confused look. "Wait a minute, 'right' has a T in it, too. And 'port' has an R in it, just like starboard. How did that go again?"

"Like I said. Port and left both have Ts and starboard and right both have Rs in them."

"But that doesn't work!"

I looked confused. "Why not? It works for me."

"Because port, starboard, left, and right all have a T in them. And port, starboard, and right all have an R. Now I don't know what's happening."

I chuckled. "Hmm. I guess you're right. Well, try this one…" and I gave him the standard version.

"OK, that one makes more sense. You had me going there for a minute." He was so earnest, it almost wasn't any fun messing with him. But we find fun where we can.

Actually, this was also part of a long tradition of messing with fresh young faces. Hazing, of course, was out of the question, and even relatively minor forms were now strictly forbidden. Two examples of "minor" hazing were the practices of "tacking on" certain insignia. For example, when a person completed his qualifications in submarines, he was given the submariners' insignia, a pair of dolphins and the conning tower (the "sail") of a submarine. One tradition was for submarine-qualified shipmates to "tack on" the dolphins by hitting the newly qualified sailor on the chest. Most of the time, this was a gentle tap, but some really hauled off. In my case, one particularly enthusiastic sailor had driven the pins through the back of the holder and into my chest. Over the years, however, examples of abuse of this and other traditions resulted in the Navy officially banning them, and they were ending during my time on active duty. The good part, of course, is that doing so helped make the Navy a somewhat more civil (and civilized) place, but I can't help feeling as though each such tradition that is curtailed takes with it some of the history of the submarine service (and the

Navy as a whole). This is not to say that I condone some of the physical harm that was done. However, we are all the sum of our history, whether as individuals, nations, or professions. It is a shame that the small fraction of those who abused this particular tradition led to the abandonment of this particular part of our Naval history.

As far as messing with the minds of our newbies, this had still not been shown to cause lasting distress, so we were permitted to continue. I tended to avoid the more traditional gags, but my "colleagues" felt no such compunctions. So we'd sometimes have new guys coming back to the engineroom asking for 25 feet of shoreline, or looking for lubrication for the military bearings, or "relative bearing grease", and the like. It was generally harmless fun, and usually just left the "newbies" feeling like idiots when they caught on to the joke.

CHAPTER 2

Reactor Start-up

One ship, one crew, one shaft, one screw.
Attributed to *Plunger* sailors too numerous to mention.

TWO DAYS LATER, I woke at 3 AM, dressed in my working dungaree uniform, and trudged down to the boat for a reactor start-up. I am not a morning person. I would rather see the sun rise before going to bed than to do so just after waking up. I absolutely hated early-morning underway times because the reactor startup had to begin about 6 hours before getting underway. So I walked to the boat through the chill of the San Diego night, cursing the Navy, the Engineer, the Senior Chief who assigned me to the start-up section, and everything that might have had a bearing on my current state of sleep and caffeine deprivation. I especially cursed the coners (the nickname given by nukes to non-nukes because they worked in the forward, conical end of the boat). But then, all nukes cursed the coners during a reactor start-up. We showed up at 3 AM to startup the reactor plant while they waltzed onboard at 8:30, just in time to kiss their wives, stow their gear, take their watch, and shut the hatch. It just wasn't fair. There was some degree of nuke-coner antipathy, but not as serious as I had heard about on other boats. Still, the CO tried to promote the "One ship, one crew" line, trying to get us all to stop using the terms and to think of ourselves as one happy family.

I groggily made my way past the topside watch, down the weapons' shipping hatch just aft of the sail, and deposited my jacket in my lab at the base of the ladder. I continued on down to the crew's mess at the foot of the ladder (actually a stairway, this time) to the middle level of the Operations Compartment. I poured myself a cup of coffee and tried to pay attention as the pre-startup briefing was given. The only part I cared about was finding out which watchstation I had for the startup. That would determine my workload for the next several hours.

"Karam; ELT." Great! That meant I could catch a few hours of sleep on the floor of Nucleonics before I was needed. Eventually I'd have to help adjust boiler water chemistry, post radiation warning signs, take the start-up reactor water sample, and do a host of other things. But for now, I could sleep a little more. I decided to throw the rest of the vile coffee away, let myself into my lab, and lay down on the floor. The floor space was five feet long, two feet across, and consisted of thin linoleum on top of steel decking. Stainless steel storage cabinets and drawers rose to waist height, and equipment was strewn all over the counters and deck. I'm 6'3", so I normally tried to sleep on the counter, feet next to the dosimetry reader and head near the lead shield (or pig) of the radiation counting system. Not this time, however; the only open space was on the floor. I was asleep in two minutes.

"Whoop! Whoop!" It was the phone in the lab going off, interrupting my sleep. I woke up, tried to figure out where in the hell I was, then stood up. I was in my late 20's, so sleeping on the floor or the stainless steel countertop was no great hardship. I remembered what we were up to and looked at my watch. Six AM, so they should be just about ready to start pulling rods. I answered the phone "Nuke Lab, ELT."

"Nucleonics, Maneuvering. Commenced reactor startup 0558."

"Commenced reactor startup at time 0558, Nuke Lab aye." I made a note in my logs, stretched (as much as possible when you're my height on a submarine), and briefly considered trying to catch another few hours of sleep. I decided, instead, to get some breakfast. The nukes were the first up for an underway, the cooks were next. Actually, in all fairness, the duty section had been up all night. The reactor operators (electronics technicians who'd been through Nuke School) were busy on the pre-critical checklist. They'd spent six hours or more checking the position of every one of hundreds of switches, the operation of all the reactor plant monitoring instruments and controls, and making sure we could start up and (more importantly) shut down the reactor in case of some emergency. The mechanical operators (more intelligent, in our opinion, nuclear-grade counterparts to A-Gangers) had been draining some water tanks, filling others, lining up valves, and preparing the lube oil systems for the next few months of operations. My duty ELT was sampling steam generators, drawing the final pre-startup reactor water sample, and filling in wherever the mechanics needed help. And the electricians were making sure we could transfer thousands of amps from shore power to ship's power at the right moment. And that reminded me; I had to relieve the duty ELT.

Every ship has both in-port duty sections and at-sea watch sections. On a fast attack submarine, the engineering department will consist of about 50 men; about 35-40 nukes and the rest in A-Gang and Interior Communications. In port, we were divided into three or four sections of roughly equal manning. Every day a different section would have duty, responsible for standing watch and doing maintenance after normal working hours. During the working day, everyone was working, and the duty section was stuck picking up loose ends, finishing jobs, and sleeping on board. At any one time there would be the Shutdown Roving Watch, the Shutdown

Reactor Operator, and the Shutdown Electrical Operator actively roaming the spaces and taking logs on what equipment remained operational in port. In addition, there was an Engineering Duty Officer, an Engineering Duty Petty Officer, and a Duty Engineering Laboratory Technician on call. All of the watches went by their initials, so we had the SRO, SEO, ELT, EDPO, SRW, and EDO taking care of business.

Before commencing a reactor startup, the engineering duty section had to be relieved by the engineering watch section. People standing shutdown watches aren't allowed to do anything except monitor equipment, unless there's an emergency. Equipment operations were performed by the off-watch personnel. In practice, a lot of people did stuff, especially at night to avoid having to interrupt the few hours of sleep you might get on a duty day. But, in order to start up the reactor and steam plant, a lot of work had to be done. So, before starting to pull the control rods and so, start up the reactor, the engineering duty section (who could only take logs) had to be relieved by the engineering watch section. And, if they were pulling rods, I was late relieving the duty ELT. So I hurried aft to try to find him.

Mackin was the junior-most person in my division, one reason I hadn't worried much about relieving him late. But, trying to be considerate, I listened to the turnover he gave me, then we both headed forward for breakfast. Whether underway or at sea, the ELT is more a state of being than an actual watch station. Not tied to any single location, the ELT was responsible for analyzing daily reactor plant water samples, doing all radiation surveys, adding chemicals to the reactor plant, checking instrument operability, and a host of other routine and semi-routine duties taking him all over the boat. A disorganized ELT could go for days without sleeping while an organized one could finish his whole day's work in three hours or so. Anyhow, this all means that, of all the engineering department watches, the ELT was the only one who was not tied to the engineering spaces. In this case, this was a good thing. I was hungry and under-caffeinated.

Halfway through the swill, the Crew's Mess phone whooped. Someone answered it, spoke briefly, then yelled to me "Andy – you're wanted in Maneuvering." I decided it probably wasn't very important and finished eating. After breakfast, I sent Mackin to the rack to get some rest before we got underway while I went back to Maneuvering (the engineering control room) to get my logs caught up and see what they wanted. I stopped at the door, pulled aside the naugahyde curtain, and unhooked the steel chain. The chain was to delineate Maneuvering from the rest of the Engineroom – you needed to explicitly ask permission to cross the chain into Maneuvering. The curtain was to protect the Maneuvering area watchstanders, so we had been told. Apparently someone ran some simulations and determined that, in the event of a major steam leak in the Engineroom, the curtain would keep the Maneuvering area watchstanders alive long enough to save the boat. After that, they'd probably die, but the rest of the crew would survive. In theory. "Engineering Officer of the Watch, request permission to enter Maneuvering as summoned."

"Enter Maneuvering. Where the hell have you been?"

"Did you try the crew's mess? I was eating breakfast. What did you want."

"Well, we've been pulling rods for ten minutes."

"I knew that. Are we critical yet?" Reactor criticality is actually a desired state. When a reactor is critical it simply means it's at the point where the control rods are pulled far enough out of the core that the number of neutrons from fission is constant. It's a physics term. A reactor won't run if it's not critical because there aren't enough fissions taking place. Most of us in nuclear power laugh at TV and movie scenes where people are running around shouting "Oh my God! The reactor's critical!" In fact, during low-power physics testing once, we spent nearly two weeks with the reactor critical, producing about enough power to heat a pot of coffee. But criticality is important because it means the reactor is running on its own. After that, it's just a matter of how much power the thing's putting out. One way to tell if the reactor is critical is to pull the control rods out slightly ("shim" them out). If the reactor power meters show a small increase and then sink back down again, the reactor is still sub-critical. If power bumps up a tad and stays there, or keeps increasing slowly, the reactor is critical.

"We're not critical yet. Ought to be in another five minutes."

"More like ten. Sir." That was the reactor operator, or RO. He was shimming rods while watching his instruments. Part of the pre-crit was predicting how far we'd have to pull rods to reach criticality. A good RO would be within a few tenths of an inch. Knowing who calculated the Estimated Critical Position (ECP) and the speed you could pull rods gave a rough time of criticality. The Engineering Officer of the Watch (EOOW) was pretty new and the RO was one of our best. I trusted him more. Now, time for some EOOW training.

"So why are you calling all over the place for me? I logged pulling rods. I relieved the duty ELT. Rad areas are posted (well, not really, but I wasn't going to tell him that). And I was trying to get some food and coffee before we pull out. I don't even bother my pets when they're eating. Sir. So do you have anything happening that I need to know about?"

I didn't hate junior officers (JOs); I just didn't respect them. They knew enough to be cocky and dangerous, but not enough to know their limits. I figured I was supposed to train them, and no lessons seemed to sink in as quickly as those accompanied by some degree of embarrassment. It wasn't polite, but it was effective. I wasn't allowed to socialize with the officers and I wasn't going to write them when we parted company. All I cared about was that they learned how to be safe as quickly as possible. And the best way to be safe was to have them realize that the senior enlisted men knew a lot more about the actual operations than they ever would. We did it for a living, and they were just passing through. So I used every tool I had to train them as quickly as possible.

"Uh, I guess not. But…."

I turned and left before he could finish and went forward where I posted all the radiation areas. Nine minutes later I heard the loudspeaker announce "The reactor is critical." I made a note in my logs.

After criticality, the next step was to continue pulling rods to raise reactor power to a useful level. Nuclear reactors work by fissioning uranium atoms. This is done by neutrons that strike atoms of uranium and cause them to break into two parts, called fission fragments. Neutrons are generated spontaneously in a shutdown reactor, but control rods, made of neutron-absorbing materials, soak up the neutrons before they can cause fissions. Pulling rods allows part of the reactor fuel to be exposed to the neutrons, causing some atoms to fission. In addition to fission fragments, neutrons are produced and these, in turn, are absorbed by other uranium atoms, causing still more fissions. Before the reactor is critical, the number of neutrons produced from fission steadily drops with time, like a ball slowly rolling to a stop. At criticality, the number of neutrons produced by fission remains exactly the same over time. At this point, pulling rods further will allow more fissions to occur by exposing increasingly more of the reactor fuel to the neutron flux. Since reactor power is related to the number of fissions taking place, pulling rods also increases reactor power. Each time the rods are shimmed, neutron flux increases for a short time and then stabilizes at a new, higher power. Eventually, the reactor is putting out enough juice to start heating the large quantities of water that comprise the reactor plant. This is called the point of adding heat (abbreviated POAH) and it is the next milestone in a reactor startup. At the POAH, the reactor is finally doing useful work and, at that point, you can start to turn turbines. That was the next log entry I made.

While it's mostly the RO's show until the POAH, nobody's really relaxing except, maybe, the Electrical Operator (EO). An engineering watch section is comprised of 11 people. They are the Reactor Operator, Electrical Operator, Throttleman, and Engineering Officer of the Watch, all in Maneuvering, Engineroom Upper Level (ERUL), Engineroom Lower Level (ERLL), Engineroom Supervisor (ERS), Machinery Space Upper Level (AMSUL), Machinery Space Lower Level (AMSLL), Auxiliary Electrician Aft (AEA), and Engineering Watch Supervisor (EWS). Of these, the RO and AMSUL are manned by electronics technicians (ET) who operate the reactor controls in and out of Maneuvering. The EO and AEA are electricians mates (EM), operating and maintaining all of the electrical systems, and the Throttleman is either an EM or an ET. The three engineroom watches and AMSLL are stood by machinists mates (MM) and, since the AMSLL watch usually maintains boiler water chemistry, he is usually an MM who has qualified as an ELT. The EWS is a supervisory watch that can be stood by a senior member of any specialty and the EOOW is the lone officer in the engineering spaces.

During a reactor startup, the RO and AMSUL are busy starting up and monitoring the reactor and the engineroom watches are lining up valves, draining some water storage tanks, filling others, readying the propulsion and electrical generating turbines, starting up the lube oil systems, and otherwise getting the engineroom ready to receive high-temperature and high-pressure steam. The AMSLL watch is busy getting ready to feed high-pressure water into the boilers (also called steam generators) and is watching the steam generators, while the EWS and EOOW coordinate and supervise the whole intricate procedure. That leaves the EO and AEA to monitor shore power until we start making our own electricity, and the throttleman typically just stands at the throttles, taking logs and helping with communications because, until we're ready to go, there just isn't much else to keep him occupied.

The entire reactor and engineroom startup procedure is tightly scripted from start to finish by Naval Reactors (the group that oversees all Naval nuclear reactors). Everything that takes place happens by the book, and the book is the ultimate authority. In this case, "the book" is the Reactor Plant Manual (RPM) and it takes up about eight feet of bookshelf in each of six locations on the boat. The RPM included technical specifications and descriptions of every piece of equipment in the reactor and propulsion plants as well as exhaustive operating procedures for all conceivable routine and non-routine operations we might be called upon to perform. Some procedures were used daily, others once every 15 years or so. But they were all there. Something as complex as a startup was controlled valve by valve, switch by switch, and action by action from Maneuvering, mostly under the direct supervision of the EWS. Although this level of control was often irritating and slow, it was also necessary. Everything we did and said was with a high degree of deliberation and accuracy because mistakes could be deadly. I, and just about every other nuke, had read the RPM nearly cover-to-cover while a student at the prototype, and then read it again after reporting to my boat.

While all this was going on, I was in AMSLL with the watchstander there, one of my ELTs. For the most part, we just followed the progress of the startup by listening to the loudspeaker announcements and conversations on the engineering phone circuit. Our actions wouldn't start for a little while yet. Once the reactor reached the POAH, things started to happen more quickly.

The RO keeps pulling rods all the way to the POAH. After that, the reactor will start to maintain its own power level, based on what it's asked to do. Speeding up will draw more steam from the steam generators. This pulls more heat from the reactor coolant, making it colder. Colder water helps to make more neutrons able to cause fissions, so this causes reactor power to increase. If reactor power overshoots steam demand, the coolant starts to heat up, dropping power back to the level that's needed. This is a long-winded way of saying that, after the POAH, the RO is pretty much done with his busy work and it's time for everyone else to get started.

The first thing that happens is that we have to let steam into the engineroom. There are big valves that keep the steam inside the steam generators when we're not operating. This is necessary because we usually keep the reactor plant hot even while shutdown so that, if necessary, we can get underway more quickly in an emergency. By hot, I mean hotter than boiling temperatures. But we also have to do maintenance when the reactor's shut down, and we might need to isolate the steam generators from the rest of the engineroom in case of an emergency. So there are big valves, called the main steam stops, that serve to shut off the flow of steam. Since each valve in the engineering plant is uniquely identified by a number and the system name, the main steam stops were called Main Steam 1 and Main Steam 2.

So large are these valves, in fact, that it's almost impossible to open them with full steam generator pressure (over 400 psi) on one side and no pressure on the other. So the first step is to open smaller bypass valves to allow steam to flow around the steam stops, heat up downstream piping, and equalize pressures. That was the next order from Maneuvering, "Bypass and equalize pressure around Main Steam 1 and 2." All through the engineering spaces we could hear the steam hissing through the pipes. Steam entered the engineroom for the first time in over a month. I made another entry in my logs.

It took several minutes to warm up the piping and raise pressure to the point at which we could open the steam stops, but within ten minutes, that order came. The throttleman turned a switch on his control panel and hydraulics forced the valves open. The next order went out to startup the port and starboard main engines and both turbine generators. These tubines, spinning at several thousand RPM each, would provide propulsion and electricity to the submarine for the next two months. At this point, too, the EOOW was less involved in procedures, turning over supervision of these activities to the EWS and ERS. The whine of spinning turbines and pumps spread through the engineering spaces as, one by one, more equipment was brought on line.

Unlike commercial plants, nuclear or otherwise, we did virtually everything by hand. Valves were opened by hand at the correct time, pumps were manually prepared and started, turbine speeds manually controlled, and all parameters watched by human eyes. I tried describing this to a friend's father once, a man who made his living designing and selling power plants. Our conversation went something like this:

"Well, who pushes the buttons to start up the engines? Is it someone in the control room?" "Nobody pushes the buttons. People do everything locally, one valve at a time." "You mean there's someone on the floor actuating hydraulic and pneumatic valves?" "No, I mean there are people actually in the middle of the plant, turning valves by hand during a startup, spinning the turbines, sweating, and working during a startup." Long silence. "You mean you actually still do things manually? Wow."

The Navy viewpoint (which I came to appreciate) was that the only way to truly understand the plant was to operate everything manually, to take all logs manually, and to just spend your time watching and operating the machinery. This way, if we had a problem or started taking battle damage, the people on watch would know exactly where to go to cross-connect or isolate systems. They'd know which gauges were important, where they were, and what they normally read, and they'd have a better chance of fixing things before we sank. We may have been over-manned and under-automated by industry standards, but commercial plants don't have to go into battle and survive. What we did was the best way to assure our survival should the worst happen.

We were starting to work in AMSLL, too. We still had no pumps running to force water into the steam generators, but steam was being taken to run the turbines. Although we had raised water levels significantly above normal operating levels when the plant was shut down, starting up the engineroom took a lot of steam. So water levels were falling and, if they fell too far, we could have some problems. In addition, chemicals in the boiler water, added to minimize corrosion, were starting to become more concentrated as water levels dropped. The duty ELT had adjusted chemistry the night before, to reduce concentrations as low as possible, but we still worried that we might end up with high levels. At this point, though, all we could do was to watch water levels drop and hope we could start a main feed pump before they got to be too low. Starting a feed pump, though, took a lot of juice, about 1000 amps, and had to be done carefully to make sure the power surge didn't trip off any other equipment. So we waited and watched the generator water levels drop.

Finally, the word came down to start the Number 1 Main Feed Pump. This single pump drew more electrical current than my entire house does now, and it could pump high pressure water at a rate of several hundred gallons a minute. In fact, it drew so much current when it first started up that we had to make special arrangements in the boat's electrical system to avoid tripping breakers and dumping off other important electrical loads. At sea, with the electrical plant in a more stable configuration and both turbine generators operating, starting a feed pump was a piece of cake; during a reactor and steam plant startup, it was far from being a trivial operation.

The valve line-ups had been completed long ago, so the AMSLL watch repeated the order verbatim, deliberately placed his hand on the correct switch, paused a second to make sure he and I both agreed he was starting the correct pump, and turned it to the "start" position. With an initial screech, the pump started turning. We opened the outlet valve and started feeding the steam generators, returning their water level to normal. Under normal operating conditions, regulating valves operated automatically to maintain steam generator water levels at the correct height. However, at very low powers, this system was a bit flaky, so we stationed a person to operate these valves manually. Once power increased enough, we'd turn it over to the machinery, but until then, it took a careful touch and a good feel for the system to do it right. It was something I'd become competent at over the past few years, but others took it as a personal challenge and were better. My next log entry was "Commenced feeding port and starboard steam generators."

I helped the AMSLL watch to sample the water chemistry on both steam generators and, satisfied that they were both all right, I returned to my lab to start getting ready for my post-criticality reactor water sample. Preparation would take me about an hour because I'd chosen to eat breakfast instead of getting right on it, but the sample didn't have to be taken immediately. While I was doing that, the rest of the crew was starting to arrive and to prepare their spaces and gear to go to sea. It was now about 8 AM and we were five hours into the startup.

In the engineroom, watchstanders were hard at work on the turbines. The main propulsion turbines and turbine generators spin at thousands of RPM. That puts a lot of stress on them. Heating them suddenly to several hundred degrees is even more stress. The process of warming them up and spinning them slowly takes some time, but the alternative is, as someone once put it, "High turbine blade particulate levels in the engineroom." In other words, if we're not careful, the turbine blades can come off, slice through the steel casing, and cause a lot of trouble. To call it an elaborate dance would be to mislead, for the choreography is not so precise nor the timing so certain. More appropriate an analogy, perhaps, is a fight scene in a movie; planned, outcome certain, but never the same no matter how well rehearsed, and with a lot of sweat and swearing along the way. Done well, it can be almost as satisfying as sex; done poorly, it's like a long, bad dream.

Eventually, the word comes in to Maneuvering "Port and starboard main engines ready to answer all bells" followed by "Port and starboard turbine generators ready for electrical loading." Ship's power is shifted from shore power to internal generators and the shore power cables are disconnected and taken to the pier. Fresh water and sewer lines, telephones and cable TV are disconnected, and we are free of our umbilical lines. All that's left is to take the tugs, cast off our mooring lines, and start off.

All the while, the pier is filling with wives, children, and girlfriends coming to say goodbye to their fathers, husbands, or lovers for two months. I rush topside, not to say goodbye to anyone (because I have nobody to see me off), but to photograph those who do have someone to kiss and hug. Another of my duties is that of ship's photographer, and taking these going-away pictures is one of the reasons I stand ELT as my reactor start-up watchstation. There are tears, reassurances, kisses, and last-minute kindnesses, and then the men must come aboard. The brow is lifted, cutting all access to the pier, and the CO orders all lines cast off. There is poignancy here as those whose work keeps them topside are too busy for any more goodbyes, and everyone else must go below. I'm the only one topside who's not working, and perhaps the only one who notices the un-returned waves of farewell from the pier. The tug pulls us away from the pier, the lines are coiled and stowed, and we move into the harbor. And, as I look, I notice a tear in the eye of the XO, a 17 year veteran.

"It must be difficult, to leave your family like that, XO," I say, trying to understand.

"It never gets any easier, Petty Officer Karam. It never gets easier." He looks to shore once more, trying to pick his wife and sons out of the crowd, looks down at the deck, and goes back to work. On board, there are those who will miss a child's birth, first steps, report cards, illnesses, and all the other triumphs and setbacks that go into a childhood. They will be missed, venerated, cursed, loved, wondered about, and hated. And, for the next two months, neither they nor their family will know anything about the other. The main engine starts and the water boils aft. We enter the channel, cast off the tug, and head to sea. I, too, stare briefly at the pier, wondering what it would feel like to leave a loved one behind. Then I head below to my lab.

CHAPTER 3

Leaving Port

Manly men are we...sailing for adventure on the big, blue, wet thing.
Fozzie Bear and the crew of the Hispanola (from Muppet Treasure Island)

WE HAD SET THE MANEUVERING WATCH about an hour ago. The most dangerous time for any ship is entering or leaving port. The wide ocean narrows down to a harbor entrance and shipping channel that all traffic must use, so ships get crowded together. On top of that, submarines are black and low to the water. Aside from the sail, only four feet of our boat was visible above the waves; not much to see. So we put every possible person on watch and all the rest on standby in the crew's mess. The theory was that, during this riskiest period, we had people throughout the ship, ready to help in case someone ran into us. My whole time on board was free of incident in the respect, but I never begrudged the maneuvering watch – it was less inconvenient than sinking. Luckily, the submarine base in San Diego is on Point Loma, at the entrance to the harbor, so the maneuvering watch was short. A half hour or so after casting off the tug the word came over the loudspeakers "Secure the maneuvering watch, set the underway watch, section 2." Throughout the boat, crew members put up the phones they'd been manning and started getting to where they needed to be. I was lucky this underway; I was the underway ELT, so I could not only set my own schedule (for the most part), but had a bunk to myself, to boot. Luxurious, no, but not bad for a submarine. For the next two months I wouldn't have to share my rack with anyone, could pretty much choose my own schedule, and might actually get more than four hours of sleep at a time.

The first thing I always did as soon as we secured the maneuvering watch was to go to my rack and change to my underway clothes. In port, we wore our working uniforms; dungaree bell bottoms, a blue chambray work shirt, white t-shirt, black work boots, and either a ship's ball cap or a navy white hat (which we called a Dixie cup). At sea, things were a little more relaxed. We could wear whatever shirts we wanted, any leather or cloth shoes (no plastic or other flammable materials allowed), and whatever hats we happened to have. We could also change into our "poopy suits", one-piece dark blue coveralls. I changed into my poopy suit, some topsiders, and my Albert Einstein sweatshirt, then headed back to my lab.

I had been topside before when we were leaving San Diego and I enjoyed it. Granted, a submarine is not a pleasure craft, and I have never been on any other ship or boat at sea, but I could see the attraction. There was a pleasure in standing on the bridge or on the fairwater planes under the South California sun, watching the pleasure craft and working boats glide past, and marveling at the purity of the blue and cloudless sky. True, there was always conversation among the watchstanders – the Officer of the Deck passing orders through the phone talker regarding our course and speed, the watchstanders talking between themselves, but every so often, all would become quiet except for the waves curling up over the bow of the boat and slipping down the side of the hull. Sometimes accompanied by dolphins or porpoises, some of the time alone, we were once followed by a whale for a mile or so before it broke off to pursue its own business. Even on a warship, there was a sense of peace when we pulled out that I always treasured.

This time, however, I was stuck below, getting ready to take my reactor coolant sample. I finished up my pre-sample instrument checks, got my gear together, and called Maneuvering to request permission to draw the sample. I received permission to do so and headed back to meet my reader.

Drawing a coolant sample is a complicated procedure and, on virtually all nuclear-powered ships, it is a requirement to have a qualified person read the instructions step by step and to help record data during the procedure. I was at the point where I could do the procedure in my sleep, and sometimes probably did, but rules were rules. And not a bad idea, either. Once, in a very fatigued state, I had operated a valve in the primary sample sink incorrectly and accidentally sprayed a small amount of reactor coolant onto an electronic panel just behind me. It missed me, but it took a few minutes to clean up the mess. Another time, I had trouble persuading the EWS to come read for me. Not having a lot of patience, I finally went to the sample sink and started drawing the sample myself. He showed up five minutes later, furious with me for having broken procedure, but he never put me off again. This time, however, the reader showed up and we drew the sample. Some analyses, mostly dealing with the amount of some gases present in the coolant, were performed right in the sample sink, others required me to take three small bottles of coolant and a few sample chambers back to my lab with me for further analysis. I placed the bottles and chambers into my plastic pail (to avoid dropping anything radioactive) and headed back to the lab.

A half hour later I finished my analyses, filled in my log sheet, and took it to Maneuvering for review by the EOOW. That accomplished, I performed my post-startup surveys of the reactor compartment shielding, and my daily routine was done. Ten minutes later, it was time to dive the boat.

Diving a submarine is not quite the white-knuckle experience that most movies would have one believe. This is partly because the stereotypical submarine movie is set in World War II, where subs were primarily surface craft that had the ability to submerge. They spent most of their time on the surface, so they were vulnerable to being spotted or run down. They dove out of necessity, and often as an emergency. For them, diving was a matter of life or death.

Nuke boats, by comparison, spend all of their time underwater except when they have to surface. As exhilarating as being on the bridge on the surface could be, I only felt safe when we were underwater. On the surface, a boat can be run into (it's hard to see a low black log against a dark sea), spotted on radar in enemy waters, or seen from the air. Plus, submarines are meant to operate underwater. With a cylindrical hull, submarines are designed to be underwater and they roll in even calm seas when on the surface. We had to spend four to six hours on the surface until we had sufficient water under our keel to submerge, but we always submerged as soon as we could. And, once submerged, there weren't many people not onboard who had any idea where we were. Invisibility was our best weapon, and we did not give it up lightly.

Another reason to dive was to get away from AGIs. I was never quite sure what AGI stood for – my best guess was "Assholes gathering intelligence". The bottom line is that they were Soviet spy ships, euphemistically called "trawlers". AGIs sometimes hung around outside the 12-mile line (in international waters) and tried to collect intelligence on boats as they came and went. This intelligence probably included sound cuts (acoustic recordings) on submarines to help with locating them by sonar, identification of boats as they left port, and possible electronic signals gathering. Some boats, if they ran into an AGI upon leaving port, were rumored to have turned around and returned to port to have their gear adjusted to change their acoustic profile. We hadn't run into any AGIs this trip out, but I had been called to the bridge on previous surface transits to photograph them. In any event, AGIs were just one more reason to want to dive. And, once submerged, we'd stay underwater until we returned to port in two months' time, barring some emergency that forced us to surface prematurely.

Although diving the boat is routine on a nuclear submarine, it was still something we did with a great deal of care and deliberation. First, the bridge crew secured all gear in the bridge, passing it down to Control, at the foot of the ladder. Next, the remaining gear, mostly electrical and electronic connections, was secured and stowed. The bridge crew then came down a ladder inside the sail, shutting hatches at the top of the sail and partway down to make it watertight. The last man down would announce this fact and the Officer of the Deck would announce he had shifted his watch to Control. Throughout the boat, the crew had already completed their "rig for dive" checklists, making sure that every opening in the pressure hull was sealed, every valve correctly positioned, and every emergency system checked so that we could operate safely at depth and if, heaven forbid, anything did go wrong, we could get back to the surface. As long as everything worked properly, the depths were our friend. The moment anything went wrong, however, they became the enemy and we thought of nothing but surfacing the boat. The sea was never a friend, at most, it was an unwilling accomplice to our mission. It was just there, trying to enter the boat any way it could, and ready to turn on us the moment we trusted it. So we checked and re-checked every possible route by which the sea could enter, and verified every possible way to make our way back to the surface.

The last step to rig the boat to dive was for the Chief of the Watch to verify hatch positions throughout the boat. The Chief of the Watch was the person manning the Ballast Control Panel. By pumping water between trim tanks located as far forward and aft as possible, the COW could keep the boat balanced and level in the water. By pumping water out or taking it on, he could keep the boat neutrally buoyant so, without propulsion, we neither rose to the surface nor sank towards the depths. And, by operating two switches, he could allow high-pressure air from our main air banks to flood into the main ballast tanks, forcing water out of grates in their bottom, and lifting us to the surface. The COW was the senior-most watch station in the non-nuclear part of the boat that was manned entirely by enlisted men; I had qualified to stand the watch so that I could learn more about the forward part of the boat, but I didn't stand it regularly. While the OOD called the shots for diving the boat, the COW had the leading role.

Right now, the COW was looking at his hatch indicators to make sure that all hatches indicated shut. Our hatches were up to 25 inches in diameter; trying to dive with one not fully shut could easily sink the ship. Each opening had its position indicated on the COW's panel; a red circle indicated the opening was not rigged for dive and a green line showed it was secured. Each main hatch had upper and lower hatch doors that were tightly dogged shut and checked by two men, but the COW had the final say when, looking at the green lines showing closed hatches, he reported "Straight line, ready to dive." With that, the COW was ordered to make a loudspeaker announcement "Dive, dive", sound the diving alarm (no klaxon, this, but a relatively boring buzzer), and repeat the loudspeaker announcement. Next, he located the switches for our main ballast tank vent valves, paused for a moment to make sure the OOD saw what he was about to do, announced his intention to vent the main ballast tanks, and opened the valves.

Submarines typically have two hulls. The smooth, black cigar-shaped hull we all see is really only a hydrodynamically-shaped fairing. Beneath this fairing is a high-strength hull of special steel that is designed to withstand full submergence pressure. It's what we live in, the pressure hull, and on my boat, it was irregularly-shaped. Wrapped around the pressure hull were the main ballast tanks. These were six large tanks that held air on the surface and were filled with water when submerged. When air-filled, they provided enough positive buoyancy to keep us from sinking. We had over 300 tons of reserve buoyancy, meaning we could take on 300 tons of water, say, during a flooding emergency, and still reach the surface by blowing ballast tanks. Of course, the two compartments most likely to flood both weighed much more than 300 tons when filled with water, but we tried not to think of that. Also beneath the fairing were storage lockers for our mooring lines, some void spaces that really weren't used for anything, and miscellaneous other things. But the main ballast tanks were most important.

The ballast tanks were mostly enclosed, but were open to the sea through large grates on the bottom. When we blew air into them, the water would be forced out these grates, displaced by the air. Now, however, we were preparing to do the opposite. The ballast tanks also had valves at the top that vented off the air now trapped in them. A submarine submerging will vent high-pressure air and entrained water, just like a whale gasping breath upon surfacing. As the weight of the submarine forces air and water out of the ballast tank vents, the sub rides lower and lower in the water until the forward deck is awash, then the deck aft of the sail, and finally, the sail itself submerges. The crew feels the boat take a slight down-angle and, in relatively calm seas, the wave motion gradually damps out somewhat until we level off at periscope depth (a depth shallow enough that we can still see out through the scopes). The vents are shut now, and the Diving Officer works with the COW to trim the boat, making it neutrally buoyant and balanced fore and aft. Then, with a last periscope sweep, the OOD orders the Diving Officer (or "Dive") to deeper depths. The Dive orders his underlings, the helmsman and planesman, to take the boat to the ordered depth. With a little more down-angle, we descend further into the sea, leveling off at the ordered depth.

At this point, we are a submarine again, a small pocket of habitability in the ocean, making our own water and oxygen, scrubbing carbon dioxide out of our atmosphere, eating, sleeping, working, reading, and, in general, living in a metal tube 278 feet long, 30 feet in diameter, and pressed upon by thousands of pounds of sea pressure for every square foot of hull. For the next 60 days, for this underway period, this is our home, our job, and our life. We may hear from our loved ones, but they will not hear from us until we surface again in late January.

CHAPTER 4

At Sea

For me, there were two types of underway periods, the short ones and the long ones. This may sound like a trivial distinction, but it really is not. Short underways, also called "weekly ops" were all off the coast of California. We'd pull out Monday morning, run drills or play war games for four days, and pull back in Friday afternoon. At sea, we were on an eighteen-hour "day". We'd stand watch for six hours; have six hours for maintenance, recreation, and personal hygiene; and have six hours for sleep. Then we'd be back on watch. It usually took two or three days to acclimate to the shorter "day" at sea and another few days to readjust to the 24-hour day ashore.

Unlike my sonarman roommate, chances were good that I'd have duty either Friday, Saturday, or Sunday, so that day would be a solid 24 hours of getting ready for next week's underway. One weekend day would be spent doing laundry, showering, and calling family and friends back home, and then we'd be back out to sea on Monday. It got tiring. We had one ten-month stretch of weekly ops and, at the end of it, we were all just about dead. One of the bad parts of being a nuke was that we just had a lot more to do. Most of the coners could just shut their equipment off and go home when we pulled into port. They had to stand duty, but their duty days were not all that strenuous. Unfortunately, we couldn't just walk away from the reactor and steam plant, and the engineering systems always had work that needed done (and I need to include the A-gang in this, too, because they did a lot of work). So I could count on a duty day every weekend, and those days were full ones.

On the other hand, weekly ops were easy to prepare for. We didn't have to stock up on supplies or spare parts, we never ran out of fresh food (milk, eggs, fruits, vegetables), only had to pack a week's worth of work clothes, and could prepare in just a few minutes to go to sea. After the first few times, I could wake up Monday morning and, in fifteen minutes, be showered, dressed, and packed for a week at sea.

All things considered, though, I preferred long underway periods. If we went out for two months, it was easy to settle into a routine that would carry me through the entire underway period without having to constantly adjust my sleeping and working schedule. So I was better rested. In addition, when we went out for a long time, it meant we were going to be keeping the world safe for democracy – the mission was somewhat more important than giving the surface navy (skimmers, in submarine jargon) practice finding boats. Going on these ops meant, too, that drills and maintenance were held to a minimum because we didn't want to make a lot of noise. So we'd go out and just do our jobs for two months without all the bullshit that drove us nuts in the SoCal Op Area (Southern California Operations Area). We all understood that drills were necessary to maintain battle readiness, but they were still a pain in the neck that interfered with sleep.

The downsides to long underway periods were the preparation that I described earlier, plus the difficulty in trying to pack clothes that could be worn in San Diego, Hawaii, Alaska, or Japan in February or March. Add to that trying to figure in advance how many books you'd need to bring to stay entertained without overstocking and taking up valuable room that could otherwise be used for pecan sandies or cans of coke, making sure you have enough personal hygiene supplies, deciding which tapes to bring, and so forth. It was a series of choices about how we'd make our time at sea more human and more bearable, and the choices were never-ending. In many ways, finally getting underway was a relief because, once the brow was lifted, it just didn't matter what you'd forgotten to bring or do before leaving. All that mattered was what you'd remembered.

For me, going to sea for a long underway period was not a hardship. What I enjoyed about being at sea was being divorced from the cares and constraints of shore. True, our days were more tightly controlled at sea, but just about everything we did mattered and was important. No superfluous administrative work, inspections, drills, maintenance, and so forth. Our primary concern was keeping the reactor running safely, keeping the boat undetected, staying afloat, and not hurting anyone. Everything else was secondary. And, truth be told, there was some relief in not having to worry about where to go for dinner, what to wear after work, or when to meet someone for a movie. All those choices were taken away from us now, replaced with the immediacy of life on a warship. In spite of the rigor of at-sea life, I always felt a sense of relief and freedom when we disconnected shore power and pulled away from the pier.

We were at sea now, and I was settling in for the long haul. Shortly after diving, we set our course for the northwestern Pacific and the CO made a loudspeaker announcement, telling us our mission. We were bound for the ocean off the Kamchatka Peninsula, near the Soviet submarine base at Petropavlosk where we'd spend the next few months. I was busy stowing gear during the Old Man's announcement, just as others were throughout the boat, getting everything ready for the heavy seas that awaited us. Because we'd lost a few days, we were already at a flank bell, pushing through the water at our top speed. For the next two weeks, we'd slow down only to come to periscope depth for radio contact, then we'd go deep and fast again. At the other end of our track waited an off-going attack boat, just finishing her op and wanting desperately to go home in time for Christmas. While none of us knew the name of the boat or any of the crew, we intended to keep our date. So we drilled through the water, boat shaking slightly from the force of our passage.

You could tell when the ship was going fast. First, of course, you could feel the boat shaking from the main engines, the screw, and the water we were forcing ourselves through. Then, there was the sound of the mains and the water rushing past the hull. And, on our boat, the whole submarine would tilt slightly down and to starboard in response to the tremendous torque put on the boat from the screw spinning back aft. In the engineering spaces, all systems were running at their maximum capacity. Lube oil and main engine bearing temperatures were high, main condenser vacuum was low, and air conditioning was struggling to keep up with the heat load we were placing on it. There was a sense of purpose, to be sure, but also watchfulness. If anything happened under these circumstances, it'd probably happen quickly and dramatically.

Moving quickly was hard on just about everyone in Engineering, including my ELTs. At high reactor power levels we had to keep a careful eye on the water chemistry in both the reactor plant and the steam plant. High power meant more frequent chem adds, each of which was followed by a post-add sample to make sure our add had the desired effect. All this was done near the reactor compartment shield, just when radiation levels were elevated from our high power run. It was not unusual for an ELT to pick up more dose during a two week high-speed run than in the next two months combined when on station at low power. This radiation exposure was not dangerous in the slightest, but our administrative limits were such that we had to try to plan our activities in advance to make sure we stayed legal. After three years, I had a pretty good feel for the reactor and steam plant both, so I knew we were in for a fair amount of work, but not nearly as much as on other, more poorly-maintained boats. I also knew that, once on-station, we'd all be picking up less radiation than if we were in port with the reactor shutdown. The first time I saw that, it puzzled me and I thought I'd made a mistake. Then I realized that, at sea, the only sources of radiation were the reactor and, if we had any on board, our nuclear weapons (and that dose was only to the torpedomen). No radon, no cosmic radiation, no radiation from radionuclides in the rocks and soil.

The first day at sea, this CO liked to let us get stowed and used to being at sea again. So I put gear away, read a bit, and started to get caught up with some of the administrative work I'd neglected the past few weeks. I was tired because of my early morning, so I ate dinner and turned in to get a few hours of sleep before the start of my daily routine.

CHAPTER 5

Racks and Sleeping

Sleeping on a submarine is an interesting matter. My rack was in the berthing area known as the forward nine-man. It was as far forward in the boat as you could get, just about ten feet aft of the sonar sphere that filled the nose of the boat. The berthing area consisted of three stacks of three racks, one stack on either side of the passageway in the forward part and one stack just aft of the first set on the starboard side. I had the middle rack in the forward starboard set. The mattress was about six and a half feet long, two feet wide, and two inches thick. It rested on an aluminum plate with a one inch lip all the way around to hold the mattress in place. This plate, in turn, covered a compartment exactly as big as the mattress and about four inches deep. This was all that most sailors had for storage of their personal belongings for the entire time we'd be gone. I was lucky, though, and (because of my seniority) was able to select my own rack. I picked one with a sizeable locker outboard, near the head of the bunk, that I kept my books and some clothes in. That, plus the storage space in Nucleonics made the trip a bit more civilized.

Each rack had a privacy curtain, a light, an electrical outlet, a vent, and a jack for the ship's entertainment system. The rack was the closest thing we had to a home. Many sailors took their own sheets, comforters, or sleeping bags to sea with them to make the rack feel a bit more personal. I did all of the above. There was just enough room between my rack and the one above me that, if I lay on my back, I could stand a paperback book upright on my chest and hold it in place against the upper rack. To turn over took some planning, so I wouldn't bump my shoulder into the upper rack and wake the sleeping sailor above me.

The very first night I spent on the boat, I wedged myself into the rack (I'm slender, but nearly 6'4" tall). During the night, I started dreaming about playing basketball and, in the course of the dream, I went to jump. In my rack, I straightened my legs and pushed off from the wall that made up the foot of the rack. This pushed me forward, and I hit my head on the wall at the head of the rack. Dazed, I woke groggily and went to sit up, smashing my face against the rack above mine. I spent the next few minutes wondering what in the hell I had signed up for, before drifting back to sleep. Today, ten years after leaving the Navy, I still sleep almost motionlessly.

As I mentioned earlier, the nicest thing about being underway ELT was not having to "hot-rack." Hot-racking meant that three people shared two racks. Each person was in a different watch section, so at any time, one person was on watch and the other two had a place to sleep. The bad part about hot-racking was having to share sheets, pillows, and storage space with others. I always hated having to give up a third of my bed pan (the name for the storage space beneath the rack) to someone else because it was that much less I could bring along. In addition, I'd sometimes get to my preferred rack, only to find someone else in it, and then I'd have to go to the other one, which wouldn't have the book I was currently reading and might not have my soap and towel, and so forth (many submariners, myself included, would carry their toothbrush and toothpaste around with us so we wouldn't have to go to our racks in order to brush our teeth).

For me, and for many of my shipmates, sharing sheets was distasteful. I never trusted my rack mates to shower frequently enough, so when I had to hot rack, I'd usually bring along a sleeping bag that I'd sleep in. This, too was not unique. In fact, one of the worst arguments I witnessed was over one person sleeping inside another's sleeping bag. Of course, sleeping bags raised their own problems. I had a nylon bag once and was sleeping on top of a nylon bed cover. The boat took a roll and, before I was fully awake, I had slid half out of the bunk, dangling six feet above the deck (I was in a top rack that time).

In general, it was more difficult to have your own rack on a longer op because of the extra people we took along with us. On a weekly op, we'd take along most of the boat's crew, but not many more. Some people would stay ashore on leave, for Navy schools, or would be on sick leave. On a longer op, we'd take as many as we needed to run the boat, and then we'd take on a load of other specialists as well. Most of these "riders" were enlisted men; sonar technicians, and electronics technicians mostly. Their job was to get as much intelligence information as possible when the opportunity presented itself. When we were deep (i.e. any depth greater than periscope depth) the radio and electronics types would sit around working on their gear (sometimes) or would talk (or, as we called it, shooting the shit).

To get back to the topic of sleeping, having a boat full of riders meant that virtually all of the enlisted men onboard had to hot rack, except for a few chiefs and the underway ELT. Hence my interest in standing that watch. And, make no mistake about it, sleep is something of paramount importance to a submariner (and probably, for that matter, to just about any serviceman). We rarely got more than a few hours of sleep at any one time; I always felt lucky to have more than four hours of uninterrupted sleep at any time. I decided very quickly that, while I resent having to spend so much time sleeping, being tired is even worse. Depending on my state of fatigue, I'd seriously consider putting sleep ahead of food and personal hygiene if I had to, because you can always find five minutes to wolf down some food or 10 minutes to take a quick shower. But getting rested takes time, and sometimes even just another five or ten minutes of sleep was precious beyond description.

So important is sleep, in fact, that we had a specialized vocabulary for it. "Going down" or "hitting the rack", of course, meant getting sleep. I was "Going down for two" since I had only a few hours to sleep. "Failing open" meant going to bed and not being able to sleep, either from being wired, having overslept previously, having too much to think about, or any other reason. An "equalizer" was having the time to catch up on lost sleep by going down for a long time. Every few weeks I might be able to catch a twelve hour equalizer, but more often we all had to do without. After an equalizer, you might end up with "rack burns" on your face; left by wrinkles in the sheets. And someone who never missed a chance to sleep was a "rack hound." There were more terms, but these are the most commonly-used.

Getting to my rack was an interesting exercise. The forward nine-man was at the end of a long passageway. On any long underway periods, we stored food wherever we could. The freeze box and chill box (that is, our walk-in freezer and refrigerator) were jammed, as was our dry stores locker. We had a centerline storage area filled with cans, and we stacked flour and coffee in the engineroom, outboard the main engines, turbine generators, and shaft. And we had food piled five feet deep in the passageway to the forward nine-man. To get to my rack, I had to climb on top of this food, using cargo netting as a handhold. With only three feet of space, I crawled or duck-walked thirty feet to the forward end of the food, then climbed back down to the deck (which had a single layer of cans on it). This is why I carried my toothbrush with me. All this happened in very deep red lighting. White light would interrupt sleeping and, without lights, the compartment was as dark as a cave. The compartment was rigged for red as soon as the maneuvering watch was secured and stayed that way, with very few exceptions, until we set the maneuvering watch again to enter port.

So, to bring us back to the present, I crawled back to my rack, took my shoes off, and crawled on top of the covers. If I were certain of having more than two hours of sleep, I would have stripped to my shorts and crawled under the covers, but I had left a wake-up call for two hours hence and it just wasn't worth the effort. I usually would try to read before going to sleep, but I was tired and just wanted to get to sleep. Within five minutes I was out.

CHAPTER
6

Working Underway

I woke, feeling someone shaking me gently and calling my name. It was the messenger of the watch, a very junior person whose job was to wake people up, get coffee for the watchstanders in Control, and convey messages. It was a lousy job, given to the most junior personnel on board. On the positive side, it was a good way for them to get to know their shipmates. On the negative side, nobody enjoyed being woken up. I felt lousy, as though I'd had no sleep at all. Looking at my watch, I realized it was because I'd been out for only a half hour. I mumbled something that was intended to be "What the hell do you want? My wake-up's not for another hour and a half" but that sounded more like incoherent muttering. He said I was to contact Maneuvering immediately, and left. I had a reputation for not being very pleasant when under-caffienated. I put on my shoes, crawled down the passageway to the nearest phone, and called Maneuvering. The EOOW, standing one of his first solo watches at sea, had a minor question about reactor water chemistry. I briefly considered being tactful, but decided against it and conveyed to him my feelings as to the importance of the question he was asking. I then told him I was going back to sleep, and returned to my rack. I looked at my watch. An hour and a quarter left until my wake-up. Just before drifting off again, I realized that I had never answered his question. He didn't call back.

Seemingly moments later, I was again woken. I looked at my watch and realized this time it was 11 PM, time to get up. I lay there for a few minutes, collecting my thoughts, and the messenger returned. Automatically, the messenger will wake up the entire on-coming watch section. In addition, anyone on board can request a wakeup time by writing their name, the rack they'll be in, and a time. I knew my sleeping habits, so I used the snooze alarm approach, putting in two wake-up requests fifteen minutes apart. For times like this, in fact, as I realized when I looked at my watch again. This time I got out of bed. The best messenger we had at getting people up was a guy who'd come by, gently shake you, and ask a ludicrous question, then leave. Five seconds after he left, you'd sit up in your rack thinking "What in the world does that mean?" and you'd be awake. Billy hadn't woken me this time, but I managed to get out of the rack anyhow, and headed aft to the head. There I went to the restroom, briefly washed my face, brushed my teeth, and headed a little further aft to the crew's mess for midrats, the midnight meal.

Tonight, midrats was simulated chicken noodle soup, peanut butter and jelly sandwiches, and bug juice. Bug juice didn't come in flavors, just colors. They all tasted the same. In dilute form, it was a beverage; in concentrated form, the cooks used it to clean stainless steel. I ran some tests on it once and found the pH to be comparable to stomach acid. I usually stuck to water, coffee, or cocoa. Most meals were somewhat structured as far as lining up for food and sitting down. Midrats was a free-for-all, chiefly because nobody not on watch stayed up for it. In any event, I wolfed down some food, poured some coffee, and went to my lab to start my daily routine.

For the underway ELT, the daily routine is the only fixed part of each day. Starting at midnight I would do the daily calibration checks of my radio-chemistry analytical equipment. This took nearly an hour, after which I would call Maneuvering to request permission to draw a reactor coolant sample. Taking the sample would usually take only 15 minutes or so, after which I'd head back to the lab to do the analysis. A few minutes of calculations followed that, after which I'd go to Maneuvering to get information on reactor power trends over the last several hours. After finishing the radiochemistry logs I'd head back forward to do my daily radiological surveys. I did daily surveys for contamination in the lab, around the primary sample sink, and along the OPSUL passageway to the Nucleonics Lab, the path along which I carried reactor coolant for analysis. I also did weekly surveys for radioactive contamination in the rest of the boat, one or two spaces daily. Some quick checks on the operability of our radiation meters finished the daily routine. My goal was usually to complete everything by 3 AM, 4 at the latest. Then I'd read for a few hours, or perhaps watch part of the midnight movie, have breakfast, and go to sleep until lunch.

There were some variations, of course. Adjusting reactor plant chemistry would require chemical additions or other operations followed by re-sampling. And, since several components of reactor water chemistry were linked together by various equilibrium reactions, changing one thing affected several others. It kept things interesting. This was especially likely during high-speed runs, when the reactor was operating at high power for long periods of time. If I was lucky, I could figure out a pattern after the first few days and then try to pre-empt the reactor plant by adjusting chemistry before it was really necessary. Or, if the plant was determined to have its own way, I'd just give in and would adjust my sleep schedule around when I expected to have to tend to reactor plant chemistry. And, some times, I just couldn't win and I'd be up for a solid 24 hours or longer taking care of things. That was the downside of being underway ELT.

Besides chemistry wars, I could also be thrown off by drills, training, maintenance, short-term watch relief (to let someone go to the restroom), real casualties (such as a reactor scram, fire, or equipment problem), or other infrequent or unplanned activities. I usually tried to anticipate as much as possible, if for no other reason than that I hated being tired. Luckily, this underway was taking us to very near the Soviet Union, so drills, most maintenance, and other noisy activities would be absent for nearly two months. Another reason to like long underways – we could just do our jobs without all the other bullshit that went along with being at sea. Mainly, we were away from Naval Reactors and the Squadron – I understand that the high standards, inspections, and all that were vitally important to having a safe and effective program, but I also understand that they put us through a lot of shit, and it was nice to get away for awhile.

I was still getting used to being underway ELT this time; I didn't finish my daily routine until nearly 5, just as the oncoming watch section was being woken up. I talked tiredly with the cooks for awhile, then went to my lab until the oncoming watchstanders had eaten. Then I grabbed some chow, brushed my teeth, and crawled to my rack for some sleep. Engineering department training wasn't scheduled until Wednesday, we didn't have time to slow the boat down for drills, and chemistry was all right, so I didn't leave a wakeup call. I adjusted to at-sea life the same way as to any other time zone change; by staying up until the time I should normally be going to bed and then crashing for as long as I needed (or was able).

In this case, I wasn't interrupted and woke nearly 12 hours later. I couldn't believe it at first, but repeated checks of my watch convinced me. I was just in time to grab some dinner before the chow line closed, then I went to my lab to start catching up on my administrative work. I always tried to front-load our spec ops so that I could kick back and relax as much as possible. Six hours later, at midnight, I started my daily routine again.

Life progressed like this for the next few days. Wake up, eat, paperwork, daily routine, eat, read for awhile, sleep. Some training, the occasional chem add or adjustment, and miscellaneous other odd jobs, but life settled down into a routine rather quickly. The only unusual thing this time was that radiation levels near the reactor compartment shield were higher than I was used to seeing, and I was receiving more dose than I expected, but it was nothing alarming and was certainly not dangerous. My guess was that it reflected the age of our plant and the fact that this was the longest high-power run we'd made since I joined the crew. We had three fewer days to make it from San Diego to Kamchatka, which meant we had to hustle. Most of the time we had a 15-18 knot average speed of advance (SOA), which was respectable. This time we had an SOA significantly higher than 20 knots, which meant we had no room to slow down below a flank bell unless we were at PD to copy broadcasts. Since our biggest advantage was in being hidden, we never surfaced the boat and we maintained virtual radio silence at all times, barring an emergency of some sort. In this case, we also kept our PD excursions to a minimum because we weren't very fast with a scope or radio mast up. We just needed to stay deep and fast for as many hours as possible. Of course, higher power meant higher rad levels. Monitoring them, making the crew aware of them, and keeping people's radiation exposure down was another part of my job.

Life at sea is an interesting blend of thoughts and desires. We all hoped and prayed for things to be boring, because excitement usually meant that something had gone wrong. But then we got tired of the same routine day after day. We would talk wistfully about all the things we left behind; family, girlfriends, good food, movies, and all. But many of us, myself included, were not reluctant to leave port. I sometimes envied those who missed their loved ones the most, because at least they had loved ones to miss and to miss them. I didn't want to have my children growing up, always missing their Daddy, and I didn't want to be always saying goodbye to my girlfriend, wife, or children, so I never even dated seriously while in the Navy. At the same time, I missed that I had nobody to miss me. I never fell into abject self-pity, tempting though that was at times, but I was always jealous of those with families or girlfriends to talk about. I think, though, that having nobody left behind helped the at-sea time go by more quickly for me than would have been the case otherwise. Nothing seems to make time crawl more slowly than wishing it to pass quickly by.

I had read Dana's book, *Two Years Before the Mast* shortly before going on this underway. I was particularly struck by his description of life on a 19th century sailing vessel, not because of the differences between his life at sea and mine, but because of the similarities. Despite the vast gulf between his time and mine and the equally vast gap in our technologies, purposes, and any other meaningful measure of the times, there seems to be something timeless about being at sea. The fundamental problems seem to be the same across time. Whether your ship is made of wood or steel, you must keep it afloat. Whether you are powered by the wind or the atom, you must care for your power plant, because to lose power is to be at the mercy of the elements, and it's a battle man is likely to lose. With limited space aboard, virtually all sailors must grow used to a monotonous diet and limited entertainment. And, even with near-instantaneous radio communications anywhere in the world, sailors and their families must endure time not knowing how the other is doing. We always returned to a strange world, because even periodic updates on the world or our families is no substitute for living through changes, hearing them in person, or reading of them in the daily paper. So, we return to a changed world, strangers to our friend and families, trying to adapt what we found to what we remembered leaving.

And it didn't stop with that. Today, I come home from work, and an important part of my day is telling my wife and son what I did for nine or ten hours. But, on a small ship, everyone knows what you did, and nobody cares to hear about it. Upon returning to port, much of what we did, we couldn't talk about, because much was classified, some would frighten, and the rest of it would likely be incomprehensible to our loved ones. So we learned to accept that we'd not be able to share our daily experiences around the dinner table, and we learned to not talk about many of the important things that happened in our lives. And, on board, our talk tended towards the mundane and the trivial because, in such a closed environment, you had to be either very shallow or very deep, and we hesitated to open up too much in front of other men.

In spite of this, though, the sea attracted me even before I knew what it would entail, and it calls to me still. I never considered any other branch of the service. My father blames this, and my love of travel, on our ancestry – part of my heritage is Lebanese, descended from the ancient Phoenicians. The Phoenicians were explorers, sailors, and merchants, mapping and pioneering trade routes through the Mediterranean centuries before Christ was born. Although I was not fond of much of my time in the Navy and I came to dislike my job, I liked being at sea from my first underway to my last. I still find myself wishing for the gentle rocking of a boat at periscope depth in calm seas, helping to rock me to sleep in my bunk. I miss equally the savage rolls of a boat at periscope depth in heavy seas, watching the depth gauge fluctuate 70 or 80 feet at a time, and hearing crashes as drawers fall open and plates smash themselves into the deck. I came to enjoy the focus that comes from knowing that the actions of a single man could mean the difference between a wonderful sea story and tragedy. Although I never felt comfortable with the responsibility, there was also reward in knowing that my actions helped to make a difference on the boat and, in some cases, participating in a mission that was reported to the Joint Chiefs and to the President. Despite not liking being in the Navy and my job, it was something I did pretty well, something that very few people have done at all, and I took pride in that.

CHAPTER 7

Angles and Dangles

THE FIRST EVOLUTION SCHEDULED was on our second day out; angles and dangles. This is the term we used to refer to taking the boat through increasingly high angles up and down. We did this right out of port to make sure everything was stowed properly. Otherwise, someone could get hurt, a vital piece of equipment could be damaged, or the submarine could be given away by a piece of gear skidding and crashing across the deck at an inopportune moment. So we did our best to stow everything, and then we did our best to shake it loose. If something could survive angles and dangles, chances were that it'd stay put during heavy rolls, sharp turns, or rapid maneuvering. This was one of my favorite activities, right up there with emergency blows. This was something we called an "E-ticket" ride – after Disney World, where the best rides require an E-ticket.

In many ways, submarines have as many similarities to airships as to surface ships. Like blimps, we maneuver in three dimensions, held up by buoyancy, and using a combination of speed, ballast, control surfaces, and angle to control our depth (or altitude). Most of the time we kept our angle close to zero, a flat and level surface. However, we were rated for up to a 45° up or down angle and up to the same rolling angle. Forty five degrees is the angle of a steep hill. For every foot horizontally you travel, you also go a foot up or down. At such an angle, driving from San Diego to Los Angeles would take you into space at the same altitude as many satellites.

We didn't start off at a high angle, of course. First, we heard an MC announcement "Rig ship for high angles. First angle will be fifteen degrees up." A minute later, the deck started to slowly rise in front of me, stopping at an angle of fifteen degrees up. In about a minute I had gone from standing on a flat surface to standing on a moderate hill. I was leaning forward slightly, looking around my lab to make sure nothing was going to fall. A minute later, we leveled off, then heard "Stand by for fifteen degrees down."

Now the deck fell away before me, and I was looking down the same moderate hill. No noise from the lab yet, although I heard some small thumps and crashes elsewhere. We leveled off again and some people, those in the compartments where the crashes and thumps originated, frantically stowed their gear better. Next came twenty degrees up and down, and then twenty five. Each time, the angle was a little steeper and the sensation of going up or down was stronger. By twenty five degrees, it was becoming hard to stand without leaning or holding on to something. At thirty degrees up, I heard a big crash from the crew's mess. Some of our equipment was shifting around, and I knew from previous experience, in the torpedo room, the weapons would be shifting slightly forward and aft in their cradles. Luckily, they were all strapped down very securely. The last thing you want is a 21 foot long Mark 48 torpedo getting loose in the torpedo room. At thirty degrees up-angle, the sliding aluminum door to my lab flew open along its track, crashing into the doorstop with a bang that almost scared me. This is what we needed to find out. If we had to take a steep angle near the Soviet Union, any of these noises would be enough to give us away. There is nothing in nature that sounds like a dropped wrench, a slammed door, or a breaking plate. These transients, as they're called, can only be man-made and they can be heard miles away. A single transient is sufficient evidence to fire a torpedo in that direction during wartime. Better to get them all out of the way now, in our home waters.

At thirty degrees up, one of the cooks took a burlap sack and started sliding along the passageway that ran down the ship's centerline in the upper level of the Operations Compartment (called Ops Upper Level, or OPSUL for short). At a thirty degree angle, a ship traveling 15 knots would move through a vertical distance of 750 feet in one minute. More at higher angles or higher speeds. We paid close attention to depth and speed when we were operating at high angles.

Try to picture standing in your office or your living room. You are having a conversation with a colleague. As you talk, the floor starts to tilt beneath your feet. You continue talking, but you notice you seem to be leaning forward slightly, and your companion seems to be leaning back. This becomes ever more pronounced until, in less than a minute, your footing starts to go. You're now standing on a steep slope, looking up at your colleague as he looks down on you. As you relax your arms, they dangle forward, in front of you, and you find yourself almost touching the floor in front of you. You feel normal, except for some stress on your leg muscles, but your surroundings are tilted at a high angle. And then, it's over, and then, reversed. You're now looking down a steep hill, and your only concern is that you'll slip, fall, and hurt yourself. Elsewhere, you hear plates, computers, and tools falling to the ground. This is angles and dangles.

At thirty-five degrees the deck in front of me was steep and slippery enough that I didn't even try to stand. I sat in the chair in my lab, braced myself with the chair against one set of cabinets and my feet wedged against the other set across the lab, and watched my world seemingly stand on end. In the crew's mess, I was willing to bet, new sailors would be watching as their more experienced shipmates showed off, leaning forward as the boat rose, looking like mountain climbers as they touched the floor in front of them with their fingertips while their feet were firmly planted on the deck. My ankles didn't bend that well. Meanwhile, in the lab, I'd managed to fix the problem with the door, and I listened for anything else there to break loose. Everything in the lab was either stowed, bolted to something immovable, or was secured with a metal strap that was itself securely fastened to a deck, bulkhead, or countertop. At thirty five degrees down, a few more things shook themselves loose, but in general, everything was put away by now. We leveled off and heard "Secure from high angles. Prepare for high-speed turns."

From the lab, I could hear the OOD give the order a flank bell. Even a hundred feet forward of the engineroom I could hear and feel the main engines and ship pick up speed. In maneuvering, the throttleman was opening the throttles carefully, making sure the engines and shaft weren't overly stressed and making sure that he didn't exceed the maximum rated reactor power. Meanwhile, the reactor operator was monitoring the reactor plant, and the rest of the crew was minding their equipment, as well.

When we reached a flank bell, the OOD waited a few minutes to give the crew and vessel a chance to settle out a bit. Then, he ordered a starboard turn with only a few degrees on the rudder. The helmsman turns the wheel slightly and the boat leans to the right slightly. The angle indicator (like a carpenter's level, only with a curved glass marked in angle of bank) moves to show a five degree bank to starboard. After a minute, we straighten out briefly, then do the same thing to port. In the next ten minutes, we run through ever-steeper banks as the OOD orders more rudder at the same high speed. Pretty soon, we're banking at nearly twenty degrees and the feeling is more akin to being on an airplane than on a ship. No crashes this time, just some minor bumps. So we're either getting everything stowed properly or we're breaking everything that's not put away. Either way, we're getting quieter. Another few minutes and the high-speed turns are over.

The last thing on today's agenda is an emergency blow. Of everything we're doing, this is potentially the most important and, to me, the most fun. The *Thresher* was the lead ship in the class of submarines of which my boat is a member. The *Thresher* sank during sea trials in the 1960s, taking with her the lives of every man on board. Annual training on what happened to the *Thresher* was given to all of us in nuclear power. Among the things that went wrong, the *Thresher* began to flood and, at the same time, her reactor shut down. With no way to try to drive to the surface, she began to sink. At some point, they tried to blow high-pressure air into the main ballast tanks to lift the boat to the surface. Because of the way her emergency blow system was designed, the air had to follow a tortuous path, through narrow piping with many bends, through a pressure reducing valve, and into the main ballast tanks. Somewhere in that path, water that was in the air froze, plugging the line. The *Thresher* couldn't blow her ballast tanks and sank with all hands.

A lot of changes were made as a result of the *Thresher*. One of these was a complete re-design of the emergency blow system. The air lines were made wider and more direct. The pressure reducing station was eliminated. Manual valves were installed in case the remote-operated valves failed. And, four times a year, we went deep and performed an emergency blow to make sure everything worked as designed.

Everything we'd done today had been done with some preparation, but not much compared to the emergency blow. We could break the surface at speeds in excess of 20 knots (about 23 miles per hour). Our submarine weighed about ten million pounds. We had to make sure we weren't going to come up underneath another ship or we'd likely sink us both. So, ironically, we made a slow, controlled ascent to periscope depth before we went deep so that we could blow to the surface again.

First, we cleared our baffles. The baffles are the area directly behind the boat, where sonar doesn't work. With a sonar sphere in the bow, any noises behind us are absorbed by our own submarine and are masked by our own noises. So the OOD takes a boat through a carefully-designed pattern of loops while Sonar makes sure that nobody is in our way. A submarine is never as vulnerable as when it is coming to periscope depth. The top of the hull may be only twenty feet beneath the waves, shallow enough for a ship to hit easily. But, until the scope breaks the surface, we're blind, unable to see anyone else. We surfaced once in the middle of the San Diego fishing fleet because they weren't running their engines and we had no idea anyone was above us. Luckily, we didn't hit anyone, just boosted everyone's pulse rate for a few minutes.

This time, Sonar announces our baffles are clear, so we begin a deliberate ascent from 150 feet to periscope depth. As we rise, the OOD mans the scope, constantly moving in a circle, looking for any shapes through the water that might indicate a possible vessel moving our way. The Diving Officer calls out the depth every five feet and, the shallower we are, the more urgently the OOD walks his circle. The seas are calm and, at a depth of about 60 feet, the OOD calls "Scope clear!" Ten seconds later, he has made a complete circuit with the scope and announces "Initial periscope sweep complete, no close contacts." We now all breathe a little easier. The OOD takes us on up to about 50 feet to put a lot more scope out of the water, giving the OOD a longer look. He takes another five minutes to do a thorough check of the horizon and, assured that we have this part of the ocean to ourselves, orders the Dive to take us down again. Another five minutes and we're back at 150 feet with the scope down.

We're not doing an emergency blow from a great depth this time, although once a year it's required. Today, however, we're only going down to 400 feet for a short blow. Dive takes us down, we trim the boat, and the announcement is made, "All hands, stand by for emergency blow." In Control, the OOD orders the Diving Officer to perform a ten-second emergency blow of all main ballast tanks. Dive repeats this back verbatim, turns, and repeats the order to the Chief of the Watch, who is sitting behind and to his left at the Ballast Control Panel. The COW repeats the order. Above the COW, at the top of the BCP are two silver toggle switches. The COW deliberately places his hand on the right-hand switch. The way the panel is placed, running fore and aft on the port side of Control, this switch is forward, and it controls air to the forward ballast tanks. We want to blow this group first because it'll lift the nose of the submarine up and we'll come out of the water nose-first instead of ass-first. The COW waits for a second with his hand on the switch, giving the OOD and the Dive a chance to stop him. The, he pulls the switch. Two seconds later, he flips the switch for the after group.

Throughout the boat, we hear the hiss of high-pressure air rushing through the lines into the ballast tanks. There, the air displaces water, forcing it through the grates in the bottom of the tanks. For ten seconds, air rushes in and water is pushed out, making the boat tens of tons lighter. First, we feel the bow lift, much like it did during angles and dangles, but without the sensation of speed we'd had then. The numbers on the digital depth gauge start to change as we begin our ascent. After ten seconds, the COW returns the toggle switches to their normal position and the hissing stops. Meanwhile, the depth gauge is changing more quickly and our speed and angle are increasing. Thirty seconds into the blow, we're at about 250 feet with a twenty degree up-angle and we're doing 15 knots. We continue rising, and the digits on the depth gauge are becoming hard to read as they change. The depth gauge goes to zero as we break the surface at 20 knots and we feel the boat come partially out of the water and splash back down into the sea. Our momentum carries us back down to about 100 feet, then we return to the surface again. Many of us smile, myself among them. As always, someone will say "That's an E-ticket ride for sure!" and someone else will agree. Of all the things we do, this is the favorite of most of the crew. It's also potentially the most dangerous, because any number of things can go wrong that could lead to disaster, as happened with the USS Greenville as I am writing this book.

This emergency blow was fun, but not the best I'd been involved with. That one took place on a dependents' cruise, when we went to sea for a half-day with family and friends. Angles and dangles, high-speed turns, and an emergency blow were all part of the activities, and one time our CO decided to really impress the dependents. All that a sailor is allowed to say is that their submarine can dive to depths in excess of 400 feet and can move at speeds in excess of 20 knots. But, if you were to ask my mother, she could tell you that, when we blew our ballast tanks, the depth gauge read 900 feet, the blow lasted almost 15 seconds, and we broke the surface at 28 knots. We carried so much momentum with us as we went over the top that we splashed back down to over 400 feet before coming back to the surface. That was a real E-ticket ride! In any event, this emergency blow was over, so the OOD orders a flank bell again as we turn again towards the northwest. We continue on our way.

After the excitement was over, I decided to catch a few hours of sleep. It was about dinnertime, but I was tired enough to forgo the meal. One thing I realized early on was that being rested was more important than food or, to some degree, personal hygiene. Tired people make mistakes. They are grumpy, and they have bad morale. It's hard to work effectively or efficiently when you're tired. In many ways, I'd rather be a little drunk than really tired because, when I'm drinking, I know it and make allowances. But after being up working for 30-40 hours, you might (and I have) started something complex only to find attention starting to drift or consciousness starting to fade unexpectedly. We were all relatively young; we thought that enough coffee and willpower would keep us up through anything. We were wrong. If I was tired, I would take whatever sleep I could find, even if only 15 or 20 minutes at a time. In any event, this was one of those times, so I took the opportunity and hit the rack.

I woke around 11, brushed my teeth, had midrats, and started my daily routine. I finished the primary sample and the daily surveys by 5, had a quick bite for breakfast, and hit the rack again. It usually took a few days to feel comfortable with my at-sea schedule, but it was worth working on. I was asleep by 6.

I woke to the general alarm. A gong-like sound. Twenty one times. All the lights went on and I was lying there, trying desperately to wake up and make some sense of the world. Then I heard "Security alert. Security alert. Send two armed guards to the torpedo room." Great. Wasting valuable sleep time on a drill. I looked at my watch. Seven AM.

Since I'd been in the rack, I'd missed the chance for my favorite running joke. The line "Send two armed guards to the torpedo room" was meant to secure the weapons with a pair of armed guards, especially if we had nuclear weapons on board. But for the last two years, I had been deliberately misinterpreting this and, when the announcement went out, I'd ask "How many?" My reasoning was that all of our guards have two arms, otherwise they'd be on disability. So far, nobody had got the joke. I figured that, if nobody had figured it out by my last security drill, I'd fill them in on it. I sincerely doubted that anyone would find the humor in it that I did, but a joke unshared just isn't as much fun. Or, another way to look at it is that it's not important to laugh at the joke, just to get the joke.

As ELT I had little to do during a security drill, so I wandered aft to the Crew's Mess, where the Chief of the Boat (the senior-most enlisted man onboard, also called the COB, or just COB) was mustering all off-watch personnel. I checked in with him and sat down on one of the benches, closed my eyes, and tried to catch a few more minutes of sleep. I'd found that if I could avoid waking up entirely, for example by avoiding playing these silly security games, then I might be able to get back to sleep a bit more readily when the fun was over.

This time it didn't work. The COB called my name and told me to pair up with another sailor and get down to the Small Arms Locker. There, we were issued sidearms and we performed a security inspection of the Bow Compartment. Looking for someone trying to steal the secret of uncomfortable mattresses, no doubt. We spent a good five minutes pretending to be serious, then exchanged a little conversation and, after 10 minutes or so, reported back to the COB that the berthing compartments were, indeed, free of un-American influences. We were then sent back to make sure that nobody tried to escape out the forward escape trunk (unlikely in a submarine at several hundred feet, doing a flank bell, in mid-ocean). We camped out beneath the hatch, pretended to look vigilant, and continued exchanging idle conversation. After an hour or so the announcement came "The security violation was a drill. All hands recover from the drill. All hands issued small arms, return them to the small arms locker."

That was a big relief. I'd thought we were about to lose secrets, and my relief at finding it was only a drill can only be imagined. Since I'd missed my first running joke, I decided to pass on the second (which was "My hands were issued small arms at birth, but they've grown since. What should I do?"). I returned my sidearm and returned to my rack. All in all, we'd wasted about an hour on the drill, enough time that I was going to have trouble getting back to sleep. But it was worth a shot.

Back in the rack, I tried to fall asleep for an hour, read for an hour, and finally realized it just wasn't going to happen. So I went aft, did some paperwork, had some lunch, and was finally able to catch two hours' sleep after lunch. Before I was woken again for a head relief for the AMSLL watch. After that, I spent another hour trying to get to sleep before giving up. I finally started getting tired about the time it was time to start my daily routine. Made it through that and collapsed around 5 AM. This underway was off to a bad start; less than 10 hours of sleep in the first two days, and no more than 4 hours at a time thus far. Plus, a high-speed transit coming up that would be quite taxing because of all the chemistry adjustments I'd have to take part in. This was not shaping up to be a good transit for the underway ELT. On the other hand, once we arrived on station, things should lighten up a bit. That's when standing this watch would start to pay off.

Casualties

Five days out of San Diego. About halfway between Hawaii and the Aleutians. We have diverted north to drop our sonar chief off in Adak, one of the Aleutian Islands. The CO received a message that the chief's pregnant wife is likely to lose her baby and the Navy has given us permission to drop him off so he can be with her. So we're driving even faster to the north to make up the time. Adak is not far out off the great circle route to our op area, but we're already pushing nearly as hard as we can go.

A day later, we pull into Adak harbor. We surfaced at the last possible moment because we're a lot faster submerged than on the surface and because we want to give the Soviets the least chance to spot us on a satellite photo. We do a quick turn in the harbor and, as we're heading back out to sea, a small boat comes alongside. The chief is standing topside, just aft of the sail, wearing foul weather gear, a life jacket, and a safety line clipped to the sub. He is carrying a few personal effects (the rest will stay with us until we pull back in) and a large sack of mail. Most of us have been up all night, writing letters to family and friends, taking advantage of this unexpected opportunity to tell them we're still doing well and we miss them. Normally, I'm supposed to be the first one topside to survey and make sure there's no contamination, but this time we're in a hurry and, as I'm doing my survey, the rest of the topside detail is up, too, getting the chief off. This is also one of the most potentially dangerous times to be a submariner – working in close proximity to a small boat, transferring personnel and supplies from one moving boat to another, and hoping the boats don't bump and that nobody falls off or is swept away by a freak wave. Everyone is in a safety harness, of course, and has a lifejacket on, but you can still lose people. Our former XO had been topside once and fell overboard. He stayed attached to the boat, but was pulled through the water for several minutes, like a hooked fish, until he could be recovered. Not fun, and I had no desire to experience that particular adventure.

The small boat matches our speed and course, edges closer, the chief walks as far down the slope of the hull as he can, and jumps across the few feet of water. Seamen help pull him aboard as the boat veers away towards shore. In a few hours he'll be on a flight back to the states and we'll be at our dive point. The CO is on the bridge. He orders a "surface flank" bell, the fastest we can safely travel on the surface, and we head back out to sea. When we reach our dive point, the bridge crew is down and we dive quickly. A half dozen people have been topside to see the sky. I was lucky to have been one of them. Back in the depths, our pace quickens from hectic to frantic as we try to make up for lost time. Our thoughts and prayers are with the chief, a good man and a good sailor.

Just before news of the chief's wife came in, we were fighting the first of many equipment casualties that we were to face. An equipment casualty refers to anything that goes wrong. A casualty can be a broken air conditioning unit, a fire, a frozen pump bearing, or anything else that can go wrong. In this case, we discovered a steam leak on the port main engine. Normally we'd just shut the appropriate isolation valve, do a quick weld or replacement, and put the system back on-line. This time, however, the leak is un-isolable, meaning this approach won't work. With steam at nearly 500 degrees and at high pressure, we can't let the leak go and we can't fix it without shutting down the entire main engine. Shutting down the port main engine takes only a matter of minutes, but the entire procedures requires writing a work package, hanging danger tags to make sure nobody gets hurt from accidentally operating the wrong valve, then doing the work, clearing tags, and testing the repair. The administrative work takes three hours, the repair is finished in 30 minutes, and the main is ready to go in another hour. The repair holds pressure, and we start up the main again.

This is where it gets interesting. This is happening on the midwatch. The EWS is the newest EWS we have, a member of my division, standing the watch to maintain his proficiency. What he doesn't know is that the main engine is going to play some games with him.

Each turbine has high-pressure steam on the inside, turning the turbine blades, and air (the "people tank") on the outside. A shaft protrudes through the casing and this shaft is what, eventually, makes the boat go through the water. To keep the steam in the turbine and out of the people tank, a series of rings come down and just about touch the shaft, sealing the steam in with the help of other systems. A lot of heat is generated as the turbine turns, enough to melt the shaft seals under normal circumstances. It gets so hot, in fact, that the 500 degree steam actually serves to cool the seals. Without this cooling steam, the seals have expanded and are in contact with the shaft. When the EWS goes to start the port main engine up, the seals start throwing sparks into the engineroom. Nobody has ever seen or heard of this happening before and, at four in the morning, we hear the general alarm (a series of 21 electronic tones) and a loudspeaker announcement "Fire in the engineroom! Fire in the engineroom!" The casualty assistance team rushes aft, fire-fighting gear in hand, to deal with the fire while the backup assistance team puts on their firefighting gear. As underway ELT, I stand by in the crew's mess to give whatever assistance is required, in case the CAT and BRT need more help.

Luckily the shaft seals cool off and the sparking dies down quickly with no injury, fire, or secondary damage. Everyone heads back forward. The oncoming watchstanders go to the crew's mess, knowing the futility of trying to sleep just an hour or less with adrenaline flowing. I am done with my daily routine, so I go to my lab to read before breakfast. This will have no impact on my day at all. Everyone else goes back to sleep.

The next casualty comes a few days later, when both our carbon dioxide scrubbers die on us. The CO_2 scrubbers are important. We all exhale carbon dioxide. It's a product of our metabolism. Too much CO_2 starts to make your thinking laborious, will give you headaches, and tires you out. Way too much CO_2 can make you sick or, eventually, dead. World War II submarines would spend most of their time on the surface, so CO_2 could be flushed away by normal ventilation. We wanted to stay submerged, though, because a submarine on the surface is vulnerable. We could ventilate through our snorkel mast, but even this was not always possible. At the top of the snorkel mast was a valve, called the head valve that served to keep water from flowing down the mast into the diesel generator or the ventilation blowers. A good cause, but the snorkel mast and head valve were large enough to spot on radar. Plus, the blower was noisy. So we tried not to ventilate unless we had to. This meant that we relied on our two scrubbers to help maintain a breathable atmosphere by removing the carbon dioxide.

Normal atmospheric CO_2 concentrations are about 335 ppm or, in the units we measured on-board, about 0.25 torr. One torr is the pressure equal to the weight of one millimeter of mercury and 760 torr equal the pressure found at sea level. So, even with global warming, there is not much carbon dioxide in the air normally. At sea, with both scrubbers running, we'd run about 3-6 torr for CO_2 concentrations. This was high, but not high enough to cause any problems. When the forward scrubber broke, our CO_2 shot up to over 10 torr within a few hours before stabilizing out. A few days later, the after scrubber started giving us problems. The scrubbers are A-gang equipment, but that didn't stop some of the nukes from trying to help. Carbon dioxide leveled off at about 16 torr, and we came to PD to ventilate as frequently as we could. Luckily, we were still in transit, so we didn't have to worry much about the head valve. It may be big, but it's hard to see something a foot across from orbit, or even from 10,000 feet. It took about a day to get one of the scrubbers running again, during which life just sucked. We had other ways to remove CO_2, but none as effective.

With CO_2 levels this high, no smoking was allowed onboard. Or, in Navy terminology, the smoking lamp was out in all spaces. The term "smoking lamp" hearkened back to the days of wooden ships and iron men, or so we were told. Before matches and Zippo lighters, a lamp was kept burning that men could use to light their pipes, cigarettes, or cigars. During some operations, like moving gunpowder, the smoking lamp was extinguished to reduce the risk of some idiot blowing himself and the rest of the ship to kingdom come. This term carried forward to the present. Whenever we moved pyrotechnics (flares, smoke signals, etc.), pumped fuel oil, moved weapons, or did any of a number of other things, the smoking lamp would be out in all affected spaces. In this case, there was no good air anywhere onboard, so the smoking lamp was out shipwide. It was a good time to not be a smoker.

That was only half the equation, of course. In addition to removing impurities, we also had to make oxygen. Unlike later boats, we did not carry equipment to make oxygen from sea water, so we carried it with us, instead. We'd ventilate when we could, but when we couldn't we'd either bleed oxygen from our high-pressure oxygen banks or we'd burn "candles" that released more oxygen than they used. One of the considerations when going out for a long time was how much time we expected to spend ventilating through the snorkel mast. This trip, not much, so we carried a full oxygen load and a full load of candles. And that, of course, meant a little less food and a little less room for other supplies. And a lot more weight. In fact, this trip out we were so heavy that we started off with an air bubble in the ballast tanks and one empty fresh water tank to offset the extra weight of our supplies.

Carrying an air bubble was not really supposed to be done because it's a tricky way to maintain ballast. As you dive, sea pressure increases, compressing the bubble, and reducing buoyancy. So a ship that's heavy to begin with gets heavier the deeper it goes. The flip side is that, coming up, you get lighter as you approach the surface, making the boat more difficult to control and keep from broaching. Luckily, our diving officers were good, so we neither broached nor sank out. The empty fresh water tanks were a more calculated move. We made our own fresh water, so we could fill the tanks whenever we wanted, provided the evaporator (which we usually called the evap, with the accent on the first syllable) ran and we could run it. Once we got on-station, sound silencing would be vitally important, and running the evap could be noisy. By draining one of our steam plant water tanks and one potable (drinking) water tank, we were betting we'd have a chance to fill them up again when the ship was lighter. If not, it meant a lot of smelly sailors, because personal hygiene was the last priority for water use, after the reactor plant, the steam plant, drinking, and cooking. Not too long ago, the ship had gone 45 days on spec op with only three chances to shower. I was in no hurry to repeat that. Of course, the old diesel boats made only about 100 gallons of fresh water daily, and they bathed monthly if they were lucky. It made me feel like a wimp sometimes, thinking about the relative comfort we enjoyed, but our living conditions were still much more challenging than when we were ashore, and I had no great desire to experience a diesel boat.

We got lighter by eating, burning oxygen candles, shooting trash, and blowing sanitary tanks. Some of this should be self-evident. Food weighs a lot. We eat the food, go the bathroom, and use high-pressure air to blow the waste overboard. With it goes most of the weight of the food we all ate. And the ship gets lighter. Similarly, as we burn oxygen candles and dispose of them, the ship lightens. And normal trash gets dumped through a device called the TDU (trash disposal unit), further lightening the ship. In fact, TDU ops (as we call it when we're shooting trash) does double duty for lightening the boat because each mesh bag is weighted with steel disks to ensure they sink to the bottom rather than floating to the surface and giving away our position. So, in addition to the weight of the trash, we also loose the mass of the TDU weights. On a typical long underway period we'll go through several thousand TDU weights, each weighing ten pounds or so. Day by day we get lighter, until we can afford to burp the ballast tanks and fill them completely with water. And, by the time we reach our op area, we hope to be able to fill the other two fresh water tanks. If, that is, the evap stays up and we have no emergencies that require a lot of water.

Ten days out. We're about a day or two from our op area and it's time to start being conscious of every noise. We don't want to go charging in, letting everyone know we're here. Plus, when we're going fast, our sonar is degraded because of the sound of the water rushing past the hull. Stick your head out the car window sometime, even moving at 20 miles an hour, and try to listen to the driver talk to you. You're probably not going to hear much.

I finished my daily routine an hour before breakfast. I decided to grab a radiation survey meter (which we called a radiac) and pay a visit to the Galley. Stopping in, I saw my timing was perfect – the midwatch cook was just pulling a tray of sticky buns out of the oven. He set them down and iced them and I stepped up to the door. Turning the meter to "battery test" (which made the needle go to the high end of the scale), I pretended to survey the rolls, shaking my head. The cook looked at me. He was a newer guy. He asked me if anything was wrong. "This roll looks hot," I said. "I'm going to have to take it."

I reached for the roll just as a more senior cook came by. "Don't let him pull that shit on you," he said. "Andy's always trying to get an extra sticky bun doing that. Just tell him to get lost."

I smiled. "Already touched it! You can't give this one out now, can you? I'll just take care of it for you." I grabbed the roll and scooted away while the cooks laughed. Deciding to stay up for breakfast, I was able to snag a second roll (we were usually limited to one at breakfast), then I hit the rack to try to catch up on sleep.

No training today, so I can relax a bit. Carbon dioxide levels are still high, but we're getting used to it. I've had a low-grade headache for the past few days, but nothing that aspirin can't handle. And we have plenty of that on board. About 10 I am woken by an MC announcement "High chlorides in the port steam generator. All ELTs lay to Machinery Space Lower Level." It takes a second to sink in, then I'm wide awake, dressing, and moving aft.

Seawater is salty because of the presence of dissolved salt, sodium chloride. Each salt molecule has one atom of sodium and one of chlorine. Seawater contains tens of thousands of parts per million (ppm) of both of these atoms. Our steam plant, by comparison, is kept at less than a half ppm total dissolved chloride atoms. Chlorine is a very corrosive atom. The chlorine atom in road salt is what makes our cars rust. In our steam generators, we have thin tubes that carry reactor coolant on the inside, boiling steam plant water on the outside. These tubes are all that stand between the radioactive water cooling our reactor and the clean secondary plant and, under the right conditions, they can corrode through in a matter of hours. Any chlorides are unacceptable because there is so little room for error. We make fresh water from sea water by evaporating it – the steam that comes off the seawater is nearly pure, and passing it through a demineralizer makes it even more pure. If something happens, though, we can have some brine carry over into the steam plant, carrying impurities with it.

The AMSLL watch samples each steam generator at least once every six hours. Among the parameters monitored is chloride concentration. This time, instead of less than 0.5 ppm, he found ten in the port steam generator. Not much, but enough to worry us. It's the highest level I'd seen, and we had to take care of it. But first, we needed all of the ELTs to arrive.

Dealing with a steam generator chemistry casualty is not as tightly scripted or choreographed as a reactor startup because it's less predictable. But there are still assigned roles, and everyone in my division had an important part to play. As the Leading ELT (by virtue of being the senior ELT onboard) my job was to do samples, calculate chemical additions, and advise my division officer, the Chemistry and Radiological controls Assistant (or CRA). Brian, an off-the-wall and slightly manic guy, manned the feed station where he was responsible for taking manual control of steam generator water level as needed to help return chemistry to normal. He put on a headset at the feed station gauge board and waited for instructions from Maneuvering. Mackin, our most recent addition, was tasked with mixing chemicals based on the adds I calculated. He was standing by in a rubber apron, gloves, and face shield surrounded by canisters of chemicals, scoops, and a triple beam balance.

The CRA arrived a little late, grabbed the book of emergency procedures, and asked to be briefed on the status of the casualty. I filled him in, told him what we were doing, and he read along in the book to make sure we hadn't missed any steps. This is something that should not be minimized; we all trained extensively to memorize the immediate actions required to place the plant in a safe condition, but we also made sure to confirm our actions and to choose from among the appropriate follow-up actions set forth by Naval Reactors over the few decades this type of reactor plant had been in operation. We sometimes managed to come up with variations they hadn't already thought of, but it didn't happen often. Louis was already on watch, so he just kept taking logs, filling in as needed, and running the other equipment on the watchstation. Had he not been on watch, he would have relieved the watchstander for this purpose. The last person to arrive was Mike, a nice guy and a good operator with a lot of experience. His job was to take care of everything else as needed; running logs, running chemicals, helping operate valves, or anything else we required of him. Mostly, he milled about smartly until we needed him. He was a calm guy with a bristling mustache and a good sense of humor. The EWS and ERS were already there when I arrived. The EWS had a headset on, in communication with Maneuvering, and was reading from the procedures, too, only his were those detailing the valve operations required to help adjust steam generator chemistry back to normal. The ERS was manning the blowdown station; a cluster of valves in an area smaller than a phone booth that allowed us to use the high steam pressure in the generators to blow contaminated water overboard where it could no longer harm the U-tubes. Since our reactor plant was at a higher pressure than our steam generators, any leak would result in blowing reactor coolant through the leak, into the steam generators, and spreading radioactivity into the engineroom, steam system, and condensate system. We wanted to avoid that.

The Engineer and XO had also arrived at the scene. The Eng was there because it was his plant and he wanted to supervise the whole operation and the XO appeared as the CO's eyes and ears. So we had five ELTs, three officers, and two other watchstanders, most of whom were crowded near the sample sink watching me titrate. During drills it got oppressive; now I just didn't notice. There's nothing like a real problem to help focus one's thoughts on the here-and-now rather than on petty distractions.

The first thing to do during a chloride casualty is to draw a sample on the other generator immediately because it's unlikely to have chlorides in just one. While that sample's underway, we operate valves to line up the system to blow contaminated water out of the port generator. First, we fill it as high as we can without damaging any machinery. This dilutes the chlorides in the generator as well as diluting our water chemistry. As we fill it up, we add some chemicals to keep everything in spec, then we open the last valves isolating the steam generator from the sea to start our blowdown (so called because steam pressure blows water down and out of the steam generator into the ocean). A steam generator blowdown is one of the few things you can hear all over the ship. My bunk was as far forward as you can get, and I was woken up once by a blowdown. What you're hearing is high-pressure water at over 400 degrees rushing through a small pipe into the ocean. Once out of the pipe, pressure drops rapidly to the point where the steam generator water flashes to steam, expanding several hundred times in volume (more or less, depending on the sea pressure at whatever depth we're at). In addition, some seawater will boil, adding to the violence of the event. You can hear a steam generator blowdown from tens of miles away. This is not something we do lightly, but because it's the only option we really have.

The blowdown lasts about five minutes, the time it takes to drop water level as far as we can without damaging the steam generators. We refill the port generator to its normal operating level. By this time, we've found out that the starboard generator has eight ppm chlorides, so we're feeding it for a blowdown. I calculate a chem add for the starboard generator and give the numbers to Mackin. The CRA reviews and approves the add and passes the sheet to Mackin. Mackin, in turn, carefully measures and weighs the chemicals to the gram calculated, then adds another 45 grams because we know that it takes that much extra to make up for chemical losses in the lines and tanks the add must pass through. I frown at him and call him over. He's new, so I tell him to add another hundred grams. When he looks skeptical, I remind him that we're going to be doing a lot of blowdowns and that, in each case, we're "blowing heavy". That is, the person at the feed station manually opens the feedwater regulating valve to raise water level. When water level gets to the right height, he's supposed to shut down on the valve to balance feed flow with steam demand, keeping water level constant. What Mackin doesn't know yet is that, in cases like this, as soon as the blowdown starts, the feed station is going to tweak the feed rate up a little bit to prolong the blowdown. This will clear the chlorides faster, but it will also dilute chemistry. So we have to correct for that by adding slightly more chemicals than calculated. This is one of the things that can't be put into procedure very readily because it comes from working with the plant day after day for years, getting a feel for the best way to handle certain situations, and getting a feel for how far you can deviate from procedure without getting into trouble. I didn't know of anyone who had pushed things in this manner to the point of causing major problems, but I suppose it might have happened at some time. The bottom line is that we had to keep our water chemistry "in spec", or in specification. This meant keeping chemical concentrations in a certain range that had been shown to protect the steam generators and other parts of the plant against corrosion.

The sample shows we're down to 5 ppm in the port generator and the rest of our chemistry is a little low. I calculate another chem add for another blow down, then start my post-blowdown sample on starboard. In the next two hours, I do ten full steam generator samples, calculate ten chemical additions, and try to make sure my division officer doesn't make any egregious mistakes. We finally get chlorides down to undetectable levels and take a final round of samples. Chemistry in both generators needs adjusting, so we do one more set of chem adds, one more set of post-add samples, and secure from the chlorides casualty. We've spent most of the last four hours frantically sampling, adding, worrying, and blowing down and we're all pretty beat. We usually sample each generator once every six hours; in the last four hours, we've sampled each eight times. In this time, too, the Engineroom Supervisor had found the cause of the problem, a very small leak in one valve on the evap, and was in the process of fixing it to prevent a recurrence. Unfortunately, this meant that we had to dump a lot of water from our freshwater tanks, but that was better than some of the alternatives.

Recovered from the high chlorides, I head aft to the engineroom. We were just starting to fill the number three potable water tank, having topped off our steam plant fresh water tanks the previous day. We've just blown a few thousand gallons of water overboard, cleaning up the generators, and not only is our potable water tank empty, but two of our Reserve Feed Tanks are nearly so, too. As I head forward, I know that I've taken my last shower for some time. Until we can fill our tanks again there'll be no showering, no brushing teeth with wet toothbrushes, no laundry, no hand-washing, and no other uses of fresh water that aren't vital for the ship or for survival.

Later that day, we crossed the international date line, skipping to the next day. Going west, we'd skip a day, returning east, we'd repeat one. This was my fourth time crossing in this direction and our return would be my fourth return. One year, we had crossed during the night on someone's birthday, missing it almost entirely. A common refrain in the Navy was "What are you going to do? Take away my birthday?" Well, for the next few years, this guy had a great story to tell, finishing with "I can't believe it, they actually DID take away my birthday!" Nothing like that this time, though, just another event on the calendar. That, and another time zone change. We always set our clocks by local time, so on a transit like this, we'd change time zones every day or so. I knew of some boats that always maintained their homeport time zone and others that always maintained "Zulu" time (known as Greenwich Mean Time to the rest of the world), but both my skippers liked to stick to local time so we were on the same sleeping schedule as those we were trying to watch. I couldn't remember offhand, but I seemed to recall that we were going to be 8 or 9 time zones behind San Diego when we quietly arrived on-station.

CHAPTER 9

On Station

As we crept into our op area, I reviewed the trip thus far. In addition to the major happenings I mentioned, we had contended with other, less major happenings as well. Our condensate headers sprang leaks, but these could be controlled by wrapping them with marlin, a tarred rope. We'd had an electrical fire, but that's not unexpected on any old boat, and ours was no exception. This one never really bust into flame, it just smoldered until we could cut the power and have the electricians fix the problem. We'd also had some minor problems with our drain system, making it difficult to pump water out of the bilges. This was more serious, because we had to pump the bilges every watch or so to keep water from slopping over the deckplates and starting to short out electrical systems. But, every time we started to have problems, someone would come up with an ingenious way to overcome them, bilge level would go down, and we'd go on with our lives. But these were all minor annoyances. It was the large problems, described above, that worried me. I hoped we wouldn't have anything big go wrong now that we were on station.

Maybe I should explain the term "on station." When we received our mission orders, we were given a piece of ocean to patrol. We were always in international water, as recognized by the United States, and we were the only US boat in the area. Some of our surface ships might transit the area, but any other submarine was going to be someone else's. This was important because our only real enemy was another sub. For the most part, we could avoid or sink surface ships. Evading helicopters could be difficult, but another submarine was most likely to be our biggest problem. So it was nice to know that, if push came to shove, we could sink any submerged contact without worrying about it being friendly. In any event, the piece of ocean we were assigned to was our operations area (or "op-area"), and as long as we were there, we were on station. For the next seven weeks, we'd pull off-station only for noisy operations we had to conduct or if we had to make a radio broadcast. Right now, our op-area covered most of the south-eastern coast of the Kamchatka Peninsula, including the big Soviet submarine base at Petropavlosk. To the north, we had to be careful of icebergs and the ice pack, but that was our only real natural worry.

Because of all the noise from the blowdowns, we crept on station in modified Ultra Quiet. In full Ultra Quiet, all personnel not actually on watch are confined to their racks. The only food is sandwiches served on paper plates, because even dropping a china plate can make enough noise to give you away. All watertight doors were latched open, the doors into the individual toilet stalls were taped open, and even the toilet seats were taped down with padding between the seat and the toilet to prevent clanging. We did constant monitoring of noise levels on all of our operating equipment and had switched to all of our quietest pumps and machinery to further reduce our sound signal, as well as securing the evaporator. No more fresh water for awhile, so a shower would have to wait another day or so. Watchstanders stayed seated with headsets on at all times they weren't actually taking logs, and we idled one of our turbine generators. All maintenance, entertainment, and other non-essential movement or activity came to a halt. All around the boat, you just saw people patiently waiting. Waiting for Ultra Quiet to end, waiting for their next set of logs, waiting for someone to come by to talk quietly with, waiting to be found.

In full Ultra Quiet, you can walk around the boat and hear things you never were aware of before. You can still hear the air in the ventilation system, but quieter because the fans are in slow speed. In the engineroom, you can still hear the steam in the piping and the turbines turning, but you can also hear water sloshing in the bilges and a pump in the next compartment is clearly audible. In Maneuvering, the four watchstanders might quietly talk or joke, and the EWS or ERS might sit down with the ERUL watch to pass the time, but the conversations are quiet and rare. We know that we can hear loudspeaker announcements in other boats, and we have to assume that the Soviets can, too. I remember listening to sonar once when we were playing with our of our own boats off the coast of California. The sonar tech informed me that a person was walking aft, based on the distinctive noises each watertight door made as it was opened and shut. A few moments later, he noted that someone else was now walking forward, and I could hear the difference he was talking about. Sound silencing was something we all took very seriously. In fact, even after ten years out of the Navy, I still have the urge to say "Shh…" whenever I hear a door slam or a tool drop.

Modified Ultra Quiet is a little more relaxed than full Ultra Quiet. We may run some more machinery and we might keep both turbine generators operating, but aside from that, there wasn't much difference. In either one, I would usually go to my rack and read or sleep. A few times, during drills in our home waters, I'd try to do paperwork or to read in my lab, but it was too easy to slam a drawer accidentally or to let the door slam open or shut. When it mattered, I just kept to my rack.

We spent about six hours in Modified Ultra Quiet, creeping in at five knots, and making sure we hadn't been detected. Then we relaxed to Patrol Quiet, and we were on-station; our home for the next several weeks.

Once on-station, our lives changed. We still stood watch, of course, in three-section rotation, and we still ate, slept, read, wondered what was happening back home, showered, and so forth. What we didn't do was anything noisy. The only maintenance we did was that which was absolutely necessary or could be done with a minimum of noise. We ran no drills. We were always acutely conscious of the fact that, here, a single moment of carelessness could result in our detection. So we did our jobs, worked on our qualifications, held training, and carried on life as normally as we could, given these constraints. Qualifications (or quals) were required to stand watch or to do just about anything other than sleeping and eating – most submariners spent the better part of two years going through all of their quals to the point where they were considered competent to do their jobs.

No matter where we were, people were working on their quals. As one of the more senior watchstanders aft, I was asked a lot of questions about various parts of the plant by people studying for various quals. Most of the time I tried to take it seriously. Sometimes, not. Shortly after we went to Patrol Quiet, I was in the Engineroom, taking some logs to Maneuvering. One of our junior people stopped me next to the turbine generators (which we usually called the TGs). "Hey, Andy," he said. I stopped and looked at him. "Got a question for you," he continued. "About the TGs."

"OK," I responded. "Shoot."

"Well, how much power do they put out? And what voltage?"

These were questions that were easy to find out on your own. His asking me meant he'd been too lazy to find the answers himself. Nonetheless, I gave him the numbers he was looking for, assuming more questions would be forthcoming.

"OK, thanks," he said. "Do you have time for another question?" I nodded. "Well, what's the rating on the TG breaker?" This was another easy one and, again, I gave him the correct response.

"You want to know something else?" I asked him. "Something that's not in the Manual?"

"Sure!" he responded. He was probably thinking "Great! Here's something I can use to impress whoever I get this checkout from!"

"See how big the cables are coming out of the TG?" I asked, pointing to the thick electrical cables. "Do you know why they're this thick? I mean, look at these cable runs here – they're only a fraction the size. And the wiring in the electronics is really thin. Why the big difference in size?"

I was on safe ground here. He was a machinists mate, and MMs were notoriously bad at electrical theory. He thought for a second, then replied "I'm not sure. I just never thought about it before."

"It's because of the voltage," I said, keeping a straight face. "See, the voltage coming out of the TG is pretty high. The current is carried by electrons, no matter what the voltage is, but high-voltage electrons are bigger than low-voltage ones. As the current goes through the wires or through transformers, the voltage keeps dropping due to electrical resistance and everything else. As that happens, the electrons shrink, so we can make the wires thinner. Copper's pretty heavy, so this lets us cut down on weight. By the time the electrons get to the electronic systems, their voltage is so low that they can fit through really thin wires. But here, at the TG," I pointed to the thick cables, two or three inches across "the electrons are over two inches across and they need a cable this thick to fit through."

He looked doubtful. "They never told us that in Nuke School," he replied.

"How much other stuff have you learned here that they never taught you in Nuke School?" I asked scornfully. "They just don't have time to teach you everything. That's why you still have to qualify once you get to Fleet."

"I guess so. Wow, that's pretty cool! Let me write that one down...." Later that day, his "sea dad", the person responsible for tracking his qualification progress came up to me.

"What sort of shit are you telling my guy, Andy? Something about big electrons and little electrons?" I related the story to him. He shook his head, then started laughing. "Well, I guess it shouldn't be too hard to undo that one. Good thing he's not an electrician."

"If I'd been able to pull that one on an electrician, we'd be in a lot more trouble because either we'd have a complete idiot on our hands or the 'trician training is going downhill fast."

Quals aside, one of the givens here was the cold. Sea temperature was right around 28 degrees, below freezing for fresh water and close to freezing for salt water. In the lower levels of each compartment you could see you breath and in the berthing compartments, temperatures hovered in the low 60s; nice sleeping weather. Beneath my poopy suit, I wore long-sleeved t-shirts and sweatshirts most of the time and some people onboard wore long johns. I loved the cold "weather", as did most of our engineroom watchstanders – it was easier to put on extra layers than to sweat in a 100 degree room for a 6-hour watch. As the trip went on, we built up a layer of ice on the outside of the seawater piping because the water on the inside of the pipes was so cold and, even with our hull insulation, we had condensation dripping from many parts of the hull. The main engines loved the cold water – we recycled the steam used to run the turbines by running seawater through thousands of tubes in our main condensers. We also maintained a pretty high vacuum in the condensers to increase the efficiency of the turbines. With the seawater so cold, we had a fantastic vacuum almost all the time.

The one problem with the cold water is that we froze up a few fresh water tanks. Specifically, one of our potable water tanks and our radioactive water retention tanks. We probably didn't freeze the potty water tank solid, but we did freeze up the pipes leading to the tank, making it impossible to get any water out of it. Despite our best efforts, we were unable to thaw it out and it remained out of service for nearly two months, almost until we pulled into Pearl Harbor. The retention tank froze up, too, but we were eventually able to return it to service. A good thing, too, because we preferred to discharge reactor coolant to it rather than directly overboard. Our daily reactor coolant sample generated a few liters of water that drained to the retention tanks, too. In fact, that's how we discovered it was frozen; during a primary sample the water suddenly started backing up into the sink.

This gave us some pause. There were two possibilities, either we had frozen the tank or it had filled with sea water. If it was frozen, we could try to thaw it out, but the boat was not in danger at all. On the other hand, if the tank was leaking and full of seawater, it meant we'd have full sea pressure on the tank's isolation valves and, if they leaked, we could have a path for seawater to enter the boat. We finally managed to determine the tanks weren't leaking, so we turned our attention to thawing them out.

Believe it or not, Naval Reactors had even thought of this possibility. The procedure called for pouring hot brine from the evaporator down the primary sample sink. The theory was that the brine would help to melt the ice plug in the pipes and then, once in the retention tanks, would help thaw the water inside. We first drained the water from the sample sink and piping leading to the retention tanks, then started pouring hot brine down the pipe. We let it sit for an hour, then we'd drain the pipes and would pour another few liters down the sink. Eventually, after a day or so, the pipes opened up. We quickly dumped nearly ten gallons of brine down the pipe to fully open it and to start work on the water in the tanks, themselves. Then, for the rest of the underway, every reactor coolant sample we drew was followed with a few gallons of brine for a "chaser." I wasn't very happy about putting brine into my sample system, but it was better than draining the sink to plastic bottles for two months. And it worked.

This spec op we were to spend most of our time deep. This got us away from the high seas of the north Pacific winter, made us less likely to broach the submarine, and let us listen for any submarines leaving port. We'd come to PD occasionally to copy message traffic, and sometimes we'd try to eavesdrop on the radio and radar transmissions of the Soviet fleet. But it usually seemed as though we were the only ship in that particular part of the ocean. As Christmas approached, morale dropped steadily with most of the crew wondering why in the world we were spending our holidays off the Russian coast instead of with our families.

About a week before Christmas, during the midwatch movie (A John Wayne flick), the boat comedian made an offhand comment that John Wayne probably had AIDS when he died because all actors were gay. Knowing Matt the way we all did, we knew he was just trying to get a rise out of someone to help pass the time. Sure enough, someone bit. "What do you mean, John Wayne's gay?"

"He's an actor, man. You know he had to be gay."

The argument that ensued stopped short of being a shouting match and it came to a stop when the movie ended. Later that day, though, one of the senior enlisted men came up to Matt. "You know, Matt, I think you were a bit harsh on The Duke. In fact, I think you were downright disrespectful. And, you know, John Wayne played a Naval officer in one of his movies, so you were actually showing disrespect to an officer. You could be written up and placed on report for that."

Matt pretty much repeated his earlier statements and offered a few suggestions as to his thoughts regarding this petty officer. Then he walked off, not thinking much more about it. He'd had his fun and now it was time for bed. When he woke up to go on watch, he found a report chit waiting for him. "Showing disrespect to a senior officer" is what it said. Matt looked at it, then looked at the COB, who had handed him the report chit, and asked "Is this for real?"

"You better believe it. There must have been at least ten people who heard you say those disrespectful things about The Duke. And he was an officer, too. Seems like a clear-cut case to me." The COB walked off, smiling to himself.

Matt was pretty sure the whole thing was a joke, but played it up anyway. "Can you believe this shit?" he asked. "I make one comment, just joking around, and now I'm on report. What a bunch of baloney!" The rest of his watch, he'd periodically be heard muttering to himself about the injustice of it all. Later that day, in the Plan of the Day (our daily newsletter, work plan, etc.), Matt's charges were published with a note that the XO had agreed to launch an investigation.

Now, before going much further, I should add that even the Navy is not this stupid. And, however arbitrary military justice may seem at times, there was no way that Matt was going to be charged with insulting John Wayne (no matter how popular he was) because of a role he'd played thirty years before. But, as a way to get people's minds off of other things, this was heaven-sent and I expected the CO and XO to play it up and stretch it out as much as possible. Luckily for them, Matt had a reputation as being one of the "wits" on board, with a caustic enough sense of humor that everyone enjoyed speculating about suitable punishments. So we followed the case and its investigation for some time in the POD.

A few days before Christmas, I ran into the Skipper outside my lab. "Hey, Captain, got a question for you," I said after greeting him.

"What's that, Karam?"

"Well, Sir, when I was a kid, we always had an electric train set up at Christmas time. And I've been talking to a lot of the guys here, and most of them had one, too."

"And your point is?" he replied warily.

"Well, what I was thinking is that we should put one up in Control around the scopes. I mean, they're right in the middle of a pretty good-sized open space. And I'm sure someone here brought along a figure-8 train track. Just think how much it could do for morale. Bringing back all those fond memories of our childhood. What could be better than that, Sir? And maybe we could hang some garland on the Ballast Control Panel, and some decorations over the Fire Control stations! What do you think, Sir?"

"I think you need some sleep, Karam. Good night." He continued on into Control. I stopped to think how lucky I was to have a CO with a sense of humor.

CHAPTER 10

Holidays at Sea

CHRISTMAS DAY. Our 15th day at sea and our third day officially on-station. Before leaving port, I had picked up small toys and other goodies for my division. After drawing my nightly primary coolant sample, I hung some yellow plastic anti-contamination booties in the lab, using duct tape. On each one I wrote the name of one of the men in my division, including our division officer. A toy, a can of soda, and a few candy bars went into each, and I went to bed. When I woke up, I found some thank-you notes in the lab, along with some empty soda cans. My mood wasn't any better, but at least my division's was.

We copied some family-grams on Christmas, too. Each of us, before leaving port, was given a dozen forms to be sent to family or friends. Throughout our mission, these could be filled in with brief messages, sent to the Squadron, reviewed for inappropriate content, and radioed to us on a time-available basis. This was the only contact with home we had, 50 words at a time. If the content was felt to be inappropriate, the Squadron censors might edit or hold back the message. For example, bad news was not permitted because, unless we could pull into a friendly port to transfer someone off, this could make someone stew or worry about something that was completely out of their control. Why tell someone, the theory went, that his father had died if there was no way to go home for the funeral. Better to hold that news until pulling into port.

Family-grams always came at the tail end of message traffic. When some were included, word spread quickly. "Hey – didja hear? They've got some family-grams this time! Fifteen of 'em!" "Cool! Do you know who got any yet? Any for me?" "Don't know, man, let's go to Radio and see." And there would be a line of people outside of Radio, waiting for the small strips of paper to be printed, cut, and handed out.

"Karam – got one for you." My lab was just down the passageway from Radio. I'd left the door open, just in case. I got up so quickly I almost fell out of my chair and hurried to Radio to take the slip of paper. I opened it up and read:

"MM1 KARAM, 12-30-88

HI. HAPPY NEW YEAR. HOPE YOU ARE FONE AND HAVING FUN. DID YOU HAVE A MERRY XMAS? SAVED $10,000 BY NOT BUYING A NEW CAR BUT NOW TURN SIGNAL DOESN'T WORK. SCHOTTENHEIMMER RESIGNED AS BROWN'S HEAD COACH AFTER LOSS TO HOUSTON. GOING TO NEW YEAR'S PARTY. MOM."

Not much, and a few typos (probably on the part of the radioman sending the message), but any news from home was good to have. I carefully folded it in half. In another few hours I'd pull it out and re-read it, pretending I'd just got it for the first time. And again tomorrow, and the next day.

Slim and infrequent though family-grams were, our families knew even less about us. My very first time to sea had been for nearly 2 ½ months and, in that whole time, I had no way to contact anyone. When we pulled into port I found ten letters from my mother, one each week, each one sounding increasingly irritated, anxious, or concerned that I wasn't writing. After reading the last one I called (we were in Japan at the time) and asked my mother if she'd forgotten that I really couldn't write from under the Pacific. Her response? "Well, you said you'd be out of touch, but I didn't know you meant completely out of touch." But she got better after that.

In any event, this was our holiday season. Cheap toys and some junk food for my division. Turkey roll, instant mashed potatoes, re-hydrated green beans, and bug juice for dinner. And a movie marathon all day and night (as opposed to the single movie typically allowed on the evening watch and the midwatch). New Year's was about the same.

Meanwhile, in the case of Matt versus John Wayne, the XO's investigation had verified that John Wayne had, indeed played a Naval officer in one of his movies (I think it was "The Fighting Seabees" although I must admit to not knowing much about The Duke's movie career). This was reported as giving more credibility that Matt's comments had, indeed shown disrespect to an officer, something that just isn't permitted. Matt had an advocate assigned to him in preparation for Captain's mast and they were reported to be busily reviewing their strategy.

After New Year's, though, things started looking up. I pulled out of my funk, which was nice, and started spending more time in Sonar and Control, learning more about the non-nuclear parts of the boat. The previous year I had qualified Chief of the Watch while on a Spec Op, and I was hoping to work on my Diving Officer quals this time out. The time in Sonar was to unwind; one of my roommates was a sonar technician, so I'd often go in to relax a little bit. Sonar was always dimly-lit with subdued blue lighting so the techs could see their displays more clearly, there was often soft music playing, and often small talk as the three or four techs and Sonar Supervisor watched and listened for anything out of the ordinary.

Most of the time the techs didn't have their headphones on at all. In front of each was a waterfall display. Our sonar sphere (and the towed array, for that matter) sent information to the sonar computers running the display. Each screen showed strips for bearing above us, at our depth, and below. A noise would show up as a bright spot. If it was a sharp noise, like a transient, a white blip would show on the screen, while a ship would show as a bright trail. If a sonar tech saw something that looked interesting, he could put on the headphones and select that set of hydrophones to listen to that specific noise to figure out what it was. Each new contact had to be identified. I'd go in, ask one of the techs to let me listen to biologics, and would talk and joke quietly while listening to the whales. It was as good a way to unwind as any I could find onboard. Although never as good as our sonar techs, I did get to be able to identify some different types of whales, fish, and clicking shrimp. And, especially when near the Aleutians or Kamchatka, we'd pick up the low grumbling that was identified as seismic sounds, probably magma shifting in a reservoir somewhere deep in the crust of the Earth.

Today, Sonar was a little busier. One of our frigates was in the area, practicing launching their helicopter. I listened for a little while, the sonar techs showing me how to tell when the helo was landing, taking off, and flying around. It was interesting, but a little busier than I wanted. Sonar was right next to my lab, so I left and went forward to Nucleonics. I shut and locked the door, set up my miniature stereo system (actually a walkman-type tape player with two miniature speakers), put in a Jimmy Buffet tape, and pulled out a book.

For whatever reason, I couldn't get sleepy. It was noon and I was wide awake. After a few hours of reading, I put my book down and went forward to my rack. I lay there for another hour, reading and waiting for fatigue to take over. Finally, around dinner time, I dozed off.

I woke just in time to catch the last part of midrats (the midnight rations). Soup and sandwiches. I started my nightly instrument checks, drew the primary sample, and decided to wander into Control. At night, Control can be rigged for either white, red, or black. Rigged for white means that white lights are on, largely because we're deep. Before coming to PD, we would rig Control for red because the deep red lights would help everyone's eyes to night-adapt. We always manned the scope when at PD, so it helped if the OOD could actually see something. Just before coming to PD, we'd turn off all lights, rigging Control for black. Part of the reason was to help maintain night vision and part was to prevent any light from shining back through the scope, giving away our position.

Right now, we were at PD and Control was rigged for black. I eased around the heavy curtain that was hung to keep the passageway light out. As my eyes started to night-adapt, I began to see the dim light of the instruments, seemingly floating in mid-air because the panels they were attached to and the people monitoring them were equally invisible in the dark. Looking to my right, I could barely see the fire control technician looking at his monitor, trying to get a fire control solution on a sonar contact we were tracking. To the left, the Ballast Control Panel was outlined by dim indicator lights, showing the Chief of the Watch only by a dark area in the middle of the panel. In front, the depth gauge, speed indicator, ship's heading, and trim indicator were visible in front of the Dive, helmsman, and planesman. And, in the center of Control, the OOD was circling around and around, looking through the #1 scope to see if anyone was going to try to run us down.

As I stood a little longer, I realized that I was hearing whale song coming out of a speaker on the sonar console. In nearly four years onboard, this was the best and most magical moment I can remember. The sea was calm, so we were rolling only a little, just enough to be soothing. The only sound in Control was the sound of the whales (humpbacks, I think) singing to each other in a darkness broken only slightly by the dim instrument lights hanging in space. The watchstanders were intent on their work and the OOD walked in silent circles, still looking intently through the scope. Nobody said anything and, after a few minutes, I left before anyone spoke.

CHAPTER
11

Exercises

Things started picking up again shortly after New Year's and we finally got to start earning our money. We received word that a Soviet boomer was going to be leaving port soon and we were to follow her. It was a Delta VI, one of their newer models, and we were to see where she went and how she got there. We moved in a little closer to Petropavlosk and made sure our sensors were working.

Our boat had three sonar arrays, two of which we used routinely. The spherical array was a set of hydrophones mounted in the very front of the boat, about 10 feet or so directly forward of my rack. The sphere was about 10 feet in diameter (or so my roommate told me) and, at sea, was kept filled with fresh water for better acoustic coupling. We could use it in both active and passive modes. That is, we could ping with it to get a range and bearing to a target and we could listen to see what we could hear. Typically we listened. Pinging was more accurate, but it also made a lot of noise – others could hear us a lot farther away than we could get a good sonar return. It was like using a flashlight – you may only be able to see 20 feet ahead with a flashlight, but someone else can see the light from a few hundred feet away. In fact, a full-strength ping could kill a man up to a hundred yards from the boat and it put so much acoustical energy into the water that we needed both turbine generators on-line to produce one.

We preferred to use our sonar in a passive mode. By listening carefully, we could not only hear a ship or submarine, but we could break the noise down into its component parts. We could hear the frequency of the ship's pumps, its electric plant, and its engines. Looking closely at the acoustic data, we could count the blades on the screw, count the number of screws the ship had, and see how fast it was turning. And, by carefully tracking the direction and angle the noise was coming from, we could eventually tell how far away the other ship was, whether it was a sub or a surface ship, and when it changed course.

We also had a towed array sonar system. This was a line of hydrophones nearly half a mile long that we towed behind the ship to listen more carefully. We couldn't go active on our towed array, but its listening ability was without parallel. The towed array was long enough that, with close contacts, we could triangulate on it alone to determine a distance to the target. The array itself was stored on a reel when not in use and was paid out through a tube that ran the length of the submarine, diverting to the outer edge of the port stern plane to avoid the screw.

The towed array did have drawbacks, of course. It took a long time to deploy, because of its length. So it was not an "instant response" type of tool. In addition, the towed array was flexible. That meant that, if we turned, it'd take some time for the array to stabilize and, for that period of time, bearing data wasn't very accurate. We had tables to help determine how long it would take to stabilize for various speeds and length of array deployed – the faster we went, the faster it would stabilize, but the less we could hear. As with anything else, a series of trade-offs.

In any event, we had the towed array out now, and had been streaming it since arriving on-station. And it was on the towed array that we picked up the Delta VI leaving port. We let it go to a distance of about 5 or 6 miles before turning to trail. Once it was far enough from port that we didn't worry much about being accidentally detected, we moved in closer.

"Man the fire control tracking party," came over the ship's announcing system. My job here was to man the periscope if we were at PD and to help with plotting sonar bearings and distance if we were deep. The Delta VI was submerged, so I went to the time-bearing plotting chart.

We had several plots to maintain during battle stations, tracking, or other similar operations. One plot chose a baseline frequency and looked for changes in pitch that could indicate a Doppler shift showing the target was moving towards or away from us. Another, the Geo plot, plotted the positions of all targets of interest against our position to try to keep track of everyone in our part of the ocean at any particular time. The Quartermasters tracked our position against known geographic hazards, like islands, seamounts, and the shore.

My plot, the time-bearing plot, tracked the bearing to a specific target of interest over time as our submarine made course changes. The theory is simple. If you're moving and someone else isn't then you can move slowly past them and see how fast they're changing their apparent position against the background. For example, as you walk past a tree, it'll seem to move against the houses in back of it. If you know how fast you're moving and you measure how fast the tree appears to change position (or relative bearing) then you can figure out how far away the tree is. If it's changing bearing quickly then it's pretty close by. In our case, things were a bit more complicated because sonar bearings shift, acoustic conditions are never perfect, and our targets were moving at variable speeds on changing courses. Nevertheless, with enough practice we could do a pretty good job of figuring out where they were and where they were going. I should also point out that we were a backup method. The primary job of tracking was delegated to our fire-control computers. But, just in case they got squirrely on us, we had human back-up for all essential tasks.

It got hectic, though. Data points came in every 15 seconds for ten minutes or so, then we'd change course. In the few minutes between a course change and the first bearing, I'd take out a circular slide rule and, using some scales designed for the purpose, calculate a distance (range) to the target. Then the next set of bearings would come in and we'd start again.

This time the Old Man was determined to not only follow the boomer, but to get some sound cuts on it, too. By doing this, we could get specific-enough information to allow the boat to be identified individually any time in the future. A good set of sound cuts would also give us more information to help identify any ships of this type in the future. Knowing if a boomer or fast attack submarine was crossing to your shores was nice information to have. Trying to get the sound cuts, though, was nerve-wracking.

First, we had to get close enough to get good data. This meant closing to a distance of less than a mile. A mile may seem far, but really isn't. One ship at 5 knots can cover a mile in 12 minutes. Two ships a mile apart, each at 10 knots on a collision course will meet in 3 minutes unless someone gets out of the way. But it's hard to get good acoustic data at a great distance, so we rigged for ultra quiet and closed in behind our target.

Towed arrays notwithstanding, the best place to try to sneak up on a submarine is from behind. The sonar sphere is blocked from hearing in back by noise from the boat itself and even the towed array can't get good directional information on noises directly astern. We came in directly astern at only a knot or two faster than they were making. At this rate, it took nearly an hour to get into position, plotting bearing data continuously to verify our position with respect to the boomer.

Once in position, we carefully drifted from port to starboard and back, all the while safely in the Delta's blind spot, or baffles. A few times she'd apparently slow down because bearing rate would start to increase. On most of these occasions, Sonar would announce a change in the turn count (the speed of the screw) and Doppler would note a change in frequency before I'd see anything on my plot.

One time, however, we changed course to get a better cut on their port side and I calculated a quick range to the target. Three hundred yards, way too close. The last range had been nearly 2000 yards, one nautical mile. I quickly rechecked everything, coming up with the same number, which I wrote down on a slip of paper, passing it to the XO. His eyes widened and he went to the CO, who had been driving the boat all through this evolution. The CO was over to my station in two steps. "How close are we, Karam?"

"Three hundred yards, Sir."

"Is that range good? Are you sure?" I was. The CO turned urgently to the Dive. "All stop! Let's open the range a bit. All we need is to run into this thing. Slow us the hell down now – all we need is to have her do a Crazy Ivan or slow down – we'll be running into her so fast it'll make your head spin."

Control went quiet. Maneuvering called back and the phone talker announced "Officer of the Deck, Maneuvering reports answering all stop." I got another set of data. Then another. The CO was glued to the sonar repeater, as though willing it to show the range.

"No course change. Let's just hope she opens up the range a bit before doing anything drastic. Karam, what's the range now?"

"Not enough data points yet, sir. We lost some TMA when we went to all stop. Give me another two points." Thirty seconds to get two more data points. Ten seconds to calculate a range. Five more seconds to check it. Two more seconds to decide if it was valid. "Nine hundred yards, sir. But I don't have a lot of confidence in the data because our speed's changing."

"Close enough. Phone talker, to Maneuvering, make turns for three knots. We'll let him pull a little more ahead of us." Control relaxed a little. Now we were just tense. And we still had our work to do and we were still worried about a Crazy Ivan.

Eventually, the CO decided we had enough data. We slowed down a bit and let the range open up, allowing the boomer to draw ahead of us. At a more comfortable distance of 5 miles, we followed her towards the Sea of Okhotsk.

The Sea of Okhotsk, or the Sea of O as we came to call it, lies behind the Kamchatka Peninsula and the Kuril Islands. The Soviets claimed the entire sea as territorial waters and they laced all passages into it with arrays of hydrophones; their equivalent of our SOSUS lines. One of their reasons for doing this is that they kept their boomers there. Our ballistic missile boats found security in the open ocean, unguarded but aware. The Soviets preferred to stick their boomers in the Sea of O and to try to deny access to anyone else. We recognized the Sea as international waters and sent surface ships in periodically to emphasize that view. We also sent subs in from time to time, albeit with less fanfare. This was one of those times.

Before leaving port, the CO had received permission to enter the Sea of Okhotsk under certain specific conditions. One of these was if we were trailing (or trying to intercept) the Akula, their latest and greatest fast attack boat. The other was if we were trailing a boomer. We had a day before we got to the most likely entrance. A day to get ready.

We were going mostly south and a little west along Kamchatka. We expected the boomer to turn to the west to pass into the Sea of O, then into the Northern Sea of Japan through the Straits of La Peruse. If so, there would be some irony in that the last submarine named *Plunger*, a World War II boat, passed this way on its way to Japan. She made it back, and I hoped we would, too.

Journal Excerpt, january 3, 1989

We're in! We snuck in last night. Luckily, the Delta IV was going slowly; giving us time to top off our fresh water tanks before hitting the Straits because we won't be able to run the evap until we're out again. Once we topped off all tanks and pumped the bilges, we rigged the ship for Ultra Quiet. The CO really means it this time, too. This is the most severe UQ I've seen yet. We taped open the doors to all the stalls in the head to keep them from slamming and we even taped down the toilet seats, just to keep anyone from dropping one and giving us away. All watertight doors are latched open, of course, the port turbine generator is secured, and nobody is out of the rack unless they're on watch. We went to UQ right after I had finished with my primary coolant sample, so I was in my rack for nearly 15 hours straight, waiting for us to secure from UQ. Slept for awhile, got up to quietly go to the head, and had dinner (peanut butter and jelly sandwiches) just before securing from UQ.

And now, of course, the question – why us? I mean, we're an old 594-class boat, and Pearl sends us through the most heavily listened-to piece of water the Soviets have. I've been told there's a 688 up around here, too; why not send them? We've not been detected during my time on board, and I've got a lot of confidence in the Old Man, but let's face it, the Los Angeles class boats are supposed to be a lot quieter than us. So why us? Who knows; we're set to go for decommissioning when we get back, maybe the Nav thinks they can save money if we're sunk out here. A hundred fifty payouts of $20 K (which is the value of our insurance policy) each is only $3 million, a lot less than the $50 million that decom will cost. Hmmm…let's hope the accountants aren't running this op.

The passage was interesting. The water here's shallow. We came through with only 45 feet of water beneath the keel and about the same above us. At one point, we took a two degree up-angle; you could barely feel it except that we're so conscious of everything right now. I never saw the CO move so quickly – in ten seconds he was in Control yelling at the Dive to get our angle under control or to get the hell out of Control. But I can see the Old Man's point. We're nearly 300 feet long and we only have 45 feet to work with either way. A fifteen degree angle will lift the screw out of the water or dig it into the mud, but a smaller angle will drive us to the surface or into the bottom in no time at all. And we don't have to hit bottom to let their hydrophones hear us. Anyhow, we got back to a zero angle pretty quickly and only went up five feet, so we're OK. I was just glad we made it through.

So now we're in the Sea of O. We lost the boomer for a few hours – they went through on the surface at a higher speed than we could manage, so they got out of sonar range. The acoustics here are pretty good, though, so we found them again without too much trouble. The downside is that that the acoustics are pretty good – they can hear us better, too. But, for now, we're in and following our boomer. Apparently, the Akula's heading this way for sea trials, so we might be pulled away from the Delta IV to try to get some intel on her. Let's hope she's not as good as everyone says. I think we can beat the Akula or the hydrophones. I don't know if we can take both of them. Here's hoping. In the meantime, all I can say is that 15 hours of UQ is too much of a good thing. I didn't think I could have too much rest, especially on an op, but there's only so much time you can spend lying in your rack, waiting. I slept for nearly 10 hours, but can't get back to sleep. Almost makes me wish our scrubbers were down again. At least the high CO_2 helps you sleep.

And that pretty much describes our transit into the Sea of Okhotsk. Long, slow, and nerve-wracking, to be honest with you. But, truthfully, I didn't really worry about being caught. Yes, it was tense, but I never really expected anything other than complete success. Which we had.

Once in the Sea of O, we caught up with the boomer and tracked it into its op area the next day. We followed it around, then got a message that the Akula had finally left port, headed for the northern Sea of Japan. So we figured an intercept course and set out as quickly and quietly as we could to try to find it.

The Akula was a big prize. It was the newest and best Soviet fast-attack boat, one of the first to come out after the flap in which European and Japanese companies had been caught selling proscribed technology to the USSR. We didn't know much about its capabilities yet because there was only one; we were trying to find out what it could do, how to find them, and maybe how to shoot them if we needed to. As far as we knew, only one US boat had managed to track the Akula; everyone else had come back empty-handed or had been caught trying to get close. Our best guess is that they were at least as quiet as us, and maybe as quiet as a 688, our best. But, on the other hand, three years ago we'd thought that the Victor III was pretty quiet and we were really worried about them. Turned out not to be a problem once we finally spent some time nearby. When we knew what to listen for, they were just not that bad to find.

We made it to the Straits before the expected arrival time for the Akula and hung around, waiting for it to show up. The next day we received another message saying it had returned to Petropavlosk for unknown reasons. We were to exit the Sea of O and head for Petr (as we were calling it by then), waiting to see if she'd head out to sea again. We transited the Straits that night, another long, quiet ordeal, and were back outside Petr late the next day. That's when Greg got sick. And, in the John Wayne case, the XO verified that at least ten people were willing to say they had heard Matt's comment that John Wayne was gay; a comment that they all knew to be false and a malicious attempt to slander a fine officer and a wonderful American.

CHAPTER 12

Appendicitis

GREG HAD BEEN FEELING POORLY FOR A FEW DAYS and finally got around to seeing the Doc about it. Subs don't have medical doctors, they have senior Corpsmen who have been through a year of Independent Duty School. Our Doc (all Corpsmen are called Doc) was one of the best. The local Naval hospital was closed when he was to be doing his equivalent of a residency, so he got to spend about six months in the Yale University Medical School, learning from some of the best. We were lucky. And Greg was lucky – the one surgical procedure the Doc was trained to perform was an appendectomy.

Doc finally diagnosed the appendicitis by having Greg lie down on his back and sharply rapping his foot. Greg looked at him questioningly for a moment, then nearly cried with pain. Doc explained that the sharp rap set up vibrations in the intestines, eventually straining the part to which the appendix was attached. The sharp pain, he said was the vibrations finally reaching the inflamed area. Greg had been disbelieving; this changed his mind. Doc reported to the XO who went to the CO. Greg went to his rack and, within an hour, we were headed off-station to transmit an emergency message.

We reached our transmit point and waited a few hours until there were no radio-capable satellites in the sky, then transmitted an emergency message to the Commander of Submarines, Pacific (COMSUBPAC) at Pearl advising them of the situation. On these special missions, we were under his direct operational control, so he was advised of everything that happened and would give us our marching orders. From what I overheard, I could tell the CO wasn't happy about transmitting because of the chance the Soviets would intercept the traffic and pinpoint our position with their direction-finding equipment. However, we really didn't have much choice, and neither did Greg, so he authorized the transmission. An hour later we received a response telling us to stay on station, treat Greg with antibiotics, and call back every 24 hours with the previous day's worth of vitals. If things got really bad, they might give us permission to pull out and get medical treatment. Considering the nearest hospital was a week away, we were under few illusions. If it came down to pulling off station, we figured either the Doc would be operating or Greg probably wouldn't make it.

Theoretically, we could handle an operation. The table in the Wardroom was the designated operating table and a socket in the overhead was designed to hold the surgical light, which we found in one of the medical supply lockers. The Doc had a supply of scalpels, drugs, anesthesia (kind of), and a reference book, plus his experience doing two appendectomies under supervision at Yale three years earlier. A number of us were given parts to play and told to study for them with the Doc. My role was lighting and photography, since one of my collateral duties was that of ship's photographer.

Taking my job seriously, I dug out the surgical light, plugged it into the socket, and turned it on. Nothing. I fiddled with it and tried again. Not a single photon emitted. More adjustments, a look at the electrical setup, and more fiddling still produced no light. I called the Doc in. He shook the bulb briefly (something I'd been afraid to do) and heard some rattling. We started to talk about Plan B.

Plan B was completely ad hoc. In my role as ship's photographer I had to do a fair amount of work copying photographs or charts on a copy stand. To get good photos with a reasonable exposure time, we had to use a lot of light. So I had four high-intensity lights we were saving for making the slide briefing that'd be shown to the admirals and whoever else was interested. A lot was riding on the quality of the slides, including the CO's evaluations and career options. However, the CO felt that giving the Doc enough light to operate by might be slightly more important and told us to rig something up that'd work. This made Greg feel better, although he was strenuously hoping that he wouldn't need this special attention. We had the lighting set within a few hours, including provisions in case one of the bulbs burned out during the operation.

I should note at this point that this was the second time in the last two years a situation like this came up. The first time had been the previous year's spec op when one of the coners came down with appendicitis. That time, too, we were told to stay on station unless the appendix ruptured. We made it back to Adak about 25 days after the initial diagnosis. Before the brow was even down, the guy was taken off the boat and rushed to the hospital. Less than two hours after tying up to the pier his appendix was out and the surgeons were closing. We all hoped this would be the same.

One thing that kept coming back to me during the whole appendectomy saga was a play I had read in junior high school. I could never remember the name of it or the playwright, but it had to do with a diesel boat during World War II on which a crewman came down with appendicitis. In that case, the Doc had to operate because their treatments weren't all that great and they were a long ways from home. I spent a lot of time trying to remember if the Doc was successful or not. I guess I was hoping for some sort of omen, if you will. Hoping that, if I could remember that the operation in the play had turned out all right, then Greg's would be OK, too. But I couldn't remember how it all turned out. Come to think of it, I still can't recall how it ended.

We pulled back on-station and the Doc came up with a rotation for some of the junior guys to keep track of Greg's vital signs. He showed them what to do, drew up a chart to fill out, and set them loose while he figured out the proper antibiotic dosing to keep the appendix under control without completely wiping out our supplies. He and I got along pretty well together, so I asked him how it looked. "Not too bad," he replied, "As long as nobody else gets sick. I can probably keep Greg out of trouble, unless he's allergic to one of these, but I don't have enough to treat an infected hangnail in anyone else unless we pull off station early."

The next day, we pulled off-station again to transmit another message to Pearl; the last 24 hours' worth of information on Greg. We were moving at about 10 knots, not too slowly, but slowly enough to be quiet. I went to Sonar to say hi and to find out if anything interesting was going on. My roommate looked puzzled, so I asked him what was up.

"I'm not sure, Andy" he replied. "We just got passed by two Victor IIIs (which were Soviet ASW-capable submarines), both going active on sonar every now and again, and moving at 30 knots. If they'd been going any slower, there's no way they would have missed us, but at that speed, they couldn't hear a thing. We're trying to find out what the hell they're doing." Earlier, I'd thought I'd heard some pinging, but dismissed it as hearing things – submarines just don't ping that often. Knowing I hadn't been hearing things, I shivered retroactively. You ping when you're trying to find someone and you don't care if they know you're around. Pinging also gives very precise information on an enemy's distance and location. If they were pinging, it meant they were looking for a submarine, they were very confident, and a sonar return would give our location to them on a platter. These were all bad.

A few minutes later, a sonar tech called in an airborne contact, flying down the port side of the boat, and a few minutes after that, another airborne contact to starboard. I was always amazed at what Sonar could come up with – in this case, they could tell which side of the boat the flybys were on and where the sonobuoys were dropped. Once, listening, I could hear a helo flying around and could even tell when it landed on the frigate, just by the quality of the sound. In this case, one of the planes dropped a sonar buoy; the splash was picked up and tracked. As we got closer to our transmit area, we noticed more and more planes and picked up a few more boats moving quickly in that direction. With all this, the CO decided enough was enough. He wasn't sure how, but assumed they were looking for us, and it was time to clear the area. We turned to the south and went to our backup transmit location.

I overheard the CO talking with some of the wardroom. He felt that the Intel weanies had screwed up and listed a satellite with radio capabilities as a photo-only bird. Either that, or someone just happened to get lucky and was listening in with two receivers at just the right time and on the correct frequency to triangulate our signal. Whatever the reason, there were a lot of Soviet boats and planes right over yesterday's broadcast location so it seemed likely they were looking for us. It also seemed likely they didn't know much more; otherwise they'd be looking in our op area and not at our broadcast location.

We reached our backup transmit location, waited until no satellites were in the sky, and squirted an augmented message to Pearl. This time we used a buoy as an extra safety measure. We recorded the message, shot the buoy overboard through the after signal ejector, and left. After a programmed amount of time the encoded compressed message would be sent off to Pearl. Meanwhile, we'd be in a different part of the ocean waiting for a response. Except this time, we were interested in more than just Greg. We wanted to find out what was happening with the Soviet Navy and what our next mission was to be.

CHAPTER 13

ASW Games

I wish to have no connection with a ship that does not sail fast
for I intend to go into harm's way.
John Paul Jones, November 1778

THE MESSAGE WE GOT BACK was interesting. COMSUBPAC's intel guys thought the Soviets were either conducting a major ASW exercise or were looking for us specifically, maybe from having sniffed out our earlier transmission. In any event, we were told to remain in the areas to monitor the operations, identify as many of the participants as we could, and get some good photos of the newer ships. We were also reminded to not get caught – as if we needed reminding. We were pretty squarely in international waters, but, off the Soviet coast, we really didn't know what to expect from them. This was just a few years after the Soviets had shot down the Korean airliner, an incident that we were well aware of.

We found out that the Soviets had put every seaworthy boat and all of their ASW surface ships out to sea, and just about every plane and helo available into the air. All were apparently looking for us. We were told to continue staying on station and that "help is on the way." The help, it turned out, was another 6 US boats, most of them sent out on short notice. We were each given our own op area and told to get as much intel as possible. We were also told to get fire control solutions on anything that crossed our path. A fire control solution is when we track a target, figure out its course and speed, and know that we could shoot it if we had to with a high probability of a kill.

Many of us got a little worried when word of all this filtered down to us. We were pretty sure of our ability to stay undetected against a few Soviet ships not looking for us, but we were about to be decommissioned, in their backyard, with as many systems broken as working. Many of us just weren't sure if the boat was up to the task of staying undetected against so many ships who knew we were somewhere out there. Our main hope was that they'd decide after a few days that we'd left when they put all their ASW assets into the water.

The first few days were as close to wartime conditions as I ever hope to experience. Although we did not go to Ultra Quiet often, we were at battle stations more often than not, making sonar approaches on submerged and surface targets alike and making periscope approaches on some selected surface targets. I went through a few pencils on the time-bearing plot and, in my other battle station, spent a fair amount of time near or on the scope.

During this time, we took a lot of good pictures of their surface ships, and even got some submarines on the surface. This last part was new to me; we stayed submerged as much as possible, even in our home waters, but the Soviets did things differently. Maybe it was easier for them to communicate this way. Who knows. In any event, we were able to ID just about every Soviet ship out there by their pendant numbers (the hull numbers painted on the sides of the ships).

Taking the photos was both busy and exciting. First, of course, we had to try to get close enough to get a decent shot. If possible, the skipper or OOD would also try to line us up for decent lighting, although this was not always possible and we'd just do our best. As we approached, we had to be increasingly careful because anywhere inside about 3000 yards (a mile and a half), the scope could be seen by either a lookout or radar. Lookouts would see the scope itself or, more likely, the wake (or "feather") it left moving through the water. So we tried to keep a scope exposure time of less than 6 seconds whenever possible and never more than 10 seconds.

When we got to within 1000 yards (and hopefully closer), the CO would have the photo team (me and the photo officer) raise our scope (we had two, a navigation scope and the attack scope) and squeeze off as many shots as we could in 6 seconds. Focusing, shooting, bracketing exposures, and calling out every shot was quite a bit for six seconds, but at less than a half mile, we had no choice. At times, if we went more than a second too long, the Skipper would just lower the scope with one of us still taking pictures. After a few knots, I came to realize that this was one time limit that was inflexible, and for good reason.

Taking pictures was, in some ways, more difficult than shooting torpedoes. Torpedoes can be fired at ten miles, but good photos require closing to a fairly short distance away from an enemy vessel that might just be actively looking for you, without being caught. At less than a half mile from a major Soviet warship, you not only ran the risk of detection, but collision, too, which would be even worse. On the other hand, there was no better way to prove you had tracked a specific target than to have a nice photo of it at 1000 yards or less, and these were often used to keep score on an op such as this. Besides, the CO loved to show nice crisp, close pictures of the latest warships at the post-operation brief with COMSUBPAC. The bottom line, all things considered, was that the CO had to balance the intelligence value of the photos against the risk to his boat; a tough job. Tougher than I ever wanted to take on.

As periscope assistant, my job was to keep track of the relative bearing to whichever target the CO wanted to look at. When he decided to make an observation, I was to raise the scope by pulling on an orange ring set into the overhead. This ring activated hydraulics, raising or lowering the scope depending on which direction I was pulling it. The procedure was easy with only one or two targets; just listen for the relative bearing (the direction relative to the bow of the boat) we'd have to look to see the target, set the scope to that bearing, and raise it. The CO would squat down to take the handles and stand with the scope, immediately looking for the target. Our goal was to have the scope exposed for only a few seconds to minimize the chance it would be seen. So it was important to put the scope up with the target in the field of view to keep the skipper from wasting even a few seconds hunting around. With more than one or two ships it sometimes got confusing and mistakes could be made. This is one of the reasons we practiced all aspects of both surface and submerged approaches in the attack trainer endlessly.

Right now we were at periscope depth (PD), tracking a surface target; a Krivak. Krivaks were a class of Soviet frigates. They were pretty ships with (I thought) graceful lines. They were also relatively fast and carried a lot ASW detection gear and a number of weapons to use against us. We'd been about ten minutes between periscope observations. Even with the risk of someone seeing our scope, the quality of the data was high enough to make the risk worthwhile. The only thing that could really catch us would be either a very good lookout who just happened to be looking our way at exactly the right time or a helo overhead and looking our way just when the scope was up. High-frequency radar could "see" the scope, too, but we weren't as worried about it because we didn't think many of their ships had this yet.

"Prepare for periscope observation, target, Master 3." This alerted everyone that we were about to take a peek at a target designated as Master 3. Normally, target tracked by sonar were identified as "sierra" and a number given sequentially. Visual targets were called "victor" with a number. This helped to organize everything. If we could definitely link a sonar contact with a visual target, both were re-designated as "Master". Most of the time we tried to give the master target the same number as the sonar target, but this was not always possible. In any event, the CO was going to look at Master 3.

"Master 3, bearing 310." Numbers were read as three numerals, so this came out "Three one zero." That was from one of the plotters.

"Relative or true?" I asked. They should have told me if that bearing was with respect to the bow of the ship (relative) or a compass bearing (true). The bearing circle on the scope showed relative bearings and, without knowing the ship's heading, I didn't know which way to point the scope.

"Relative." Came the quick response. I positioned myself at the correct location around the scope and waited. The CO took a quick look at some of the plots, the Fire Control screen, and the sonar waterfall display. I assumed he was assembling a mental picture of where everyone was, but for all I knew, he could have been going over his tax return and looking busy. After a minute, he came over to the navigation scope.

"Up periscope" he said. I reached up, twisted the ring to the right, and the scope rose. I quickly snapped down the handles on either side and hauled the scope around to point at a relative bearing of 310 degrees, about halfway between port and forward. The scope was designed with this sort of operation in mind; around the lower part of the scope was a black circle engraved with the various compass headings, just like a circular protractor. It was also set up for the periscope assistant – the bearings were 180° off from the direction I was looking, so the scope would come up on the correct relative bearing. In other words, the relative bearing of the ship's bow was 0°, the same as due north. But, when I was facing the bow of the ship and looked at the bearing circle, it showed 180 degrees because I was always on the side of the scope opposite the CO and, if I was looking forward, he was looking directly aft. The CO squatted and put his eye to the eyepiece when the scope was at about waist level, standing with the scope. As the scope hissed to a stop, he started panning slightly, up and down and side to side. "Where's the damned target, Karam? There's nothing here."

I looked at the Geo plotter. He frantically reviewed his data, looked at me, and shrugged. Nothing else from anyone else. I reviewed quickly, but didn't have a good picture of what this target had been doing. I replied "Not sure, Sir. Scope's on the last known bearing. 310." Sometimes I had a good feel for whether or not I was getting accurate information, more often not. This time I didn't have a good feel for the data and had to just accept it. Too bad it turned out to be wrong.

The skipper looked for another two seconds, stepped away from the scope, and called "Down periscope." He looked at the XO. "Scope exposure time?"

"Eight seconds."

"Too long." He turned to the Geo plotter. "We have a target a few miles away. It's a Soviet warship designed to find and sink submarines. She draws about 30 feet of water, and our sail is less than 10 feet down. And she doesn't know we're here. We need to visually sight this thing now, before she runs us over and decides we're too hard to be a whale. I've only been depth-charged once, and I don't want it to happen again."

Unlike some COs, this one rarely raised his voice and yelled even less frequently. However, he could make you feel worse by making it obvious that reasonable expectations hadn't been met because you screwed up. "Let's try this again. Do we know where Master 3 is? Geo?"

"330 relative, Sir."

"Sonar? Do you concur?"

"Sonar concurs, Captain."

"Very well. Periscope observation, Master 3. Up scope."

I raised and positioned the scope again. This time, the CO seemed pleased. "Right in the crosshairs, Karam. Bearing, mark!" He pushed the "pickle", a button on the handle of the scope that automatically sent the bearing information to the fire control computers. "Range, mark! Down scope!" I lowered the scope again. "Scope exposure time?"

"Five seconds."

"Better." He closed his eyes and concentrated for a moment, visualizing his last view of the target. "One point three division at high power. Use a masthead height of 125 feet."

This meant that, in the graduated scale visible through the scope, the Krivak took up 1.3 divisions and the scope was at its highest magnification setting. I had a circular slide rule on a string around my neck. When I was first assigned as time-bearing plotter I had snagged a circular slide rule for myself, just to make sure I didn't have to root around for one when we went to Battle Stations. Since becoming the Periscope Assistant, I had cut some notches into the outer rim to show which scales to use for high power and low power periscope observations. I now lined up the number of divisions with the high-power notch, moved the hairline to a masthead height of 125 feet, and read off the range from the third scale in. I called out the range loudly enough for everyone to hear and everyone input the data into their respective plots or computers. That was one thing about being Periscope Assistant; if you made a stupid mistake, not only was the Old Man there to catch you at it, but it was impossible to hide from anyone. I was usually right with the ranges, though, and had got to the point where I could check them in my head quickly before calling them out. Most of the time it took about five seconds to come up with the range, assuming the other ship wasn't unusually tall or short. And, of course, the range was only as good as our identification of the other ship, the information we had on its height, the CO's quick count of the number of divisions it covered, and a number of other variables too numerous to mention. However, I was impressed with how frequently we got it right.

The CO continued. "Angle on the bow, port 30 degrees. Nice bow wave, so they're at a high speed. No other contacts." So they were coming our way at high speed. At least they were alone. "Dive, make your depth 350 feet. Heading, 050. Ahead two thirds. Let's get out of his way." The Krivak was to the west of us, so this course would take us out of his path before he could come over top of us. We had no indication anyone knew we were there, but it was best not to take any chances. We went down at a 15 degree angle, angling away to the east.

"Fire Control, do you have a solution yet?"

"Yes, sir."

"Good enough to shoot?"

"Yes, sir."

"Very well. Fire Control, course and speed?"

"Course, 175. Speed, 15 knots, based on sonar turn count. Range, 8000 yards."

"Sonar, do you concur?"

"Sonar concurs, sir."

"Very well. Now let's get out of his way and find someone else."

Whenever we went into unfriendly waters we went with weapons in three of our four torpedo tubes, something we never did in friendly waters. It was a sobering sight to go into the Torpedo Room and see the massive breech doors shut, three of them with a red sign that said "Warshot loaded" on them. That was the biggest difference between the SoCal Op Area and what I called the SoKam Op Area (for South Kamchatka Operations Area) – off the coast of California we never had anything more lethal than water loaded into the tubes. We usually deployed with up to 24 weapons, a mix of Mark 48 torpedoes, Harpoon anti-ship missiles, and Subrocs, tactical nuclear anti-ship weapons. Had we really meant to shoot a torpedo, the CO would have designated a specific tube to use. Torpedo tubes 1 and 3 were on the starboard side of the boat and tubes 2 and 4 were to port. Typically, we'd try to shoot using a tube on the same side of the boat we expected the target to be on when the weapon found it. This was because the torpedoes were tethered to the submarine with a long wire that sent back telemetry data and through which we could steer the weapon if our fire control solutions suddenly changed. However, if we maneuvered too violently or put too much strain on the wire, we'd lose it. We were also unable to use that tube again until the torpedo hit, ran out of gas, or we cut the wire. If we did lose contact with a live torpedo, it'd go into an automatic search pattern and would still have a greater chance of finding something than a dumb weapon would have, but we tried to maintain contact with them as long as possible.

To shoot a weapon, we would have flooded the tube, prepped the weapon, and had a much more formal sequence of actions. The last step would have been to either take one final periscope bearing and range, take one last set of sonar bearings, or generate a final bearing based on computed data. Once that was done, the CO would have given the command "Match final bearings and shoot!" and the FTOW (Fire Control Technician of the Watch) would have launched the weapon on its way.

Even the simple act of launching a torpedo on its way had complications. Torpedoes were 21 feet long and 21 inches in diameter. The tubes were barely larger than the weapons. Unlike diesel boats, our tubes were in the middle of the boat and they were canted out at an angle of 15 degree. This was to make way for our large bow-mounted sonar sphere and the electronics that ran it, also in the forward part of the boat, directly beneath my berthing area. So torpedoes left the boat at an angle.

The tubes themselves were not much longer than the weapons, but they intercepted the outer hull at an angle. Because of this, the ends of the tubes were covered with an angled shutter, a steel tube that conformed to the shape of the hull, had a hole through the middle, and turned around its long axis. When we opened the shutter, the hole lined up with the tube, letting the weapon leave the boat. When closed, the shutter door would close, making the hull again smooth and hydrodynamic. Inside of the shutter door, at the end of the torpedo tube, was the muzzle door. This was designed to take full submergence pressure and was a massive piece of metal. Both the shutter and muzzle doors were hydraulically operated.

At the other end of the tubes was the breech door. This door, another massive piece of metal, was made of gleaming brass and ours all had red nylon line wrapped around the handles. These doors were also designed to handle full submergence pressure because, when the weapon was fired, the tube was at full sea pressure. We had several interlocks and warnings designed to prevent opening both the outer and inner doors at the same time and, to the best of my knowledge, this had not happened to any US submarine in decades, if ever. If both doors did open simultaneously, it'd be pretty bad. We would have a two foot hole in the boat with water pouring in at hundreds to thousands of gallons per minute. The boat would not survive and neither would we.

To fire a weapon, of course, we had to have one in the tube. The torpedo was our weapon of choice, and we carried more of them than anything else. They were fast, relatively smart, and we could stay in touch with them as they went hunting. Torpedoes were stowed on skids in the torpedo room, lined up in deadly rows, mixed in with the harpoons and the white subrocs off to the starboard side. We had two tubes on either side of the boat, one atop the other, and we kept two layers of weapons in the Room (as we called the torpedo room). This trip out, we had 24 weapons with us, although I never counted to see how many of each we had on hand. To load a tube, the torpedomen could either use muscle power or they could use hydraulic rams to push the skids laterally across the Room, to push weapons forward into the tubes, or to bring them back out into the Room. Our torpedoman chief told me that his guys could load a tube in one or two minutes, including hooking up the telemetry wire and securing the breech door.

With the weapon in the tube, my direct knowledge of events vanished. I've seen the weapons moved and loaded, I've seen them shot, but I've not seen them prepared for firing. So we'll fast-forward a little bit. Once loaded in the tube and prepared, the FTOW announces "Tube 3 (or whatever tube is to be used) ready in all respect." The CO then makes sure:

"Fire Control, tube ready?"

"Tube ready, aye, sir."

"Weapon ready?"

"Weapon ready, aye, sir."

At that point, we're ready to go and the next order will send the weapon on its way. On the order to shoot, the FTOW reaches out to grab a small handle. The handle does not move easily because it should take more than a casual pull to launch a weapon. However, it does turn, sending a signal to the torpedo room.

In the Room, that signal triggers a solenoid valve that opens to admit high-pressure air to the top of a piston. The air pushes the piston violently aft. The other end of the piston is submerged in water, filling the tube it is in. It follows the connecting rod, pushing the water in front of it. The water in the tube has only one place to go, through a pipe, into the torpedo tube, and out into the sea. As it rushes out, it pushes the torpedo out with it. The piston reaches its limit, the solenoid valve shuts, and the air vents off into the Room. The whole sequence takes just one or two seconds and it is neither gentle nor quiet. When you shoot a torpedo, everyone within ten miles will know because they'll hear it. And, if they miss the sound of high pressure air and thumping machinery, they're sure to pick up the sound of a torpedo whirring towards them, sounding on sonar like nothing more than a high-speed blender. A high explosive blender. In the boat the noise and sensation is very noticeable. Along with a steam generator blow-down, shooting a torpedo is one of the few things heard and felt all over the ship. You hear and feel the thump of the water impulsing the torpedo on its way, you hear the hiss as high-pressure air vents inboard, and you hear the further thumps as valves reposition themselves and huge pumps struggle to refill the impulse tanks, the tanks from which the water came.

But, in this case, and in the 27 other ships we (simulated) bagged over the next two weeks, everything past the fire control solution was just in our imaginations. And, if we might have fantasized about what an actual shooting war might be like and how well we might do, we were just as happy to not have to find out. I know that I was ready for the possibility of war or self-defense, but I sincerely hoped I would not have to take part in either. I don't know that all of the crew agreed with me on this, but it was my observation that the last people who want to fight a war are usually those who are on the front lines or who are likely to be sent. It wasn't cowardice, pacifism, or any personal weakness so much as a heightened awareness that, if it came down to shooting, we would be the first to draw return fire, and we all had a lot to lose. If need be, we'd do our best for God, country, family, and democracy, but we'd just as soon go home at the end of our mission without those particular sea stories to tell.

Completing the drill, the CO turned the scope back over to the OOD and turned back to the sonar display, looking for our next target. We were off to the side of a group of skimmers. Some were dedicated for ASW, some were support ships, and some had just shown up. A submarine at PD is vulnerable to any passing ship because we were hidden, but shallow enough to be hit and sunk by accident. Since we were actively trying to avoid being seen, we were completely responsible for avoiding all accidents. So, every time we were at PD we were making sweeps with the scope and sonar to make sure nobody was going to accidentally run us down. Since the CO had just got off the scope and Sonar wasn't showing any close contacts, the OOD wasn't terribly concerned and took a few seconds to look around Control, trying to build a picture in his head of what was going on. It was not a terribly bright thing to do.

The OOD finished his mental inventory of ship's status and put the scope up. As the scope came up, he was crouched down, looking through the eyepiece, right arm hanging over the grip. He began going around, straightening up as the scope rose. "Scope's clear. Starting sweep," he announced. Starting off looking to starboard (the way the scope happened to be pointing), he began a running commentary. "Scope's clear, no close contacts." He circled quickly clockwise, continuing the commentary. "No close contacts aft. No contacts to port." He continued on around, facing forward. "No close contacts forward. No...shit! Emergency deep! Emergency deep! Dive, make your depth 150 feet. Left full rudder! Ahead standard!" He put the scope down and stepped away, shaking.

An emergency deep will get any submariner's attention. They are ordered when we're about to be run down by someone, and those two words set into motion a number of actions. The stern planesman, under the Diving Officer's supervision, puts the planes into a shallow dive at first, to avoid lifting the stern of the boat and the screw out of the water. Doing that would not only show everyone in the area that we were right there, but would take away our propulsion. At the same time, the fairwater planes would be put into a dive to drop us down as quickly as possible. A standard bell was ordered because it was the fastest bell we could answer without worrying about having to shift the reactor plant around. A submarine dives faster if it's going faster. So, even though increasing our speed put us closer to the ship that was (knowingly or unknowingly) trying to run us down, if we could get underneath his keel, we'd miss him. Depth was more important than a few hundred extra yards. Besides, that was what the course changes was for, to take us away from the track of the Krivak. We wanted to get deep and break off away from him. All this took place in less than ten seconds and in utter silence. Those with something to do were doing it. The rest of us were listening for anything that would let us know if we'd been found, if we were going to be run down by accident, or if we'd managed to get away. Active sonar would be bad. A depth charge would be worse, but not as bad as the sound of a torpedo in the water. Worst of all would be hearing the deep thrumming of the Krivak's screws followed by the crunching sounds of a collision at sea. I looked over and saw the Diving Officer's hand near the collision alarm. Anywhere else in the world and he would have already set it off, letting the crew know that we were potentially in trouble. Here, we still valued secrecy over the extra few seconds of readiness. There was still the chance we hadn't been found. Besides, there wasn't a person on board who didn't know something was happening. We were at a 25 degree down- angle now, and that's something you just don't do without warning unless there's an extremely good reason. We waited, doing our best to hear through the hull.

The CO had been on his way out of Control when he heard the emergency deep called. He was back in Control within seconds. "What's happening?" he demanded.

"Krivak, sir. Starboard bow, about 45 degrees relative. Zero angle on the bow, less than a mile away, big bow wave."

"Shit. Did she see us?"

"Don't know, Sir."

"We'll find out. Sonar, where is he?"

"Ninety degrees, relative, Sir. Not changing course."

"Depth eight zero feet, sir," announced the Dive. "Course?" We still had the rudder full over with no final heading ordered. The Dive was gently reminding the OOD that, without further orders, we'd just be going in circles instead of clearing the area.

"Helm, make your course 225 degrees, ahead two thirds."

"Course 225, ahead two thirds, aye, sir."

"Sonar – where is he?"

"Passing astern, Sir." More like right over top of us. We were still shallow and we could hear the screws churning the water above us. I looked at the depth gauge – 80 feet. The top of the sail was less than 40 feet underwater, only 10 feet beneath the Krivak. That shallow, and we'd have hit him if we put up the scope.

"What's he doing? Is he turning towards us?"

"No, Sir. Looks like he's turning to rejoin the task force."

"So what happened, Sonar? How'd you miss him?"

"Don't know, Captain. We were looking at someone else and he just snuck in on us."

The CO turned to the OOD. "So what happened?" Spoken mildly, now that the excitement was over, but the reproach was present, nonetheless. If there was going to be a chewing out, it would take place later, out of earshot of the enlisted men and as many other officers as possible. Right now, the Skipper was probably furious, but was intent on making sure that everyone in Control learned something from the experience. As he and the OOD discussed the matter, we continued down to 300 feet and cleared the area at a one third bell. This took us below the thermal layer and got us out of the area, just in case they had any inkling we might be there. For now, exercises took a distant second place to remaining undetected. And, while the CO and OOD talked, the rest of us continued doing our jobs, happy to have escaped.

During these two weeks, we still pulled off every 24 hours or so to broadcast Greg's condition to Pearl, and each day we were told to stay out just a little longer. Greg was rapidly tiring of his confinement to bed, but the Doc wouldn't let him do much more than go to meals, to the head, or to shower. During this time, too, we could run the evap only sporadically, when there were few contacts around. So we ran low on fresh water, showered infrequently, and had one more thing to complain about. But things rapidly fell into another kind of routine, a routine in which we spent most of our time either seeking, stalking, or pretending to kill ships and submarines as quietly and efficiently as possible. By and bye, the Soviets gave up trying to find us and Pearl started rotating the other US boats to more distant op areas, leaving us again on our own.

The last incident in this affair came 17 days after Greg was first diagnosed with appendicitis. I was hanging around in Sonar that evening and one of the techs suddenly leaned forward, reaching for the headphones. He called the Sonar Supervisor over and they conferred briefly. The Sonar Supervisor reached for his microphone and called Control. "Control, Sonar, we have a contact designated Sierra 5. Contact is identified as a warship based on sound (merchant vessels were noisier and just sounded poorly-maintained next to a warship). Contact appears to be submerged."

"Sonar, Control, aye. Track Sierra 5." Although things had been quiet lately, we were still cautious. The OOD called the CO in his stateroom and explained the situation. In a minute the CO was in Control, looking at the sonar display in Control.

Back in Sonar, efforts were underway to identify the contact. Surface ships weren't too bad to deal with. Other subs were. If this was a sub, we wanted to know exactly where he was, where he was going, and what his capabilities were. The sonar tech who'd initially identified the contact was giving it his all. Looking at all his displays, he reported the number of blades on the screw, the screw speed, and a few specific tonals, or specific frequencies, we could detect. Then he started stretching his abilities a bit. "Sounds like steam noises, and I think they have a hard-mounted pump that's got a bad bearing," he reported. Steam noises were easy to pick up, and the pump was plausible, but sometimes difficult to tell for sure. "And, you know, it kind of sounds like they're cooking or something. Doesn't that sound like dishes? Or maybe they're just cleaning up from a meal." This was really stretching it. Some of the other sonar techs called him "Jonesy" after the character in Tom Clancy's book, The Hunt for Red October. Our sonar was good, but, unless someone drops a dish, you're not going to hear it. And, even then, you'd have trouble telling the difference between a dropped dish and a wrench.

"Jonesy" continued to give us descriptions of life onboard the other boat while his fellow sonar techs became increasingly amused. "What are they having for dinner?" one asked. Another asked what movie they were watching, based on the quality of the sound. But I had to hand it to Jonesy, he stuck to his story and his convictions.

Meanwhile, Control was starting to do some TMA maneuvers to get a better fire control solution on Sierra 5. Even though we felt safer than last week, this was still a potential enemy who might try to shoot us. We had to be able to shoot back. So we started doing our TMA legs, changing course every five minutes to try to get a fix on the target.

Unfortunately, every time we changed course, the other boat would, too. This continued for nearly an hour until finally, with some degree of concern, the CO realized that the other boat was doing TMA on us. This was bad. Not only were we detected, but we were possibly nailed because the other boat might have a solution on us by now, and we were still trying to get him pinned down. The concern grew and the CO tried going deeper to get below the thermal layer. Over the next hour, we tried crossing back and forth through the layer, but he apparently had a towed array that was drooping below the layer while he stayed on top. This meant that he could hear us all the time. We tried opening our distance, but we had to do so without putting him in our baffles because we needed to keep tracking and listening. In any event, it didn't work because he stayed on us. Finally, Jonesy came through again.

"Sonar supervisor; look at these tonals. We finally have a good set." He pointed to the frequency analysis screen. "See here, and here? This's a 637!" A 637 was a submarine in the class of boats starting with hull number SSN-637, also known as Sturgeon-class boats. US boats. The Sonar Supervisor called Control on the intercom.

"Control, Sonar. Contact Sierra 5 is identified as a 637-class submarine based on tonals." The CO was back in Sonar in moments.

"What the hell do you mean, it's a 637?" he demanded. "There aren't supposed to be ANY other boats in this op area! What the fuck are they doing here?" The Sonar supervisor showed the CO the tonals.

"See here, sir? That's the main coolant pump frequency. And that one looks like an electric plant, and that one's got to be their feed pump. It's one of ours, Sir. No Soviet boat has any of these, and it's missing anything we'd expect to see in one of their boats."

The CO agreed that it was a US boat and stopped doing TMA. We returned to our original course and, within ten minutes, the contact suddenly broke off and cleared the area. It was generally agreed that they must have realized around the same time we did that we were each tracking the other and that we were both on the same side. And we undoubtedly both breathed a huge sigh of relief as we went our separate ways. Being tracked by anyone else is not a good feeling, especially when you're in enemy waters.

Food and Hygiene

WE SECURED FROM THE FIRE CONTROL TRACKING PARTY and, a few days later, declared that particular exercise over. We were nearly five weeks into our op. Nearly half done. Nearly halfway home. I looked at my watch, which I kept clipped to my belt, right next to my knife and my radiation dosimeter (I didn't like wearing it on my wrist). It was about 10 PM. Too late to try to catch a few hours of sleep, although I'd been up for nearly 24 hours, so I decided to take a quick shower (we had fresh water again), get some midrats, and hurry through my daily routine. If I hurried, I could finish by 3 and, with luck, get caught up on my sleep. I headed down a level and on up to the forward nine-man to my rack. On my way, I had to pass by the crew's head. I glanced inside quickly to see if there was a line for the shower. One person in the shower, one waiting. With luck, I might not even have to wait long.

I crawled the thirty feet through the passageway to the berthing area (we hadn't yet eaten our way through to the deck). There, I quickly stripped, wrapped a towel around my waist, grabbed soap and shampoo, and hurried back to the head. Two others had shown up ahead of me, but the guy in the shower had just finished up, so I only had two people in line ahead of me. Plus the guy in the shower. Not too bad.

To understand personal hygiene on a submarine you first have to understand the water supply. As I mentioned earlier, water is almost always in short supply. It's even worse on an op because of noise. The evaporator makes water quite nicely by using steam to boil seawater. The water that boils off is nearly pure, so it is condensed and pumped to holding tanks. The remaining brine is much saltier and must be pumped overboard. This is where the trouble comes in – water pressure changes with depth so, as we dive deeper, the sea pressure increases and it becomes harder to pump brine overboard. For this reason, our evaporator (or evap, as we called it) had a quiet low-pressure brine pump and a noisy high-pressure brine pump. The LP brine pump normally acted as a booster pump, sending water to the HP brine pump. Alone, it was good when we were on the surface and down to about 50 or 60 feet. After that it just couldn't pump any more and brine would start to back up in the evap. Any deeper and we had to run the noisy HP brine pump. In these waters, though, the HP brine pump made more noise than we felt comfortable with and we preferred to not run it at all. We had received permission a few years earlier to operate on the LP brine pump only down to about 60 feet but, at this depth, even a small angle on the boat could drop the stern down far enough to flood out the evap and ruin our water supply. One of our ERLL watches had hung a weighted piece of twine from the side of the evap. If we were at PD and the angle was any greater than about 10 degrees he knew to shut down the evap or to dump it to the bilge because it was going to flood. Any depth change could flood it in a heartbeat, and, of course, this only worked when we were at PD. The last op, we'd spent a lot of time at PD, but this op was more a sonar op. We weren't shallow very often, so we didn't have much chance to run the evap.

In addition to problems running the evap, any abnormal demand from the steam plant or reactor plant would deplete our fresh water reserves. We had separate tanks to store water for the reactor plant, the steam plant, and potable water. In fact, we had three tanks for each of these purposes, plus another three tanks for miscellaneous purposes. All told, we could hold about 12 thousand gallons of fresh water, 3400 of which were designated for human use. If we started running low on potable water, showers and laundry went first followed by use of the sinks. Right now we were lucky, our tanks were topped off (pretty much so, anyways) so the showers were open. It was a common bone of contention that riders liked to shower after every watch, and their hardest work was getting up to refill their coffee. Most of us, if we wanted to wash our hair or ourselves more often than every 2-3 days had to have a watch like ERLL or AMSLL, where we could draw off some condensate or other fresh water for an illicit cleaning. The bad part of this was getting caught, like the time a friend was washing his hair from a tank sampling line and a small fire broke out.

Even in the best of circumstances we had precious little water, and on-station we were always expecting the worst. We were limited to three minutes of water time during our showers. On some boats, this was strictly enforced. I had heard stories of people standing outside the shower with a stopwatch and, if the person went over their allotted water time, they were reported to the XO or to the Chief of the Boat (COB). We weren't that bad, but someone spending too much time in the shower was invariably met with calls of derision, verbal abuse, and the label "water buffalo." Three minutes sounds like a short shower, and it certainly wasn't long, but it was manageable. I brushed my teeth as I waited. I always tried to spit the toothpaste directly into the drain so I wouldn't have to run the water. If successful, it meant I didn't have to wipe down the sink after using it. I tried to avoid this because the sink sponges weren't changed out very often and were often pretty gross. Didn't make it this time, so I had to rinse the sink and clean it up. Sigh.... The preceding two people having finished their showers, I was ready for mine.

I stepped into the shower, like the rest of the crew's head, a study in stainless steel. The door shut behind me and I opened a small locker door to stash my towel. I took a few seconds to make sure the soap and shampoo were readily accessible and turned on the water. It took me about 10 seconds to get the temperature about right, and I quickly wet my body. Then I reached up and turned a small knob on the shower head, stopping the flow of water. So far, about twenty seconds of water time. I lathered myself up; face, arms, front, back, legs, feet. Then I turned the water back on and rinsed. Once the lather was gone, I shut off the water again. I was up to about a minute and a half of water time. I found my shampoo, turned the water on again for about ten seconds to wet my hair. I lathered, rinsed quickly, then lathered up again. I had about a minute of water time left, so I luxuriated in a full minute to fully rinse my hair, soak the rest of me a little bit, then turned the water off. Next I reached down and picked up the shower sponge. It was our responsibility to wipe down all moisture on the walls after we showered. This took a few minutes and several wringings. Luckily the sponge wasn't too disgusting yet.

Reaching into the locker, I pulled my towel off and dried myself. Then, opening the door, I dried the bottoms of my feet before stepping out so the deck wouldn't be slippery. I wrapped my towel around myself and squeezed past the next guy. Looking around, I saw that the line was now about five people long and congratulated myself on good timing. I made my way into the passageway and forward to my rack to get dressed.

Dressed, I looked at my watch again. Ten thirty. Midrats would start in a half hour, but I couldn't eat for at least 45 minutes. Normally I'd read, but I was tired enough I'd fall asleep and I knew that meant I'd either oversleep or I'd feel even worse if I managed to wake up in time. So I went on into Sonar for awhile to see what was happening and pass the time.

Mealtimes are normally broken into two distinct segments. First to eat are people going on watch, the on-going watchstanders. The oncoming duty section eats first so they can go aft and relieve the watch section, giving them time to eat before the meal's over. Relieving the watch late was a cardinal sin. Most of us tried to get there by about quarter or twenty past the hour, and showing up later than half past was really frowned upon. The crew's mess seated 24 at four tables that, in a restaurant, would have seated four people each. One of these tables was the "Chief's table", reserved for the Chief Petty Officers, and was off-limits to regular enlisted personnel unless invited by a chief. At any one time, we'd have ten enlisted nukes on watch, four in sonar, two forward roving watches, a torpedoman on watch in the Room, seven enlisted men on watch in Control, and one in Radio. Plus, on this op, a handful of riders in each section. All in all, we had to push 25 enlisted men (perhaps three of whom were chiefs) through the crew's mess in 15-20 minutes. Midrats was less structured than the other meals, but we still tried to respect the division between on-going and off-going watchstanders. As ELT, I was neither, so I usually ate with the off-going watch. Since I was on a 24 hour day to their 18 it also meant I ate with a different group of people at every meal.

Looking at the clock, I noticed it was about time to head for midrats. I went forward from Sonar to the ladder, down to Ops compartment middle level, turned to the right at the bottom of the ladder, and headed into the crew's mess.

The crew's mess was less organized at Midrats than during the other meals. At breakfast, we lined up outside the Galley, filled out a breakfast chit for the food we wanted, took our plate, and sat at the first available space. Lunch and dinner, we lined up in the passageway, waiting for a table to empty, then sat. Very junior enlisted men took turns as "mess cranks", bringing food, plates, and silverware to the tables, cleaning them, and cleaning the crew's mess after the meal was over. For Midrats, however, food was brought from the Galley to the Crew's Mess, placed on the tables, and a free-for-all ensued. Free-form might be a good way to describe Midrats. Every Friday was pizza night on *Plunger*; the rest of the time we had soup, sandwiches, corn dogs, or whatever else the cooks came up with. Nutrition was not a high priority.

This far into an underway our eating habits had changed considerably. We had run out of fresh fruit and veggies before we even made it to Adak, and our frozen veggies had run out a few weeks later. Fresh milk made it for four or five days into any underway, and fresh eggs usually lasted for two weeks. On a long underway such as this one we could also expect to run out of hot cocoa, coffee creamer, a lot of meats, and miscellaneous other supplies. We made our own bread daily, so we usually had plenty of that, but we'd run out of yeast on a spec op two years ago and the supply officer tried to grow more so our flour wouldn't go to waste. About the only thing we never ran out of was coffee, or what passed for coffee in the Navy. Although, on one spec op a rumor went around that we were almost out of the stuff. It was the only time I ever saw a bunch of Chiefs panic. They immediately sent a Chief back to the Engineroom to grab two 35 pound cans of coffee, moved them to the Chief's Quarters (also called the Goat Locker), and placed them under guard. We later found more coffee, but they refused to surrender theirs until we pulled back into port, ensuring their continued caffeine supply. I heard stories about boats that were extended on station for a few weeks and pulled into port having eaten ham sandwiches and chicken soup for every meal for two weeks. We never got that bad, but our menus did get steadily more boring as an underway went on.

Most of us brought our own food for long underways like this one. I had learned early and brought more food each time. This time I was lucky. I had my own rack with an outboard locker and, as Leading ELT, I could give myself a little more space in Nucleonics. This time, I had brought three cases of soda (one can for each day we were to be at sea), a few pounds of ground coffee and four cans of flavored coffee mix (enough to have a liter of coffee every day plus a cup of flavored coffee every few days), two or three bags of pecan sandies (two cookies a day), two jars of dry roasted peanuts, a dozen sticks of beef jerkey (one each week), and a few other goodies to celebrate Halfway Night and our last night at sea. There was no way to bring enough food to last an entire underway, the goal was to be able to give yourself a little treat every so often. In my case, every so often was daily.

My pet peeve was Navy coffee. I was convinced it was really roasted soy meal with amphetamines and black food coloring added. It tasted horrible. That's the reason I brought so much coffee – the only way I could stomach the Navy stuff was to mix it with a pouch of hot cocoa, and I knew that wouldn't last more than a month or so. There were times I had no choice but to drink it, but I always hated the stuff.

People in the surface navy always told me that submarines got the best food in the fleet. That may well have been the case. I was stationed on a frigate while in the Reserves and I ate on the submarine tender a few times while in port and I can attest that our food was better than theirs. But that doesn't mean our food was good, it was just better. Part of it was the recipes our cooks were forced to follow, part of it was some less experienced cooks, part due to cramped galley space, and part due to poor ingredients. There were several occasions where I saw cooks opening tins of food that were older than most of the crew. I know. I read the dates on the containers. I also saw cases of meat labeled "USAF reject", meaning that, for whatever reason, it wasn't good enough for the Air Force. And I can vouch for the fact that, while steak and lobster may sound pretty good, most of us dreaded it because the lobster was usually soggy and the steak was usually so stringy and tough that it just wasn't worth the effort to chew. Not that there was much meat left after removing the gristle, bone, and fat.

I sincerely believe that most of our cooks tried to do their best to give us the best meals possible. And with good reason; few things bring morale down faster than an unending string of bad meals. But even the best-intentioned cooks can only do so much with poor recipes and poor ingredients. And the Navy frowned upon diverging even a little from the given recipe. One of our cooks had a special hat made up for this trip. Playing on the unofficial submarine force slogan "Death from below", Pat had a had with the specialty insignia designating a mess specialist (i.e. cook) and the words "Navy cook – Death from within."

We were about at the point of this underway where powdered eggs were starting to taste normal and I couldn't remember what fresh fruit looked like. This was my warning. In another few weeks, when powdered milk started tasting normal I'd know it was about time to go home. Unfortunately, this underway, we'd still have another two or three weeks to go at that point.

Like everything else, all our food had come onboard during the days before we got underway. We'd get to the boat in the morning and find out we'd have a stores' load later in the morning. A few hours later, word would be passed and we'd drop what we were doing. Going topside, there would be a pile of boxes and cans on the pier. We'd form a line from the boxes to the weapons' shipping hatch, down the ladder to OPSUL, down the ladder to OPSML, and into the Crew's Mess. Then we'd start passing cases and cans of food along the line. We usually didn't have more than a few seconds between loads and, if you were slow, the whole line would start yelling at you for breaking the rhythm. Sometimes a can or box of food might slip out of someone's grasp, ending up in the harbor. Liver seemed particularly slippery. Odd, too, how it never seemed to be dropped by people on the pier where it could have been rescued.

As food wound up in the messdecks, the cooks would carefully stow it. We filled up the chill box (refrigerator) and freeze box with meat, milk, and other foods requiring refrigeration. Everything else went into Dry Stores. When that filled up, we filled up the centerline storage area, an area about 20 feet long and three feet across that lay between the Crew's Mess and the Wardroom. When we loaded weapons, this area was cleared out, the deck taken up, and weapons loaded into the torpedo room below. At sea for long periods of time, this became storage.

After the obvious storage places were filled, the line would shift and we'd start passing food forward, filling up the passageway to the forward nine-man. When that filled, the line would shift again, running aft along the top of the boat to load food down the engineroom escape trunk where it was stacked outboard the main engines, turbine generators, and shaft. On a long underway such as this one, we'd take smaller cans (a gallon or smaller) and stack a single layer on the floor beneath the tables in the messdecks, on the floor of the berthing compartments, and wherever else we might find room.

At the end of this underway, we'd pull into Pearl Harbor and do another stores load, probably on our first full day in port. This time, however, there'd be fewer complaints. We'd be outdoors, in the sun, and able to grab fresh fruit from the boxes as they passed from hand to hand. Maybe not heaven, but a pretty good approximation after a few months at sea.

Most meals were eaten pretty quickly. The on-coming section had to eat quickly to relieve the watch. The off-going watch section had to eat quickly because the messdecks closed down after 45 minutes for cleaning. And most of ate quickly as an act of culinary self-defense. The faster we ate, the shorter the amount of time food was in contact with our taste buds. We savored the food we brought; the rest, we wolfed down as quickly as possible.

For this meal, there was only so much the cooks could do to ruin it. Still, out of habit, I was finished within three or four minutes. I made a cup of flavored coffee, went to my lab, and started my daily routine. Three hours later, exhausted after nearly 30 hours awake, I went to bed, hoping to get caught up on my sleep. And I got lucky this time; I was able to sleep for six hours before someone woke me up. Almost enough to be rested.

CHAPTER 15

Halfway Night and other Entertainment

I woke around 9, groggy, but a lot better than before. I didn't wake voluntarily, but at the insistence of the Messenger, shaking me and whispering in my ear that we needed to get into the port aux tank. I looked at him blearily. "Good morning, dear. Although, I've got to admit, you're not really the person I was hoping to wake up next to." He looked at me, puzzled. I continued, "To be honest with you, I was just having a really nice dream, and you weren't in it at all. And you're a lot uglier than she was. But, it's an imperfect world." I rolled out of the rack and told him to inform the OOD that I'd been properly awakened. He left, muttering something about "damned Nukes" and shaking his head.

The class of submarines I was on had several tanks designed to hold ballast water. This ballast water helped us to submerge (or, if blown out, to surface). The forward and after trim tanks helped to balance the boat forward and aft while the auxiliary tanks (or aux tanks) were designed to balance the boat side to side. But, when the boats first took to the water, it was discovered that the engineering and construction was so good that the aux tanks were superfluous. They were rapidly converted to more storage space; space badly needed for longer ops such as this one. There were only two problems. The tanks were directly adjacent to the reactor compartment shield and they were not normally ventilated when sealed. The former meant that a radiation survey had to be performed prior to any entry while the latter meant that the atmosphere had to be sampled as well to make sure it was breathable. Otherwise, we'd be doing the equivalent of a canary test with me as the canary. Not my first choice.

The aux tanks were located directly beneath the deck in the Torpedo Room, all the way aft, just forward of Air Regen. (Air Regen was the room holding the HPAC that Lumpy blew up, delaying our underway. It also held our forward scrubber and some other atmosphere controls equipment.) The only entry to the tank was a hatch about two feet long and eighteen inches across. The tank had never been intended for routine entry and the entrance had never been modified to make it any easier. The Doc was already there, taking air samples to make sure oxygen, explosive gases, freon, and other gases and vapors made it safe to enter. To a large extent, this was all a formality, even my part. To the best of my knowledge, no tank entry had ever been postponed due to bad air because the tank was vented continuously to the Torpedo Room. And, even at 100% reactor power, I'd never had an instrument reading above 1 millirem per hour, a fairly low reading. It would take 5000 hours at that radiation level to reach any exposure limits. That's 100 hours each week for an entire year, assuming you take two weeks off for good behavior. Anyhow, rules were rules. I had stopped by Nucleonics to grab a meter, so I squeezed down the ladder into the tank to take some readings. On the way down, the Doc called to me "Make sure you turn it on this time, Andy!" I assured him I would and continued climbing, radiation meter in one hand, flashlight in the other, gripping the ladder with my fingertips.

The tank was something like seven feet high, perhaps 20 feet long, and 20 feet across. The bottom conformed to the shape of the hull, so it got shallower as you moved outboard from the centerline. When we left port five weeks ago, it was jammed full of non-perishable items. Toilet paper, TDU weights, oxygen candles, napkins, and anything else that wouldn't spoil. Right now there was room to walk in some areas and you could actually see most of what was left. This entry was for oxygen candles. And, looking around, I saw precious few of them. Nowhere near enough to finish the op. I reminded myself to check the pressure on our oxygen banks when I came back out.

Now, however, it was time to look for zoomies. I had already checked to make sure my meter was in calibration. I'd also checked the battery, the physical condition of the meter and cable, and its response to a radioactive source. So I was sure it was working properly. And, contrary to the Doc's assertion, I always turned the meter on when I was surveying. I might not always report the readings accurately, but I always turned the meter on. Now, at the bottom of the tank, I turned my meter on as I moved to the after bulkhead and I started my survey. Within a few minutes I reaffirmed the complete absence of radiation in the aux tank. As I turned to thread my way back to the ladder, I dropped my flashlight. I know, a standard way to build suspense just before you get lost or attacked. This time, though, it was just clumsiness and fatigue. The tank was too small to get lost in and, although I had my detractors onboard, nobody hated me enough to try to jump me in the aux tank. One the other hand, the tank was too dark to find the flashlight in without getting on my hands and knees and groping around in the dark. Not too slimy, but I had better things to do. I found the flashlight, turned it back on, and left the tank. As always, I counted myself lucky that I wasn't claustrophobic because, even with the flashlight on, the tank was small, dark, and confining. But, then, no claustrophobe would ever had made it overnight on a boat at sea.

About a dozen guys had assembled to unload the oxygen candles from the aux tank. Since it wasn't my turn to help, I simply told the man in charge that rad levels were OK, made a note in my logs, and went back to bed. I looked at my watch. 9:45. With any luck at all, I could get another two or three hours of sleep.

I woke some time later, feeling somewhat groggy. I looked at my watch. 10:30. The lights were out, but berthing areas are always rigged for red. So that wasn't any help. I felt too rested to have slept only 45 minutes, but not nearly rested enough to have slept for over twelve hours. I looked at my watch again. Unfortunately, it was a cheap one that didn't tell me if it was AM or PM. I listened for activity, hearing none, but this was inconclusive. The problem was that if I'd only slept for 45 minutes, crawling aft to see which meal was being cooked would wake me to the point that I'd not be able to get to sleep again. And waking up at 10:30 in the morning would throw off my whole sleeping schedule. On the other hand, if it was 10:30 in the evening and I didn't get up, I could fall asleep again and not finish my daily routine. Finally, I heard someone mention pizza. That decided me. We have pizza for midrats, not for lunch. I'd not only slept, but I'd slept through lunch, dinner, and most of the day. I still felt groggy, but it felt more like a lack-of-sleep groggy than from oversleeping. Anyhow, I climbed out of the rack, dressed, and headed aft to finish my daily routine.

In the crew's mess, a movie was playing. Unusual at this hour. Come to think of it, so was pizza because today was Wednesday. Then I remembered. It was Halfway Night. Halfway through our mission, this would be our only celebration until pulling into port. From here, it was all downhill.

I had slept through most of the festivities, unfortunately. One favorite was the "Crank for a Night" competition, in which people would pay a quarter to vote for a senior crew member to help serve dinner to the crew. Actually, the top five people worked, serving dinner in the Wardroom, the Crew's Mess, and washing dishes. Although I had gathered a few votes, I was a long way out of even the top ten. Serving dinner in the Crew's Mess were the Captain, the Navigator, one of the junior officers, and the vocal A-gang leading first (the senior enlisted man below the rank of chief). The leading quartermaster and the sonar chief had served the officers in the Wardroom.

The rest of the day had been more of less low-key. The boat still had a mission to do, the reactor plant still had to be taken care of, and the boat still had to run. And there was no alcohol on board. So festivities were limited. What they did have was a movie marathon, cribbage and euchre tournaments, and the Crank for a Meal at dinner. The celebration would continue on the Midwatch with some amateur entertainment (one of my ELTs was actually a quite accomplished musician and singer and would be playing), more movies, and the Miss *Plunger* competition. The Miss *Plunger* contest won't be described right away, but don't worry – there's nothing even remotely off-color about it.

We usually went to sea with quite a video library. I have read that WW II boats would sometimes rendezvous at sea to swap movie reels, rowing them across from one boat to the other while trying to protect them from the salt water. We had it a little better. We had three VCRs on board, one each for the Goat Locker, the Wardroom, and the Crew's Mess. And we carried about 400 movies with us, plus what individual crew members brought. Movies ranged in age from classics (we'd watched *Rear Window* earlier this underway) to movies released only a few months earlier. They also ranged in quality from horrible to pretty good. Once, in an attempt I think to bring some culture to the unwashed masses, we ended up with *Amadeus*. I managed to convince everyone to watch it one night by telling them it had a lot of female nudity in it. After over an hour everyone realized I'd lied, but by then it was too late to change to another movie, so we watched the whole thing. Another time, I persuaded everyone to watch *The Princess Bride*. Imagine my surprise when it turned out to be one of the most popular movies on board. I can still picture the Crew's Mess full of sailors, some sitting on the floor because all the bench seats were taken, watching *The Princess Bride*.

Most days we could watch two movies. One, shown during the evening watch (right after cleaning up from dinner) was open to everyone and was specified by the XO. The second, shown on the midwatch, could only be watched by those crew members who had completed their submarine qualifications. That one was chosen by consensus, a process that sometimes took almost as long as watching the movie. And then we had our movie marathon days. Sundays and on Halfway Night.

There were two things I did for entertainment. I read, a habit I'd picked up early in life and never tried to kick, and I'd watch movies. They were both ways, if I really concentrated, I could immerse myself in someone else's world. I could forget for a time that I was stuck in a piece of metal sewer pipe underwater off the coast of Russia, surrounded by sailors, eating lousy food, breathing bad air, and taking orders from idiots.

For the reading part, I'd always take as many books with me as I thought I could finish, then I'd load in another few. On a WestPac, I'd restock during the trip, mailing my completed books back to my father and buying more. On a surge op like this one, if I figured wrong, I was stuck. One time I'd guessed wrong, running out of books with two weeks left. I borrowed everything I could find that was readable and, after that, I was actually borrowing *Playboy* magazines from people to read the articles (*Playboy*'s literary standards were much higher than any of the other magazines typically brought onboard). Each time, too, I would try to bring a few of the classics that I might not be able to wade through otherwise. Last time I'd read *Les Misérables*. This time, I had *War and Peace*. It was a standing joke with the XO that I should read while laying on my side. Otherwise, he said, I might fall asleep and smother to death beneath the weight of the book. Reading was my pastime of choice because I didn't need to get consensus on which book to read and I could read just about anytime I wasn't on watch.

There were a few others who shared my passion for reading. We'd try to read in the Crew's Mess between meals, but it was often taken for divisional training, lay church services, movies, and so forth. So we'd read wherever we could. My lab was usually a good place, as was my rack. And the Sonar Equipment Space and the Diesel Compartment were usually empty, too. But, in a pinch, we'd sit on the ladders, just next to the watertight doors, or anywhere else we could have a chance to immerse ourselves in someone else's world. I don't know about my shipmates, but when I read, I tuned out almost everything else, concentrating with all my effort on the book and its story. It was one of the ways I coped.

And that brings us back to the rest of Halfway Night. I hurried through the rest of my daily routine, finishing just before midrats ended. I was pretty hungry by this time, so I made it the Crew's Mess as the cooks were bringing out the last pizza. Grabbing a few pieces, I jostled for a seat and wolfed them down. I snagged a few more pieces from the tray, ate them almost without tasting (probably a blessing), and felt a little better. Still groggy, though, but probably nothing that some coffee wouldn't help with. Returning to my lab, I started today's routine with the daily instrument checks. Pausing briefly to look at the CAMS (central atmosphere monitoring system), I noticed that CO_2 levels were sky high and oxygen levels were low, about 18%. Atmospheric oxygen concentration is about 21% and at least 16% is needed to sustain life. We were at 18% right now. High CO_2 and low oxygen. No wonder I was groggy. Curious, I went to Control and asked the first person I saw what was up.

"After scrubber's down again," came the reply. "And we're low on oxygen. So the CO wants to run with low O_2 levels for a while to see how it works."

"Well, that explains why I feel so bad," I replied, "and why I slept for so long. Any idea how long we're going to do this? And what about the scrubber?"

"Don't know. The Old Man's got a hair up his ass. Said they ran like this all the time on his last boats and we're just a bunch of wimps. Sounds like a bunch of bullshit to me. And on Halfway Night, too. Go figure."

We commiserated a little more, then I returned to my lab to get permission to draw my primary plant sample. I sampled, finished the analyses, and returned to the messdecks in time for the last round of the Miss *Plunger* contest.

My second spec op was the time of the first Miss *Plunger* competition. As I mentioned earlier, there was absolutely nothing sexual or effeminate about it, it was just a way to blow off some steam. The premise was that whoever was interested could dress however they felt was most appropriate and compete for the honor of being named Miss *Plunger*. There was a talent competition and a question-and-answer segment, after which the judges (this time, the

CO, COB, and Bull Nuke) would vote. The Miss *Plunger* contest wasn't my favorite part of Halfway Night, but it could be pretty entertaining, depending on the contestants. This year we had a few who seemed to be taking it seriously and one who wasn't.

In some of the reading I've done, I've come across a number of references of similar events, going back several centuries. In the days of wooden ships and iron men, sailors would routinely make journal entries about having dances onboard, having skits in which some men would dress as women, and even some competitions similar to ours. I don't know if all-female crews would have something similar or not, but there seems to be a long tradition with men. But enough on that – it's time for the contest to begin.

The first segment is the "beauty" contest. Matt, the first contestant is medium height and slender. There's not much storage space, of course, so he's wrapped a bedsheet around himself for his evening gown, put some silk flowers behind one ear, and managed to find enough of something to make himself look pretty statuesque. He's one of the few onboard who hasn't grown a beard, which helps the illusion somewhat, and he must have brought some of his wife's cosmetics with him because his cheeks are blatantly rouged. According to some of the wives he's not a bad-looking guy, but even after a month at sea he's far from comely. He strikes a pose, is met with a smattering of applause and some catcalls, and is ushered back out of the messdecks.

The next contestant, Ken, moonlights as a male model when we're in port. Like Matt, he is wearing some makeup, but not quite as blatantly applied. Kent actually borrowed a dress from his wife and also found a way to become buxom. His only problem is that he works out and he's just a bit too muscular to look like anything more than a man in drag. He bats his eyes flirtatiously, curtsies, and thrusts his shoulders back to show off his falsies. Ken also receives a little applause before leaving.

The last contestant is the one not taking things seriously. Hammy is built like a fireplug, about five and a half feet tall and nearly the same across. He has used a wet mop as a wig, the gray strings framing his bearded face. He, too, is using a sheet for his evening gown and, as he sashays in with a hand on one hip, he's clutching a plastic rose in his teeth and has a pink feather boa around his neck. Beneath the sheet, he must have wadded up two other sheets to serve as breasts because he looks like he has two Mark 48 torpedos attached to his chest. Arriving at the front of the messdecks, he tosses the rose to the Old Man, cocks his head, and smiles bashfully at the crowd. The messdecks erupt in laughter and applause, the CO shakes his head, and Hammy waltzes off the messdecks to wait with Matt and Ken for the talent show.

In the talent show, Ken and Matt were again pretty conventional. Ken sings (and actually does pretty well) while Matt plays his guitar (also quite well). And then Hammy comes out. Someone puts a tape into the tape player and Spanish-sounding music starts playing. Hammy grabs one side of his "gown", looks flirtatiously at the assembled crew, and launches into a mock flamenco dance. He's got several obstacles: The space he has to dance in is only two feet across and three feet deep, the music sounds horrible, the crowd noise is enough to drown out most of the music in any event, and it's evident that Hammy's knowledge of flamenco dancing (or any other, for that matter) probably dates back to watching Saturday Night Fever ten years earlier. Plus, his shoes consist of steel-toed work boots. Nonetheless, for three minutes or so we have the incredible bearded lady prancing and stomping around the Crew's Mess, throwing his boa around the CO's neck, pulling him close, then falling backwards holding his nose as thought he Old Man has horrible breath. When he's done, the entire messdecks erupts in laughter and I'm glad we've checked to make sure nobody with decent sonar is anywhere near us.

The final part of the competition is a short interview, but by this point the result is a forgone conclusion. Matt and Ken gamely try their best, but Hammy steals the show by sitting in the CO's lap, wrapping the feather boa around his neck, and asking for a date. The Old Man, having survived ten spec ops, emergencies at sea, high-level inspections, and who knows what else, is in a state of near-shock and at a complete loss. All he can do is shake his head and laugh. In the end, Hammy wins the Miss *Plunger* contest hands down and sashays off the messdecks back to his berthing area to change.

The final event is a pie-in-the-face contest. In this case, the cooks made up five whipped cream pies that were to be auctioned off. As with the Crank-for-a-Night contest, all the proceeds went to our Recreational Fund, which was used for ship's picnics, holiday parties, softball teams, and the like.

The first three pies went for pretty low prices and for people nobody could really get too excited about. The fourth pie went for about $50 and was used on the Navigator, a pretty innocuous guy who, with his beard, reminded most of us of the groundhog in the movie Caddyshack. Except that the groundhog looked a bit smarter. Not to take anything away from the Nav, who was no idiot, he just hid it well behind a look of pretty constant befuddlement.

Bidding for the final pie started at $50. The bidder was a pretty junior topedoman named Eric, a tall young guy who was always in a pretty good mood. He was countered by the Quartermaster chief bidding $60. A senior A-Ganger bid $75, which was countered by Eric with a bid for $80. This continued for awhile with the stakes rising to nearly $200. At that point, Eric started getting some help from his friends, bid $225, and the other bidders gave up. Then, the moment of truth. "Who's the victim?" asked the COB.

"The Old Man! How else do you think I got these other guys to go in on it with me?"

The CO was brought back from his stateroom and told the score. I really wondered what he was going to do. On the one hand, he was an officer and a bunch of enlisted men were planning on smashing a whipped cream pie into his face. Kind of undignified, especially for an officer. On the other hand, he had known all along that anyone who did not specifically exempt themselves from this event was fair game. The Old Man was a good sport. "How much did the pie go for?" he asked. When told, he looked disappointed. "That's all I'm worth? I'd have thought you'd have got at least $500 for the skipper." And then he took a seat, waiting for the inevitable.

As leader of the consortium, Eric got the honors. He took the pie and moved to stand at the CO's side. Then, instead of just whacking him with it, he sat on the table in front of the CO and dipped his finger into the whipped cream. He looked at the CO and smiled. "This is for Christmas at sea," he said, and dabbed the whipped cream on the CO's nose. "And this is for New Year's at sea." Another dab, this time on the skipper's right cheek. "And one for Super Bowl Sunday!" A dab on the left cheek. "And the stupid ORSE at the end of the whole damned trip!" With that, he gently rubbed the rest of the pie into the CO's face, up over the top of his head, and tried to find some more for the ears. The whole messdecks erupted into laughter, the CO included. The Old Man simply said "You're awfully lucky the showers are running," toweled off as much as he could, and went back to the wardroom to clean up. That done, Halfway Night was over.

Or so we thought. During the festivities, someone had snuck into the Officer's head and unbolted their toilet, hiding it somewhere onboard. Within minutes of the CO leaving the messdecks, he was back, politely inquiring as to the whereabouts of the Officer's toilet. Blank stares all around. A half hour later it was still missing. And shortly after that, a loudspeaker announcement.

"Attention all hands. The Wardroom toilet seems to have disappeared. Anyone who happens to stumble across it should return it to the Wardroom at your earliest opportunity. We'll assume it got lost and no questions will be asked."

Half an hour later, we heard this announcement. "Attention all hands. The Wardroom toilet is still missing. I have ordered all sanitary tanks be pressurized. I used the Crew's head just before I gave that order. Sanitary tanks will be depressurized after the Wardroom toilet is returned. Let's see who can hold it longer."

Our toilets flushed to sanitary tanks. Between the toilet bowl and the sanitaries was a ball valve, a steel sphere with a hole drilled in it attached to a handle. To flush the toilet, we turned on water and rotated the ball valve to let everything flow into the sanitaries. Since solids don't pump well, we would pressurize the sanitary tanks and use air pressure to blow everything overboard. Needless to say, this made flushing impossible because opening the ball valve would result in blowing everything back in your face with up to a few hundred pounds of air pressure behind it. Messy. With the sanitaries pressurized, nobody was going to the bathroom unless they used the bilges, and we frowned on that on *Plunger.* Another 45 minutes went by and the loudspeaker activated again.

"Attention all hands. This is the Captain. The missing toilet has found its way back home. Sanitaries have been depressurized. You can stop holding it now." Now, Halfway Night was over.

The first submarine ordered by the Navy was the SS-1, named the USS Plunger. Ordered from the Holland Torpedo Boat Company in March 1895, it failed its sea trials and the contract was cancelled by the Navy in 1900. The Navy used the funds to order a second submarine, also named Plunger from Holland in 1900.

The second Plunger (SS-2) spent its first years helping to develop weapons and tactics for submarine warfare, underwater communications devices and ship design. One of the high points of this period was a visit by President Theodore Roosevelt, the first presidential visit to a U.S. submarine. The SS-2 was decommisioned at the Charleston Navy Yard on 6 November, 1909 with Ensign Chester W. Nimitz, commanding.

Launched, 9 December 1961

The commissioning of the USS Plunger on 21 November, 1962 at the Mare Island Naval Shipyard. Originally homeported in Pearl Harbour as part of Submarine Division 71, she served as the Submarine Force Flagship in 1963, and was transferred to San Diego in 1973 to join Submarine Squadron 3.

Aft portion of the Plunger viewed from the conning tower (normally called the sail). To the right is a long hump through which our towed array sonar passed when it was deployed. It curves down along the hull underwater and is attached to part of the stern planes to keep the cable from becoming entangled in the screw (propeller). The path down the center of the hull is covered with non-skid paint, and the narrow line just to the port side of the non-skid is a track to which our safety harnesses were clipped when we were topside at sea. Further aft, just beneath the first group of seagulls, is the cover of the Engineroom hatch, which leads to an emergency escape trunk. Other bumps and circular openings are a variety of seawater penetrations, sensors, and other engineering devices.

The Bowfin, a WWII diesel boat and the Plunger. Notice the difference in hull shape –
Bowfin was designed to run on the surface and has a v-shaped hull, while Plunger, designed
to be submerged all the time, has a rounded hull. The round shape, smaller battery, and
smaller diesel gave Plunger much more interior space than the Bowfin, even though the
overall dimensions (length and beam) are similar for both boats. In addition, Bowfin sits
higher in the water and her conning tower is much further aft than Plunger's. In this photo,
Plunger is moored alongside the USS Proteus in Chinhae, South Korea in April, 1988.
The photo of Bowfin was taken at the Bowfin Museum in Pearl Harbour, Hawaii in
January 1989.

Plunger in drydock. This photo shows the real size of the boat. First, compare the amount
of hull you can see here with what shows above water in some of the other photos. Like
an iceberg, most of the Plunger was below the waves. On the other hand, Plunger is in a
drydock designed to handle Los Angeles-class boats. A 688 would fill the dock completely,
whereas Plunger fit like socks on a rooster.

Plunger *leaving port for her final spec op. The little girl probably had no idea that small black thing was taking her daddy away for two months, or where it was taking him.*

The Plunger *patch. SS-2 and SS-179 are the two previous boats named* Plunger. *"What is past is prologue" is the ship's motto.*

LT Brian Belcher greets his daughter after returning home.

One of the Navy's publicity shots. We never had hull numbers showing except for publicity reasons. This was an old photo – there is no towed array fairing on the port side of the boat, the mini-sail had not been added yet, and the masts look a bit different than when I was on board. The very first mast is the snorkel mast; its large diameter and the large size of the head valve (the mechanism on top that kept water out of the mast when we were submerged) kept us from raising this mast for fresh air unless we had to. The other two masts look like periscopes.

Inscribed version of this photo reads: "MM2 Karam - My personal congratulations on your rapid qualifications in submarines. Your accomplishment of this demanding goal in less than half the time allotted was nothing short of IMPRESSIVE! I welcome you to a tradition of service to country and professional excellence shared by all 'DolphinWearers'.

G. A. Gradisnik
Commander, US Navy
Commanding Officer
USS Plunger (SSN-595)
8 May, 1986

Andy Karam receiving commendation from CDR William R. Large III.

SUBMARINE QUALIFICATION CERTIFICATE

MACHINIST MATE SECOND CLASS (SS)

PHILIP A. KARAM

Having successfully completed the rigorous professional requirements for qualification in submarines, having gained a thorough knowledge of submarine construction and operation, having demonstrated his reliability under stress, and having my full confidence and trust, I hereby certify that he is

Qualified in Submarines

Given this _8TH_ day of __MAY__ 19 _86_

On Board U.S.S. _PLUNGER (SSN 595)_

G. A. GRADISNIK, CDR, U. S. NAVY
COMMANDING OFFICER

NAVTRA 1650/1 (7-73)
S/N 0115-LF-016-0500

DEPARTMENT OF THE NAVY

The Secretary of the Navy takes pleasure in presenting

the **NAVY ACHIEVEMENT MEDAL** to

Machinist's Mate First Class (SUBMARINES)
ANDREW PHILIP KARAM
United States Navy

for services set forth in the following

CITATION

"For professional achievement in the superior performance of his duties while serving as Engineroom Supervisor, Time Bearing Plotter, and Photo Petty Officer in USS PLUNGER (SSN 595) from February to August 1988. Petty Officer Karam performed his demanding duties, while deployed to the Western Pacific, in an exemplary and highly professional manner. His determined personal efforts were directly responsible for PLUNGER's successful Western Pacific deployment. Displaying superb initiative and responsibility, he exhibited unsurpassed expertise as a Photographic Developer and Printer significantly improving several post-deployment reports and briefs. As Engineroom Supervisor and Time Bearing Plotter his aggressive watchstanding and attention to detail under conditions of high stress, contributed significantly to the highly successful conduct of operations of great importance to the Government of the United States. Petty Officer Karam's exceptional professional abilities, initiative and loyal dedication to duty reflected great credit upon himself and were in keeping with the highest traditions of the United States Naval Service."

For the Secretary of the Navy

W. R. LARGE
Commander, U.S. Navy
Commanding Officer

Coming in to port

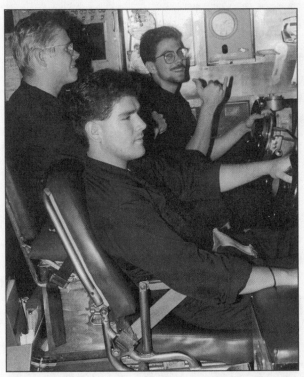

Driving and diving

Bunk spaces in the Torpedo Room, directly above the torpedoes.

Crewmembers in the torpedo room

Christmas at sea. I bent the rules and hung up 'stockings' for the other ELTs and our division officer. These are actually disposable anti-contamination booties, normally worn to enter radioactively contaminated areas. These, of course, had never been used. The large machine to the left is our radiation dosimetry reader, and our pH probe is on the far right.

Al Moran reading in the mess

Nucleonics lab

The other half of Nucleonics, partly hidden by the author. Judging from the two chevrons on my utility jacket, this photo must have been taken during my first extended underway period. The décor was not exciting, stainless steel, but it was easy to clean up.

The author reading on the messdecks in his own underway hat, poopy suit, and Albert Einstein sweatshirt (although you can't see Big Al). Just above the table is the ship's store in its entirety. Behind the wall is the OPSLL centreline storage compartment, and the sloped part of the wall to the right is where the ladder comes down from OPSUL. Directly above this table is Nucleonics.

Part of Engineroom Lower Level, showing Dave Sewell (facing the camera), Al Moran (back to the camera) and a lot of pipes and equipment. The box just in front of Al's head is a battery-powered battle lantern, for use in a power failure.

Mealtime on the Plunger. This is facing forward on the messdecks. The Chief's table is at the far end on the starboard side, just in front of the stereo system. Each table seats six. The ice cream machine is in the foreground on the right. The plaques on the forward bulkhead show that we won the "DC" award for being the best boat in the squadron in damage control for two years. The small locker barely visible to the right of the stereo system is the ship's library. Damage control gear and some food were stored in the benches we sit on. Not visible are the bug juice machines, hidden behind the ice cream machine on the starboard bulkhead.

Stores load – this one in Chinhae, South Korea during WestPac. This was a relatively minor one, so the number of boxes was pretty small and only the duty section was called to assist. A full-blown stores load included a line of sailors from pier to hatch and, inside the boat, from the hatch to wherever the food was to be stored. Those were all-hands affairs.

Transferring personnel from Plunger at Adak in the Aleutians (see Chapter 7 for the story behind this incident)

Tied up alongside a resupply vessel.

A view through the scope. This is one of ours; a Ticonderoga class cruiser in the SoCal Op Area.

The Delta IV (Soviet Union)

An Soviet Akula class sub

A Soviet Victor III on the surface. After we got used to them, they just weren't too difficult to deal with. Suspicions are that the pod on the tail houses a towed array sonar.

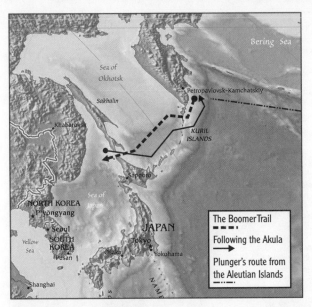

The Boomer Trail

Following the Akula

Plunger's route from
the Aleutian Islands

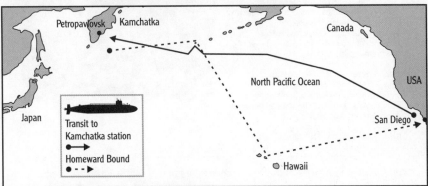

Transit to
Kamchatka station

Homeward Bound

The end of the line. Plunger enters San
Francisco Bay, passing beneath the Golden
Gate, on her way to Mare Island for
decommissioning. She would tie up to the
pier and shut down her reactor for the last
time in less than five hours.

CLOSING

One ship leaves the Navy today,
One ship of hundreds
Will feel the ocean one last time.
This one submarine which carries in her name
The history of all such craft
That have ever flown our nation's flag.

Our Navy's first craft
To plunge beneath the waves
Is an honored ancestor.
She carried, in her time, a president
And an ensign named Nimitz.

A second ship bore the name PLUNGER.
She fought for that honor bravely.
Sixteen ships she sank
And thirteen battle stars won.
She served her country with pride.

The third PLUNGER is before us now,
A fit successor to a noble name.
Twenty seven years serving freedom
Have left their mark.
What was once smooth hull and pristine lines,
The newest and the best of all,
Now shows scars from welder's torch;
From repairs and patches made of necessity.
No innocent youth, this ship,
She wears her age well, with pride,
For even at the end,
She is among the best.

One ship leaves the Navy today,
Soon to take her final voyage.
Yet she takes with her the knowledge
That she has served her nation and her men
As well as any ship could.

MM1/SS P. Andrew Karam

Excerpt from the Plunger *deactivation ceremony program, 10 February 1989.*

CHAPTER

16

Fire

I FINISHED MY DAILY ROUTINE and went back to sleep. With high CO_2 and low O_2 levels, most of us were asked to stay in the rack unless we were actually doing something. I'd checked the pressure in the oxygen banks and found that we had gone through nearly half of our oxygen. The oxygen banks were a number of large, high-pressure cylinders in the ballast tanks that were kept filled with pure oxygen. We tried to use them in conjunction with the candles to keep our oxygen levels at 21%. Unlike newer boats, we did not have the capability of making our own oxygen from the seawater. With the O_2 candles that were left, it was just enough to get us back to Pearl at the end of the op, maintaining oxygen at 20%. It didn't leave any room if we were extended on station or if we had a fire that consumed too much oxygen. Things weren't dire, and we were a good sight better off than a diesel boat would have been, but we had to be careful. My best guess was that the CO wanted to run with low O_2 levels for a week or so, ventilating whenever we could stick the snorkel mast up, to build a cushion. After that, I hoped, we'd go back to 20% and life would be a little easier.

The other half of the equation, of course, was CO_2. With one scrubber down hard and the other limping along, we could barely remove enough carbon dioxide to keep us at even the high levels we were currently at. Many of the crew were starting to get CO_2 headaches, we all felt lethargic, and some of us were starting to have bouts of diarrhea. All of these were classic symptoms of excessive CO_2 in the air. Another symptom, increased irritability, was hard to determine on a crowded submarine off the coast of the Soviet Union over the holidays. A certain amount of irritability just went with the mission. Ventilating through the snorkel mast would help the air situation, but being depth-charged would probably be worse for us in the long run. So we stayed in our racks, slept, didn't smoke, and hoped A-gang would fix the remaining scrubber. I made it through my daily routine each day, then went to my rack unless I was needed for anything. There, I could usually manage to read for a half hour or so before falling asleep. From talking to my shipmates, most of us were sleeping nine or ten hours out of every eighteen, and we were still groggy.

On the fourth day of this, I decided to stand an EWS watch. We were required to stand at least one watch monthly for each watchstation we were qualified on to maintain our proficiency. For me, that meant I had to stand three watches at sea, EWS, ERS, and AMSLL. I was qualified ERUL, too, but the ERS watch covered that proficiency. After qualifying EWS and becoming the Leading ELT, I dropped my proficiency on ERLL, mostly because I didn't have time, I never expected to have to stand the watch, and I hated that watchstation more than any others. To retain ELT proficiency I just had to draw at least one primary coolant sample each month; not a problem this underway.

I arranged with the EOOW and Engineer to stand the evening EWS watch. I figured that the evening watch should be pretty calm, given our location and current situation. Mostly, the EWS supervises the operation of the engineering plant in the spaces. In an emergency, the EWS is the man-in-charge at the scene until someone better comes along (usually the XO or Engineer). During complex evolutions, the EWS supervises the procedure step by step to make sure nothing goes wrong and to be there if it does. Once each watch, the EOOW is required to tour the spaces and review logs; while he does so, the EWS takes his place in Maneuvering. According to the CO, if anything weird happens in the engineering plant, he's going to ask the EWS what's happening because the EOOW is usually a junior officer who's never operated a piece of equipment except under supervision while the EWS is usually the most experienced person on watch at any given time.

To qualify as EWS I first had had to qualify all of my "in-rate" watches, those watches normally stood by machinist's mates. To do this, I had to know enough about each of the mechanical systems to know how to run them and to keep them running in an emergency. Other systems, the electronics and electrical stuff, I just had to know the basics. For EWS, I had to learn the other systems to a nearly in-rate level of knowledge. For the entire reactor plant. But more on qualifications later. For now, it's enough to know that the EOOW is in charge, but the EWS makes things happen.

In any event, I finished dinner and headed aft. I stopped in Sonar to say hello, but noticed they were tracking a few submerged targets, so I continued aft where I took a quick pre-watch tour of the engineering spaces. Most important was to find out what pumps were running. Some pumps were powered from the starboard side of the electric plant, others were on port. If we lost a turbine generator or popped a breaker, I had to know which pumps we'd lose so I could recommend starting alternates powered from the other side. I had never been able to remember everything, so I had a little laminated cheat sheet that listed, for each side of the electric plant, which pumps were powered from where. I just circled those that were running on this card, slipped it into the chest pocket on my poopy suit, and found the off-going EWS for turnover. He told me what was happening, what was expected for my watch, and headed forward. I went to Maneuvering to let them know I'd relieved as EWS.

After that, I headed to AMSLL to talk with Joe, the ELT on that watch now. After a few minutes of idle talk, we heard a low hum from somewhere above us. I popped my head up the ladder and looked down past the electrical switchboards that lined that side of the boat. One of the heavier sonar techs was on the treadmill, so I figured that must have caused the sound. I reminded him that we were still restricted in activity due to our atmosphere and ducked below again.

A few minutes later, the AMSUL watch stick his head down the hatch. "Do you smell anything, Andy?" he asked. I sniffed and shook my head. "Can you come up here? I could swear I smell something acrid." That got my attention. Acrid smoke is the hallmark of an electrical fire. Caught early, they're not hard to extinguish; you just cut the power. Left too long and they can be nasty. The previous year, we'd had a 1000 amp circuit breaker blow up on us. The current surge tripped off every other breaker on the boat, scramming the reactor, forcing us to blow to the surface, and leaving us without lights, navigation, sonar, or battery power and with fires in both ends of the boat. It was so quiet in the engineroom that you could hear waves breaking over the hull. That was off the coast of San Diego. Something similar here would be bad. I went up to investigate.

This time, as soon as I cleared the hatch to AMSUL I could smell the smoke. However tempting it was to find the source, it was more important to report the problem. That only took a few seconds and would mean that someone outside of the two of us would know there was something happening. If we were somehow overcome by smoke, others would still be on the way. It could save our lives and it could save the boat if the casualty were serious enough.

I picked up the phone and spoke into it. Normally I would have pulled a lever on the orange box directly beneath the phone. This would have piped my amplified voice over the Maneuvering loudspeaker, letting anyone who wasn't deaf or dead know what was happening. But that made a lot of noise and, in my opinion, we didn't yet need that level of alert. Besides, all phones were monitored by Maneuvering continuously. "Maneuvering, EWS. Acrid smell, machinery space upper level, starboard side. Cause unknown. Investigating."

"EWS, EOOW. Say again." That was the EOOW picking up the phone. He must have been drifting or doing something else.

"Maneuvering, EWS. There is an acrid smell in AMSUL on the starboard side. I just found out about it. We're trying to find out where it's coming from. Don't know any more than that right now, sir."

"Very well. Keep me posted."

"Keep you posted, aye, sir." I hung up the phone. Like I was going to keep anything like this a secret.

In Maneuvering, the EOOW would be calling the OOD to report the smell. He, in turn, would contact the Engineer, the XO, and the CO to let them know what was going on. Within two minutes of my call to Maneuvering, most of the crew knew of the potential problem. The off-going watch section was headed aft with fire extinguishers, hoses (in case something non-electrical started burning), and other damage control (DC) gear. The on-coming watch section was being woken. Some of them would muster in the Torpedo Room to don Nomex suits, oxygen breathing apparatus (OBAs), and still more DC gear. They'd wait, ready to respond if needed, but not until. Too many people was almost worse than too few in the cramped quarters we had. The members of the watch section were busy manning phones and rigging their spaces for fire and general emergency. Watertight doors were being gently shut to confine any fire that might break out, and emergency procedures were being reviewed to make sure everyone knew what to do if the worst happened. And I was trying to figure out where the hell the light gray smoke was coming from.

Fire at sea is bad. Surrounded by water, your options are to put it out, to go overboard, or to die. On a submarine, you usually don't have the option of going overboard. All submariners were trained in fire-fighting, using real fires and mock-ups of a variety of submarine spaces. I'd put out my share of fuel oil fires, lube oil fires, electrical and metal fires, and burning solids. On shore. We'd had over 30 fires in my time on *Plunger*, most of them minor. I should add to this that reporting light smoke or an acrid smell was considered reporting a fire under the assumption that, if there's not one now, there will be soon without proper action. And proper action meant doing just what we were doing right now. Treat everything like the real thing because you might not get another chance.

Within five minutes, the Electrical Division chief, called the EMC (short for Electrician's Mate, Chief) was on the scene. With acrid smoke, it was a fair bet his division would be involved, and if we found an electrical panel to be the problem, he'd need to supervise shutting off power to it, opening, and inspecting it. I had a high degree of respect for all of our nuke chiefs, but especially for him. He was a big, burly, easy-going guy who knew our electrical plant about as well as the guys who'd designed it. You couldn't pay me enough to go into a live 450 volt electrical panel; he made it look boring. I was glad to see him.

I told the EMC what I knew, which took about ten seconds. Within another few minutes, the rest of his division was on hand, so we divided up the starboard side among us. Smoke was getting steadily thicker and we were starting to narrow the location down to the forward part of the space.

We weren't happy about that. The high-voltage panels were aft of where we thought the smoke was coming from, but the affected panels were all reactor plant electronics panels. Losing any of them could scram us out; not something we wanted to do just now.

In Control, the CO was on the scene in a few moments. He sized up the tactical situation and instructed the OOD to break contact with everyone. I felt the boat take a small down-angle and bank slightly to port as we turned away from anyone who could hear us. We wanted to get as far away from anyone as we could so that, if we had to start making noise or come to PD, there'd be less chance of being detected. I guessed, too, that the CO was trying to get beneath a thermal layer to further hide any noises we might have to make. Good from the perspective of stealth, but it took us further away from the surface, where we might end up needing to go if we couldn't get things under control.

Control had two concerns right now. The CO had a fire back aft that was, as of now, an unknown. He didn't know what, if anything, it would do to his ability to hide, fight, or escape if anyone found us. And he had some submarines around that were certainly capable of finding us if we had to start making enough noise to put the fire out. So he had to balance the two concerns, taking care of the fire versus keeping us quiet and undetected. This is why he broke contact and moved away. This way, if anything happened, we'd at least have some breathing room and a chance to prepare for anything else that might happen. And, in making that decision, he left the casualty to the Engineer to fix, concentrating on the tactical situation. The Captain's priority was the whole boat, of which this fire was only a part. An important part that had the capability of limiting his options, but still only a part of the big picture.

We were still looking for the source of the smoke. One of the electricians had determined it was coming from a transformer box, but that box drew power from both the port and starboard sides of the electrical plant. Unless we knew exactly which part of the box was smoking, we couldn't do much more. I was standing by the switch near the middle of the compartment, looking across to where the electricians were trying to get better information. The problem was this: I could take the switch to select either the port or starboard power source. If I was right, the fire would go out. If I was wrong, the fire would continue. Sooner or later, it would cause a short circuit that would trip the circuit breaker supplying power to the panel. When that happened, this box would lose all power and the reactor would scram because our reactor plant controls were powered from the box. The reactor would be safe, and we could still blow to the surface, but we didn't want to have to run the risk. So I stood by the switch, hoping someone would give me some good information to go on because this was not a decision I wanted to have to make on a guess.

Meanwhile the smoke continued to thicken. The general rule of thumb is that, when you're having trouble breathing, it's time to put on a mask. I shouted to the electricians that they were to put on their emergency air breathing masks (EABs). These were full-face respirators that plugged directly into the ship's 100 psi air system, reducing pressure to about a half psi through a pressure reducing valve clipped to the waist. EAB manifolds were scattered throughout the ship, so most of the time it was just a matter of grabbing an EAB, putting it on, checking for a good seal, and plugging into an EAB manifold. The electricians turned to put their masks on. I told Maneuvering we were donning masks and was then going to put mine on. As I reached for it, I glanced across the aisle and saw the bottom of the box glow orange and then erupt in flame. I pointed to it and yelled "There it is! What side of the plant is it?"

One of the electricians started to answer, but the machinery made it moot. The switch I'd been holding suddenly flipped to port. This meant the starboard power supply was bad. When it went, the current surge tripped the starboard breaker and the power-seeking switch had automatically supplied power from the remaining source.

With the breaker tripped and the selector switch in the port position, there was no more electrical power to the fire and should have gone out. It didn't. By the time the breaker tripped, the heat had lit off the inside of the electrical panel and, instead of stopping, the smoke intensified.

"Phone talker, to Maneuvering, electrical power to fire secured when breaker tripped. Fire continues to burn as a class A fire. Fire fighting efforts underway." The phone talker repeated back to me, then repeated the message to Maneuvering. I looked at the EMC. "Chief, want to tell Maneuvering what happened?"

"Yeah, I'll head on back." This was important. I didn't know as much as the chief, and describing everything over the phones would take too long. Better for the one person who knew the most to give the report in person, to avoid any possibility of misunderstanding. In the meantime, the immediate electrical problem was over and we just had to fight the burning insulation. We had plenty of people on hand for that.

Now it was my turn to put on an EAB because the air was getting pretty thick and was starting to burn my eyes and throat. I realized I was already holding one – someone must have handed me one earlier when they were passed out to the fire fighters. I nestled my chin into the rubber chin cup, pressed my face against the soft rubber seal, and pulled the five rubber straps over my head. Next, I reached back behind my jaw and felt around for the tabs at the end of the lowest straps. Finding them, I pulled them tight, to seal the bottom of the mask. I then repeated this with the forehead straps, leaving the top strap alone. In the past, I had accidentally ripped hair out that got caught in the straps. Irritating in a drill and not even noticed in a real emergency. Next, I took a quick breath in, sucking the air out of the mask. The EAB collapsed against my face and, after a few seconds, was still tight. Amazing, because I had a pretty good beard now – that usually kept you from getting a good seal. I was lucky.

The next step was to plug the end of the hose into the nearest EAB manifold. There was one right above me, and it still had an open spot, so I took the dust cover off and jammed the end of the hose into it. I took a breath of good air, fresh from the ship's air banks. It's an effort to breathe with an EAB since it's what's called a "pressure-demand" regulator, but it's better than breathing smoke. The good part was that I could breathe now. The bad part was that I was tethered to the EAB manifold by a six-foot long rubber hose, and I could only move by unplugging myself (and holding my breath) and scurrying to the next manifold. If that one was already full, then I'd either have to find another, or plug into the "buddy connection" on the regulator of someone else, and hope they didn't take off on me. Another drawback was that it was hard to talk intelligibly with an EAB on – just like listening to people in the movies talking with gas masks on. Talking on the phones was even more difficult because you couldn't talk and listen at the same time – the handsets wouldn't reach from your ear to the speaker diaphragm. So we could work and operate the boat in EABs, but it wasn't easy and was certainly not fun. The longest I had ever had to "suck rubber" had been about six hours, a few years earlier. I didn't want to have to do that again.

By this time, too, the XO and Engineer were on the scene, along with the chiefs. I gave the XO a quick summary of what was happening, he sized up the situation, and he relieved me as man-in-charge at the scene. Someone else took over the phones, and I went back to being EWS, which meant checking in on the rest of the watch section.

Moving around the engineering spaces was becoming inconvenient because of the fire. First, the EABs made any movement difficult. Second, as part of our emergency procedure, all the watertight doors were shut and dogged (to dog a door you turn a central handwheel which mechanically locks and seals the door). Going through a door meant undogging it, opening it, going through, shutting it without slamming it against the seal (which would make too much noise), and dogging it again on the other side. And EAB lines couldn't go through the doors for obvious reasons. Nonetheless, I had to go back to the Engineroom, report in to Maneuvering, and make sure everything was going well there. Not that the watchstanders couldn't be trusted to do things the right way; they knew their watches far better than I did. But there's no substitute for having the supervisor actually making the rounds.

After checking in with Maneuvering and the ER watches, I headed back to the machinery space. Smoke was thicker than ever, and I had noticed that it was even starting to build up in the ER. This wasn't due to any problems with our isolation, but every time someone went through the watertight door, some smoke went with them. I spoke with someone who'd come from up front and was told it was the same story there. In Control, Sonar, Radio, the Torpedo Room, and elsewhere, watchstanders were sitting at their consoles or manning their watches in EABs, plugged into the nearest manifold, and listening on the phones to find out what was happening. The air conditioning plant and ventilation were secured, so temperatures were rising all over the boat, and sweat was pooling in the EABs while they fogged up and began to itch. My beard was starting to really hurt, now that the initial excitement was over, and the effort of pulling air into the EABs twenty times a minute for the last hour was tiring everyone out.

As uncomfortable as it was in the AMS, I was happy to be there rather than elsewhere. At least I was able to do something, and I knew what was happening. I had been on the other end of casualties before, and I hated it. I could imagine the people in the forward part of the boat. They knew better than I did how many Soviet skimmers and subs were around, and the different ways they could find us. And, on top of that, they were stuck in Control, sucking rubber, and listening to the phone traffic going back and forth, trying to find out if we were going to be able to put the fire out before *Plunger* had to snorkel. Powerless to help, and almost totally dependent on our ability to put out the fire before it turned into something that might endanger the boat, I guessed they were feeling both helpless and frustrated. I know that's how I always felt, in similar situations. Nonetheless, they would be doing their jobs the same as before; jokes a bit strained from tension and speaking through the EABs, but making as few concessions to the extra strain as humanly possible. I returned to the fire to see what was happening. We were now into the second hour since I'd first called away the acrid smell.

At the scene, it looked a little better. Smoke was still thick, and a little found its way through my beard into the EAB. But there didn't seem to be any more smoke coming out from under the panel, and from the number of spent extinguishers around, I could imagine why. The electricians were setting up an electrical safety area, preparing to open the panel to make sure the fire was well and truly out. The Doc was on the scene, just in case someone was electrocuted, and the EMC was putting on thick rubber gloves to open the panel. A rope was tied around his waist so that one of his electricians could pull him out if, in spite of everything, the panel was still "live" and he became electrocuted, and rubber mats were over every metal surface to provide electrical insulation. Just outside the electrical safety area, men were standing by with fire extinguishers, because there was a chance that a smoldering fire would burst back into flame as soon as the panel opened, feeding it oxygen. I suppose the EMC could have delegated this dangerous job to someone more junior, but I had never seen a chief do that. No matter how much we might joke about their life of leisure, their four-section duty, and their waistlines, when it came to anything really important or dangerous, most chiefs were right there, doing the work. Part of it was leadership, because just about all Navy leaders were taught to lead by example, and this was the example to set. Another part was that the chiefs were the most experienced onboard in their areas, and were the logical people to choose for ticklish operations. And, in part, I think that many chiefs just wanted to make sure that everything went right, and were confident enough in their abilities and experience that this meant doing it themselves. So the EMC was (hopefully only figuratively) on the hot seat, getting ready to go into a potentially burning, potentially live high voltage panel to see if we really had put out the fire. Personally, I'd have rather put my hand into the cage of a rabid dog – you can survive rabies with medical treatment. You really can't survive being dead.

The panel opened to the right. The EMC stood on the right (or hinged) side of the panel and put his hands on the upper and lower latches. On the left, facing the panel, stood two electricians, each wearing an EAB and electrician's gloves and holding a CO_2 fire extinguisher. Their job was to hit the panel with CO_2 if it looked like it was flashing back into an active fire. The EMC tightened his grip on the latches and, with a smooth move-ment, opened them and swung the panel open. The XO and Eng were standing between the two electricians, peering into the panel. As it came open, a huge cloud of smoke billowed out, and the electricians' grip tight-ened on the extinguishers. But no more followed, no flame, and no sparks. In a few seconds, the smoke had cleared as much as it could given the atmosphere, and we realized the fire was out. The XO turned to the phone talker. "Phone talker, to Maneuvering. The fire is out." For the first time in nearly two hours, everyone on board started to relax. And, in Control, they realized that our mission could continue.

At this point, we were still not out of the woods. True, the fire was out. But we still had heavy smoke in the machinery space, and no way to ven-tilate to the outside. And we had a power supply to the reactor control instruments that was tenuous. We needed to fix all these things, find out exactly what the fire had hurt, and figure out what to do next. Time for the electricians to earn their pay.

Within three hours the electricians had a pretty good idea as to what had happened. This transformer was mounted close to the hull. In the cold waters of the winter North Pacific, condensation forming on the hull (in spite of our hull insulation) had dripped onto it. Normally the things were splash-proof, but constant dripping for over a month was just a bit much. It shorted out, frying most of the internals. We normally ran a three-phase electrical system, we could salvage the transformer and pretty much restore the electrical plant by running the thing on two phases. The EMC assured us it could be done, the Eng checked his calculations and concurred, so

E-Div went ahead and fixed it up. Had the work done in another 12 hours. As ship's photographer, I took a full series of photos to document it for posterity. And for the CO's post-mission slide show. We had to reduce electrical load on the transformer, of course, but that could be done. The important thing was that we again had port and starboard power to the reactor control instruments. Next thing to do was to call home and tell them.

I was in Control when we started coming up. Riding below the weather, we usually have a pretty smooth ride. Shallow, however, a submarine has no keel and, with only a round hull, we rolled a lot. This time, I started feeling some gentle rocking at about 300 feet. This was interesting, because we normally didn't feel anything until about 150 feet, even in bad weather. Luckily, I had never been seasick. By the time we got to 150 feet we were taking 20 degree rolls or more. I hurried to Nuke Lab to make sure everything was stowed and spent the next ten minutes taping drawers and locker doors shut, stowing gear and books, and lying the stool down on the deck. As we went up, the rolls became increasingly violent. I wasn't in Control, so I couldn't see the official gauge, but we'd hooked up a crude plumb bob with a protractor in Nucleonics, just for the hell of it. When we finally made it to PD it was showing 45 degree rolls, the most I'd experienced. All over the boat, people told me, doors flew open, people were thrown from their racks, plates crashed, cans fell. Luckily, the same storm was making so much noise that these sounds were unlikely to be noticed in the general din, so we were safe from that perspective. Provided the storm didn't roll us over. We were built to take a lot, but that wasn't one of things we were designed for.

I braced myself in Nucleonics, figuring it was best to stay there to try to take care of things. There was no way I'd be able to sleep, draw a sample, or do anything else. And there was no way I wanted to be walking around the boat now, bouncing off the bulkheads and maybe missing steps. So I braced myself, sitting in the chair with my feet against the counter opposite the lab, wedging myself into a corner. Every so often, despite the taping and latches, a drawer or door would fly open and various pieces of gear would try to escape. I'd try to catch them, shut the door, and tape it shut again.

The rolling went on for almost an hour before we finally got the broadcast off. Gradually, I felt the rolls diminish from insane to violent and finally to almost imperceptible. I left Nucleonics and went back to Control. Talking with the helmsman, I found that the largest roll we took was over 50 degrees, more than we were designed to take and more than halfway to rolling over on our side. I also found out that the depth gauge had been fluctuating between 16 and over 100 feet from a nominal depth of 50 feet and, with nearly 20 feet of scope out of the water, we kept having waves breaking over the top.

Winter in the North Pacific, I am told, rivals anything you can find in the North Atlantic. After three ops in the North Pacific in winter, I am ready to believe that. But this was the worst tossing around I had ever experienced and I was hoping I'd not have to go through its like again. Luckily, this op was mostly a sonar op, so we didn't spend much time at PD. Things were calming down and, as it was nearly midnight, I started my daily instrument checks. While they were going through their checks, I grabbed some midrats.

The XO investigation of the John Wayne disrespect case was nearly over and a date had been set for the Captain's Mast. It would happen within a week. While following it had been amusing and gave us all something to talk about, for me it was starting to pall a bit. But it was certainly better than no entertainment at all and, in Matt, they had found a perfect person to "victimize." Normally a rather vocal person, this gave him a continuing chance to spout off about the injustice of it all, which he did loudly and humorously for all to hear. I assumed he was just playing his part very well, and he certainly was funny.

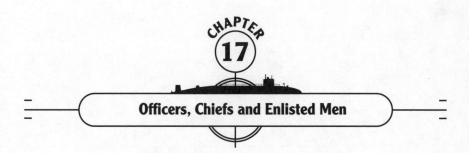

CHAPTER 17

Officers, Chiefs and Enlisted Men

It is by no means enough that an officer should be capable… He should be as well a gentleman of liberal education, refined manners, punctilious courtesy, and the nicest sense of personal honor… No meritorious act of a subordinate should escape his attention, even if the reward be only one word of approval. Conversely, he should not be blind to a single fault in any subordinate. True as may be the political principles for which we are now contending…the ships themselves must be ruled under a system of absolute despotism. I trust that I have now made clear to you the tremendous responsibilities… We must do the best we can with what we have.

John Paul Jones, September 4, 1775,
excerpts from a letter to the US Naval Committee

A FEW THINGS that are essential to understanding life in the Navy do not lend themselves nicely to describing within the confines of this story. For that reason, I've chosen to simply talk about them outside of the confines of the story line, after which I'll return to the main narrative. The most important of these topics is the distinction between officers, chiefs, and enlisted men.

The Navy, and most of the military for that matter, is an interesting contradiction. In order to preserve our egalitarian society, we worked in a very strict hierarchy in which officers reign supreme, enlisted men are on the bottom, and chiefs occupy an uneasy middle ground. Ideally, there was to be absolutely no mingling between these castes. I didn't socialize with the officers or chiefs except under tightly controlled situation. At ship's events, I could tip a glass with my division officer and, if he chose, he could invite the entire division out to dinner or to his house for a cookout. But I was only once invited to an officer's house for dinner, only twice went socially with an officer, and only twice with a chief. In the submarine navy, these were the major distinctions; in the surface navy, the stratification was even more detailed.

Part of the reason for this was operational and for battle efficiency, the theory went. We might end up in a situation where the only way to save the ship was to order someone to do something that was likely to be fatal. It would be easier to give that order to Petty Officer Karam than to tell Andy to go and get himself badly burned. Similarly, I was thought more likely to blindly do follow the orders of the Engineer Officer, even if it meant being hurt, than I would be to do what Bob, my drinking buddy told me to do.

Personally, I thought this ludicrous. In his books, Stephen Ambrose relates quite convincingly that most fighting men performed deeds both heroic and routine because failing to do so would be letting their buddies down. And I saw this on board, albeit under less extreme circumstances. Most of us would whatever we had to in order to pull our own weight, to do our jobs, or to save the boat. And most of us would do whatever it took to not let our shipmates down, even if it meant going in harm's way or putting others there.

I'm not sure about my shipmates, but this is something I thought about a lot. I remember looking at the watertight door between the bow compartment and the ops compartment, wondering if I would be able to shut it on sleeping or screaming people in order to save the boat. I still don't know if I would have been able to. I convinced myself I would, but I'm glad I never had to put that conviction to the test. But, logically, that would be the only thing to do if leaving the door open meant that the ship would sink, killing everyone. And this is the sort of situation that was given as an example of the reason to maintain a strict separation between the castes. So that the Engineer could say "Karam – we're flooding in the bow compartment. Go forward and shut the watertight door." And, instead of thinking about Joe and Scott and Brian, all of whom might be stuck in the bow compartment, and instead of thinking that I might drown trying to reach the door, I'd simply say "Aye, aye, Sir," and do my best to shut the door.

I think that this strict separation was also a tradition that nobody wanted to change. Granted, in any organization there must be a boss, middle managers, and underlings. And granted, too that the exigencies of wartime make it more desirable to have instant, unthinking obedience. But I think the way the Navy did things was the result of what we called 200 years of tradition unhampered by progress. Heavy industry, mining, even construction workers find themselves in situation where a boss or foreman orders men into harm's way, and people do what they have to because they don't want to be looking into a beer one day, alone at the bar, listening to others talk about how John died because that no-load at the bar there didn't have the guts to save him.

I think the Navy is the way it is because the Navy remembers the days of aristocracy, when officers came from the upper classes and enlisted men, from the lower. Many of our naval traditions come from the British including, I think, this one. Who went out drinking with their field hand? So why do so with a lowly enlisted man; someone who was likely to be dirty, unrefined, uninteresting, and beneath one's station? And part of this was instilled in officers early on. The only problem is that this division should not have survived events like the American Revolution, mandatory education, and the change to an all-volunteer Navy.

Admittedly, things were more extreme in the surface navy, but it was noticeable in submarines, too. And, in my opinion, the very worst offenders were officers who attended the Naval Academy. A great many officers seemed to come out of the Academy thoroughly convinced of their importance and talents and equally convinced that anyone who was not gifted with an Academy education was somehow lacking, both socially and intellectually. In my opinion, the Naval Academy was the nation's premier facility for taking perfectly normal young men and turning them into elitist snobs in just four years. The very worst officers I worked with were all graduates of the Naval Academy.

Now the flip side. The very best officers I worked with were also Academy graduates. They were the ones who came out the Academy impressed with how much they didn't know. The ones who realized that the enlisted men could teach them something and who were willing to listen. They were the ones who realized that a diploma from the Academy did not confer infallibility. And, they were the ones who didn't demand respect, who didn't yell if you forgot to salute, who didn't scream when you made a small mistake, and who didn't turn red when you dared disagree with them. I enjoyed working for them.

Officers came in three "flavors"; junior officers, department heads, and the CO and XO. Junior officers (JOs) were each responsible for a specific division of men. As LELT, I reported directly to the Chemistry and Radiological Controls Assistant (CRA), the JO responsible for making sure my division did everything correctly. The CRA, along with the Damage Control Assistant, the Electrical Officer, the Mechanical Division Officer, and the Reactor Controls Assistant, reported to the Engineer Officer, the department head for all of Engineering. And the Engineer reported to the XO along with the Navigator and the Weapons Officer, the other department heads. Sitting by himself at the top of the food chain was the CO, our local deity and arbiter of all disputes. What the CO said was always final.

Enlisted men were the other extreme in this spectrum. We did the dirty work. We sweated, grunted, cleaned, put in 24 hour days (or longer). We ran the equipment, turned valves, wrote work packages, crawled in the bilges, contorted ourselves to reach bolts. And we knew our part of the boat better than anyone because we traced out systems, operated machinery, tore apart pumps and electronics, fixed things, and did everything else that kept the boat running. The officers knew what the books said about our systems, but we knew in our fingertips how a pump felt when a bearing was loose and our noses knew what burning packing smelled like and we could look at a gauge and tell how a dozen other parameters were changing because this was our job and our life. Or, as one of my skippers put it, "A ship manned with only enlisted men would come back dirty. A ship manned with only officers probably wouldn't come back."

The lowest of the low were the non-rated seamen. These were the kids, usually 18 or 19, who had joined the Navy without any guaranteed training. They were really junior, since you can't be a petty officer unless you've got a rate, or field of specialization. They were generically called seamen, although if someone wanted to be in a specific rate they were a "striker", a person striking for a specific rate. Generally, these guys came onboard the boat and were assigned to "Seaman Gang", our pool of indentured servants. Until they settled on a rate and advanced in rank, they'd spend most of their time painting, carrying, cleaning, washing dishes, and doing all the other menial jobs that had to be done, but not by more senior people. There were three ranks for non-rated personnel, Seaman Recruit, Seaman Apprentice, and Seaman.

To further complicate matters, if a person went to a specialty school but was not a petty officer, instead of being called "seaman", they were designated by their rate and rank. My rate was machinist's mate, an engineering rate, so, as a non-petty officer, I had been called "Machinist's Mate Fireman (or MMFN) Karam." After advancing to third-class petty officer, I was Petty Officer (or MM3) Karam and my rank went from third-class petty officer (1 chevron on my sleeve) to first-class petty officer (three chevrons) by the time I left the Navy. And, the piece de resistance, when I qualified in submarines, I became MM1/SS Karam, meaning a first-class petty officer machinist's mate qualified in submarine warfare.

In between the two castes were the chief petty officers, usually just called chiefs. Chiefs were enlisted men who stayed in long enough, had good enough evaluations, and had impressive enough records to be elevated to that level. Unlike other branches of the service where there was no great distinction between one paygrade and the next, the Navy places its chiefs on a short pedestal. Chiefs are the ones who make things happen. At least, good chiefs are. I can speak with a limited authority in this one because, although never a chief on active duty, I did make chief in the Reserves.

Chiefs can be summed up in a few lines from some standard jokes.

"The Chief is always right."
"In case the Chief is found to be wrong, refer to the above rule."
"The Chief is always the Chief, even if dressed in only a towel."
"The Chief is never late. He is unavoidably detained elsewhere."

And so on.

Most chiefs in the submarine navy were very good at what they did. In spite of the standard stereotype of a coffee-swilling fat guy stalking around giving directions and doing little else, chiefs on *Plunger* (and on the frigate I was assigned to when in the Reserves) worked as hard as anyone else. They were in a sense caught between two worlds. Their technical prowess and abilities helped them to become chiefs, but after this elevation, they started doing increasingly more administrative work and less of the technical work they usually loved. A good chief understood and accepted this, dirtying his hands from time to time when he could find a good excuse, and always remaining the technical expert in his area. The poor chiefs either refused to shoulder their administrative responsibilities or they ignored their technical ones. Working for a good chief was a joy; working for a bad chief was worse than working for a bad officer because we had more daily contact with the chiefs.

The way the work went was like this. At the start of the day, the officers would meet and discuss work to be done that day. They would, in turn, meet with their division chiefs who would then go to their divisions and parcel out the work and some sort of plan for accomplishing it. In this process, the chiefs would sometimes have help from their "leading first", the senior-most first class petty officer (the rank directly junior to chief). Some chiefs would leave the daily operations entirely to their leading first, some wanted direct control over everything, and some would share the duties. From there, it was up to the rest to make things happen, calling upon the chief for advice, reporting progress to him, and, if need be, recommending alternative approaches if things started looking troublesome.

I took a somewhat jaded view to the whole hierarchy. On the one hand, I was always a pretty rabid egalitarian and I had a very hard time being treated as anything less than a complete equal by anyone. On the other hand, I'd signed the papers and had to take everything that went with enlisting. What this meant was that I gave chiefs and officers exactly the amount of respect required of me, as a minimum. In general, I noticed that people demanding respect rarely deserved it. If they deserved more than that (in my opinion), I gave them more. If I thought they were incompetent idiots or insufferable asses, I'd make sure they were aware of this, within the constraints set forth by the rules under which we operated.

For example, I worked for the CRA and was supposed to do what he said. Each time we got a new CRA, I'd give him the same talk, explaining that it was my division, I was happy to teach him anything I could, and that I'd keep him out of trouble as long as he didn't try to tell me how to do my job. I had one CRA who chose to ignore this advice. After two weeks of arguing with him, I simply told my division to do exactly what the CRA said, no more and no less. And we sat back and waited. Within another two weeks, a tired and frustrated CRA caught up with me on the pier and told me "You win. It's your division. What do we do now?" I told him not to worry, called a short division meeting, and we were caught up within a few days.

Many of us enlisted men were less than subtle when teaching our division officers. And not without reason. They had a lot to learn in a very short time. We couldn't afford to be patient or subtle. Good division officers had to be taught as much as possible in the short time they were going to be with us because, someday, they'd be the engineer, XO, or CO and they needed an appreciation of what you did. And, if they were bad officers, we just didn't want to take the time or energy to walk them through something. We threw it at them, hoping it would stick, knowing that if they didn't get it, at least they'd only be our division officer for six months or so.

I can think of one specific instance that vividly demonstrates the difference between good and bad officers quite nicely. Following one of our spec ops, we pulled into the Aleutian Island of Adak. At the time I was feverishly studying for my oral board to qualify EWS, a big deal for nukes. A few days after we pulled in, someone found out that another boat was going to be pulling in with a bent scope. Apparently they had come to PD beneath an iceberg, something we'd been very careful not to do ourselves. For some reason, our XO was determined to get some pictures of the boat, bent scope and all, so he could give them to our Submarine Squadron Commodore when we returned to San Diego. I guess he thought it would make *Plunger* look good and the other boat look bad. In any event, when they pulled in, he was standing there, camera in hand taking pictures.

After he'd shot off the roll of film, he took it to our photo officer and said that he wanted some 8x10 glossies as soon as possible. The photo officer didn't know much about developing and printing film, so he was more or less dependent on me to do this. However, knowing I was studying for my EWS boards, he decided to wait until after I had passed to ask me to develop and print the film. I passed the board a week later, just after we left port again. That's when the photo officer told me about the XO's photos. I noticed he was looking a bit tired, but didn't know why. The photos were lousy; dark, grainy, and out of focus, so it took a lot of time and work to get some decent enlargements. As this went on, the photo officer kept looking more and more haggard. I finally figured it out when I happened to find a note to him from the XO saying "Photo Officer – I asked you for 8"x10" glossies of the bent scope several days ago. You have consistently failed to produce them. By so doing, you have squandered all your credibility and good will. You are not to sleep until you have delivered pictures to me suitable for presentation to the Commodore upon our arrival in San Diego."

To me, this was astounding. I couldn't believe a senior officer so intent on embarrassing another ship and currying favor for himself as to forbid a junior officer's sleeping until the photos were done. Not only was it petty and childish (not to mention churlish), but it showed a complete disregard for safety since the photo officer was standing watch as EOOW and, if too tired, could miss something important. I found the photo officer and asked him about the note.

"Sir, when did you get this?"

"Oh, nearly a week ago, Karam."

"Why didn't you say anything? We could have had some photos for the XO within a few days."

"Well, you were studying for your EWS board. How could I ask you to take the time from something so important for this?"

The conversation went on from there, of course, but I was as amazed by the photo officer as by the XO. In this case, however, I was impressed rather than contemptuous. I simply couldn't believe that he was willing to give up his sleep and take so much heat simply to give me a better chance of passing my EWS board (which was not a done deal; I had failed my first oral board a few weeks earlier). I had had disagreements with this officer a few times in the past and, to some extent, had often viewed him as overly conservative and rule-bound, but it never happened again. I told him to find a place to sleep where he wouldn't be caught and then locked myself in the Nuke Lab (also our darkroom) until we had some decent photos for the XO.

As a sort of epilogue to this incident, it's worth noting that the XO left *Plunger* shortly after this incident to take command of a submarine. On one of their first underways, they managed to run aground and (if I remember correctly) he was relieved of his command. When we heard about it, the entire crew was highly amused, joking that he probably had the crew painting the bottom of the hull while they were waiting for the tide to come in so the tugs could pull them off the sandbar.

In a lot of respects, the feelings of these three castes towards one another was mixed. Although I cannot speak for all enlisted men, I know I respected and even had genuine admiration for really outstanding officers and chiefs. I resented the fact that I was working under a relatively strict hierarchical organization, and I had no use for officers and chiefs who placed themselves on a pedestal and expected us to genuflect whenever they approached. At the same time, however, I didn't particularly care for the officers and chiefs who made a big deal about spending time with the enlisted men. It was almost like wealthy people making an effort to wash their own cars or shop at K-Mart; it just rang false and was seen as either slumming or trying too hard to be one of the guys. Better were those who, although they might dislike the system too, at least acknowledged it existed and resigned themselves to playing within the rules we were given, but who treated us like people at work and at ship's functions. And best of all were those who, in addition, actually respected the enlisted men working for them. But, unfortunately, this last group was rare.

CHAPTER
18

Qualifications

One thing every submariner spent an inordinate amount of time at was qualifications. We were allowed to use our racks, cutlery, and the toilet without formal qualifications. Just about everything else required us to complete a formal qualification process to learn and demonstrate we could do things the right way. This was accomplished with "qual cards", lists of required knowledge or demonstrated practical factors ranging in length from a single sheet of paper to several pages, densely packed with requirements. In my welcome aboard, I had been given qual cards for phone talker, ELT, ERLL, ERUL, AMSLL, primary valve operator, submarine warfare, Control Point watch, TLD reader, Basic Engineering Qualifications, and ERS. As time went on, I would complete these and would add qualifications as EWS, COW, and LELT.

With each of these qual cards came qualification "curves". We were required to make progress on each of these cards at a certain rate and were given due dates for each qualification. For example, if I failed to make the required progress in my engineering quals, I could be required to stay onboard (if in port) or to stay awake pursuing quals until I caught up to the required curve. If I continued to fall behind or if I failed to qualify in a suitably timely manner, I could be sent to Captain's Mast and punished by being reduced in rank, paying a monetary fine, or being confined to the boat. I could also be kicked out of the submarine navy and onto a skimmer. The reason for this is that we simply had no room for people who were unwilling or unable to shoulder their fair share of the burden. And a lot of the burden was standing watch. It might take a newly-arrived machinist's mate 18 months to qualify ERS. In that time, he might go from being the most junior person in his division to being one with middling seniority. As senior people left, junior ones would move up to take their watches. Someone unable to fill in ERUL or ERS due to failure to qualify could leave a hole in the watchbill or could force someone else to stand a more senior watch that they weren't quite ready for yet. And, unlike surface ships, on submarines, everyone was required to complete their ship's quals. A surface sailor could make it an entire career without completing their surface warfare quals. A submariner who didn't qualify in two years would likely receive disciplinary action at Captain's Mast and be kicked out of the submarine navy forever. Because of this, and not without justification, many surface sailors thought we viewed them as the dumping grounds for everyone too dumb or too lazy to make it on the boats. Just another reason they loved us.

There were three distinct parts to each qual card; academic knowledge, practical factors, and examinations. I'd like to talk about each of these in turn, although we worked on the first two in parallel.

Each watchstation had specific systems that were important to know. For example, someone standing watch in AMSLL had to know how to operate the feed system, the after CO_2 scrubber, the steam generator blowdown and sampling system, and several others. Knowledge of the main steam system was not essential because there wasn't a single main steam valve or pipe in AMSLL. Similarly, although parts of the electric plant were located in AMSLL, they were operated by electricians, so MMs didn't have to worry about them. On the other hand, we did have to know the feed system backwards and forwards. Not only did we have to know it, but we had to persuade someone else we knew it. This was done through a process called a checkout, so called (I think) because it was where qualified watchstanders would check out our knowledge of the system. To prepare for a checkout, we had a list of important things to know and we'd study the technical manuals to try to learn these things. For example, I had to be able to draw a simple diagram of the entire feed system, showing the relative locations of the major valves, gauges, pumps, and so forth. I had to know where the feed pumps drew their electrical power, what system alarms there were (and their setpoints), what would cause the feed pumps to automatically trip offline, how much electrical power they required, their pumping rates under a variety of steam generator pressures, water temperatures and other parameters in various points in the feed system, the modes of operation of the feedwater regulation valves, approximate flow characteristics of the feed reg valves, how to deal with several possible emergency and casualty situations, and on and on and on. This level of knowledge was required for all systems I might be called upon to operate as a machinist's mate and was called "in-rate" knowledge. Luckily, knowledge of electrical and electronic systems was considered "cross-rate" knowledge; I had to know the big picture, but the details were optional. When I thought I knew a system well enough, I'd find someone authorized to give that checkout and they'd grill me. Anything I didn't know would be given as a "look-up", something to find out and get back to the person on. Once all of my lookups were finished, they'd sign and date that line item, showing I met the knowledge standards for that particular item.

The practical parts of qualification, called practical factors (or prac facs) was similar. Here, instead of demonstrating the ability to read and memorize, we had to show we could do things "hand on." For each watchstation, I had to stand four watches under the instruction of a qualified watchstander. It was not enough to simply stand the watch under instruction, we had to do things, too. Prior to the watch, I'd decide which prac facs I wanted to attempt (or would be forced to do) and I'd try to walk through them, procedures in hand, to locate the valves and switches I'd be operating. It helped, but not enough. Once on watch, in the real world, things got interesting. For example, to start up the evaporator, the procedure might say to turn this valve, wait until you saw water level rise to a certain point, and then open another valve. What the procedure doesn't say is that the first valve is tucked away beneath the evap where only a gibbon has a reasonable chance of reaching, the water level indicator is behind the evap and nearly invisible, and the second valve is in the overhead hidden behind a pipe. The procedure probably won't say, either, that you have all of 15 seconds to do all of this or the evap will overflow and trip a dump valve, dumping hot water into the bilges and filling them up. This is what you learned from the watchstander and this is why all of our training was intensely personal – never more than two students for one instructor in our initial training and usually one-on-one on the boat.

Some prac facs were easy to get, others were much more difficult. If we were conducting weekly ops, you could start up the engineroom and shut it down on a weekly basis, but we might never have to add water or chemicals to the reactor plant. On a spec op, by comparison, we might add reactor plant chemicals five times on the first transit alone, but we'd go for two months and only start up the plant once. And, once on station, we wouldn't do anything except the bare basics until pulling off again seven or eight weeks later.

After completing all prac facs and getting signatures for all the required systems for a particular watchstation, it was time for testing. First, we'd have to take a written, closed-book exam. This was graded by qualified watchstanders and required a score of 2.5 on a scale of 1 to 4 to pass. After the exam, there were interviews with the division chief, the division officer, and, finally, with the Engineer Officer. These interviews were, in some respect, mere formalities. Everyone in the food chain had to have their own chance to decide whether or not I was fit to stand a particular watch. The only interview I really worried about was the one with the Eng – he was pretty possessive about "his" reactor and propulsion plants and bore the ultimate responsibility for making sure everything and everyone worked well at all times. And he could be hard to get hold of. You'd think that, in a small submarine, everyone would be easy to find. But not the Eng. Sometimes I think he hid from me, other times he was on watch, and he was a pretty busy guy. I always had my best luck catching him on the midwatch, if everything else permitted. Eventually, I'd always track him down, persuade him (or remind him) to see me, and we'd take care of everything. For most quals, the process ended at the Engineer's stateroom. Others, ELT, LELT, and EWS, required an oral board and the Captain's approval. This could be grueling, too, and I failed my first board for EWS. In my case, I learned from my mistakes and flew through the second EWS board. As with so many other things, being intelligent never hurts, but being determined is a lot more valuable.

In addition to our "working" quals, there was ship's quals to contend with. These were the mother of all qualifications for many submariners, and what allowed us to put "SS" after our names and wear the dolphins, trademark of submariners worldwide, on our chests.

The ship's qual card was deceptively simple in appearance. A double-sided sheet of paper, it had but five sections and a total of 68 signatures in 10 areas, with "block sigs" required for each separate area. For example, one block included the HP air, service air, ballast tank blow, and low pressure blow systems. Once I completed checkouts on these systems, I had to find a submarine-qualified officer or chief for the block sig. He'd give me a checkout on all the systems, give me some lookups, and then sign for the block. Virtually all systems on the ship's qual card were non-nuclear ones, and the people authorized to sign off on them were mostly non-nukes. So, in addition to having to learn the systems, there was sometimes some nuke-coner animosity to overcome. Most of the guys were pretty straightforward, but there were some who enjoyed their only chance to one-up a nuke. And some people just enjoyed having the chance to say "no" to someone else. Or wanted to show off their superior knowledge of a particular system. For the most part, we could all figure out who these people were and, in my case, I just avoided going to them unless I had no choice.

After completing all the checkouts and block sigs, I had to go through a final walkthrough of the boat with my division officer during which he asked me questions about power supplies, damage control equipment locations and use, systems components, and so forth. And then I had my ship's qualification board. One chief, three submarine-qualified petty officers, and me crammed into the diesel generator room for over four hours. I was asked to draw diagrams of six ship's systems and answered questions about all of them. Then I was grilled about some emergency response procedures, weapons capabilities, circuit breaker locations (in case of electrical fires you need to know how to secure power to the gear), and on and on. The last step was for me to take a mental tour of the entire submarine, every level of every compartment, and describe every piece of damage control equipment; what it was, where it was located, how it was used, where the backup piece of gear was, and, in some cases, where it could be plugged in. Every piece of equipment I missed became a lookup. This was actually the crux of the board. It was nice to know how the systems and the boat worked and, originally, one of the purposes of ship's quals was to give everyone a sufficiently good knowledge of every system that, in an emergency, anyone could pitch in to help run and save the boat. But that was in diesel boats. The *Plunger* and, for that matter, any nuke boat was sufficiently complex that one person simply could not learn everything to that level of detail in the 14 months we were given to qualify. Not if they were doing their jobs, too. So submarine quals changed with time, keeping pace with reality. Now, we had to learn the most important facts about each system, but the emphasis (in my opinion) was on what anyone should be expected to do in a pinch; doing their part to help save the boat. So, for example, I learned all the specifications of the emergency blow system, but the important part was learning where all of the manual isolation and override valves were. Knowing that, I could bypass the system if a remotely-operated valve stuck, helping get the boat to the surface. Similarly, knowing the location and type of every fire extinguisher on board allowed me to get the right fire extinguisher and take it to a fire quickly, rather than trying to rack my brain remembering where to go. The *Plunger* was an exceptionally capable submarine; in order to have those capabilities, we had great complexity. With increasing complexity came increasing vulnerability to technical or engineering problems and with enhanced capability came working closer to danger zones. Things were more likely to go wrong and, if they did, we had a higher chance of being at a depth or in a location where training and reaction time mattered greatly.

Once qualified, we received our dolphins in an awards ceremony. The CO gave a brief talk, pinned a set of dolphins on our chest, and gave us a certificate and photo of the boat. After that, we could change to the better barracks (for qualified personnel), watch the midwatch movie, wear a ship's ball cap with dolphins, wear our dolphin belt buckle, and in general, be considered fully human and a contributing member of the crew. For the coners, ship's qualifications were a really big deal because it was usually the first (and sometimes the only) such process they had to go through. With nukes it was a bit different because of all the other quals we had, but for most of us it was noteworthy, too, if only because failure to qualify meant exile to the surface fleet.

And for nukes, the qualification process never ended! It would usually take over a year and a half from the time a nuke came onboard until they finished with the required watchstation and ship's quals. Then, every two years, we had to re-qualify each watch. And we were pushed to qualify advanced watches such as EWS, even if there was little chance of ever standing the watch. So, at most, we'd have perhaps six months of rest, then we'd start the requalification cycle and go through it again. And, when we reported to another boat, even an identical boat, we went through it all again. It got easier each time, of course, and some requirements could be waived based on previous ships, but some degree of qualification and requal was always required and was always a pain in the ass. But that's why they paid us the big bucks....

In other news, the continuing saga of Matt versus The Duke finally ended at Captain's Mast. Captain's Mast is also called Nonjudicial Punishment. After hearing all of the evidence on both sides, including giving the person charged a chance to speak for himself, the Captain decides what an appropriate punishment (if any) should be. It is considered non-judicial because there is no formal hearing or trial. While the CO can mete out significant penalties, there is a limit to what he can do; loss of rank, forfeiture of half of one's pay for a few months, or confinement on a bread-and-water diet for a few days. Don't get me wrong – none of these are desired punishments, but they're better than being busted out of the Navy on a Bad Conduct or Dishonorable Discharge. And, to make these less at the whim of the Captain, at least one uninvolved person is present as a witness to the proceedings. My turn had come my first week on the boat, before I had a chance to get to know anyone. It had been instructive and reinforced my desire to not have to participate in one as the accused. Which was probably part of the rationale for sending me then, rather than later, to be a witness. I guess that would be the "scared straight" approach.

In any event, at the Captain's Mast, Matt admitted to saying things about John Wayne that, in retrospect, could be construed as disrespectful, acknowledged that he had no first-hand knowledge of the sexual preferences of any actor or actress, and agreed to not say such things again. The CO noted that playing an officer in a movie, no matter how skillfully acted, is not quite the same thing as actually being one and, in any event, the movie was sufficiently old that some statute of limitation undoubtedly applied, and dismissed the case. All of which meant that the POD was about to get a lot less intersting.

I was talking with the Eng after the results of Matt's Captain's mast were announced. I mentioned it was time for me to get some rack time, to which the Eng replied "Well, pleasant dreams, Karam."

I looked at him and said "We're at sea, Eng. I always have pleasant dreams at sea." He looked at me quizzically, so I explained further. "Look at it this way. In port, I have a pleasant reality, so my dreams are bad. Here, the reality is bad, so I have good dreams. That way it all balances out."

He looked at me for a few long seconds, obviously trying to think of something to say. Finally, he just shook his head and turned to leave. "You are probably the oddest person I have ever met, Karam. And that's quite an honor. I majored in Math in college, so I met a LOT of odd people."

"Thanks Eng! Nicest thing you've said to me in a few weeks. Have a good one, Sir!" And we both headed off to the rack.

WPlg-12 *8
PLUNGERINST 1510.1G

NAME *KARAM, Philip A.*   RATE *MM2* DATE REPORTED ONBOARD *12 MAR 86*

QUALIFICATION CARD

PHASE I 1. Read the following and discuss with LPO:
SSORM CHAPTERS 1 & 2
DATE DUE: SSORM CHAPTER 4, SECTIONS 1 & 2
26 MAR 86 SSORM CHAPTER 4, SECTION 3

2. Receive brief from designated individual on the following:
(See Qualification Guide for contents)
BATTLE STATIONS PROCEDURES   (LPO)
FIRST AID   (MDR)
POWER PLANT INDOCTRINATION   (EOOW/EWS)
TOPSIDE ARRANGEMENT   (DCPO)
TANKS AND COMPARTMENTS   (DCPO)

3. Spend about an hour at each of the following watchstations:
TOPSIDE   (WATCHSTANDER)
BELOWDECKS (OR AEF OR AUX
OF WATCH)   (WATCHSTANDER)
MANEUVERING   (WATCHSTANDER)
SRW (OR ERUL, ERLL & AMSLL) (WATCHSTANDER)

4. Obtain the following check-outs:
SECURITY   (DUTY OFF/DCPO)
ATMOSPHERE CONTROL   (DCPO)

PHASE II   DAMAGE CONTROL INDOCTRINATION   (DCPO)
RADIATION CONTROL   (ELT)
DATE DUE: SSORM EMERGENCY BILLS   (DCPO)
12 APR 86 INTERIOR COMMUNICATIONS SYSTEM   (DCPO)
IC PROCEDURES   (DCPO)
ELECTRICAL DISTRIBUTION   (DCPO)
DAMAGE CONTROL, OBA/EAB   (DCPO)
TAGOUT PROCEDURES   (DCPO/EDPO)

PHASE III Initial Departmental and Watchstation
DATE DUE: qualification complete.
12 Jul 86   (DEPT HEAD)

PHASE IV:

DATE DUE: 12 JAN 87   5 PTS/WK

	PTS	DATE	PTS	DATE
Ship Construction, Tanks, and Compartments*	3 QPO			
TRIM*	3 QPO	mm 3/55		
DRAIN*	3 QPO	mm 3/55	OFFICER/CPO	wng 86
SANITARY AND PLUMBING	1 QPO	mm 2/8		
RESCUE, ESCAPE & SALVAGE*	3 QPO	9 Ec mm 3/55		
SIGNAL EJECTOR & MAGAZINE FLOOD	1 QPO	4/19/86		
ANCHOR WINDLASS/CAPSTAN	1 QPO	4/17/86		
HP AIR SYSTEM*	3 QPO	4/28/86		
SERVICE AIR SYSTEM*	3 QPO	ECE/55		
HP MBT BLOW SYSTEM*	3 QPO		OFFICER/CPO	
LOW PRESSURE BLOW*	2 QPO			
MAIN & VITAL HYDRAULICS*	3 QPO			
STEERING & DIVING	3 QPO	16 7/67		
EXTERNAL HYDRAULICS	1 QPO		OFFICER/CPO	

Enclosure (2)

Andy Karam's Qualifications Card from the USS Plunger.

```
WPlg-13 *8
PLUNGERINST 1510.1G
```

	PTS			DATE	PTS		DATE
VENTILATION SYSTEM*	3	QPO			8		*OFFICER/CPO*
SNORKEL SYSTEMS & DIESEL	2	QPO					
ATMOSPHERE CONTROL EQUIPMENT	2	QPO					
BASIC ELECTRICAL*	3	QPO					
NORMAL & EMERGENCY LIGHTING*	2	QPO			5		OFFICER/CPO
400HZ DISTRIBUTION*	2	QPO					
WEAPONS	2	QPO					
FIRE CONTROL	2	QPO					OFFICER/CPO
ELEX COOLING	1	QPO					
POTABLE WATER	1	QPO					
AIR CONDITIONING SYSTEM	2	QPO					
REFRIGERATION SYSTEM	1	QPO					OFFICER/CPO
FUEL OIL & COMPENSATING WATER	2	QPO					
PRIMARY PROPULSION	2	QPO					
SECONDARY PROPULSION	2	QPO			5		OFFICER/CPO
OXYGEN	1	QPO					
BASIC NAVIGATION	2	QPO					
BASIC OPERATIONS	2	QPO			8		OFFICER/CPO
BASIC SONAR	2	QPO					
MASTS & ANTENNAS*	1	QPO					
TOPSIDE AND BRIDGE AREA	2	QPO					
BOW COMPT UPPER LEVEL	3	QPO					
BOW COMPT LOWER LEVEL	3	QPO					
OPS COMPT UPPER LEVEL	3	QPO					
OPS COMPT MIDDLE LEVEL	2	QPO					
OPS COMPT LOWER LEVEL	3	QPO			5		OFFICER/CPO
AMS COMPT UPPER LEVEL	3	QPO					
AMS COMPT LOWER LEVEL	3	QPO					
ENGINEROOM UPPER LEVEL	3	QPO					
ENGINEROOM MIDDLE LEVEL	3	QPO					
REACTOR COMPARTMENT	1	QPO					

PHASE V Walkthrough complete   DIVISION OFFICER

DATE DUE: Final Board   DATE: 7 MAY 86

EMI(SS)   Milord Thomas IC$^{?}$(SS)   MM(SS)

- -

Recommendation for Qualification in Submarines

DATE: 5/7/86   _____
                     (QUALIFICATION OFFICER)

DATE: 5/8/86   _____
                     (EXECUTIVE OFFICER)

- -

Designated as "QUALIFIED IN SUBMARINES" USS PLUNGER (SSN 595) as of 5/8/86

                     _____
                     (COMMANDING OFFICER)

- -

Service Record entry made: DATE: 10 May 86 YEOMAN: YN(SS) W.E. Styl

CHAPTER
19

Bagging the Akula

Just as, by the pawprint alone, one deduces the lion.

One of the Bernoulli brothers,
describing anonymous work by Isaac Newton

On our 51ˢᵗ day at sea, word came down suddenly to rig for ultra quiet. It happened suddenly, without even time for rumors. We had just finished copying radio traffic and I was waiting in my lab for either a family gram or for the radiomen to put the latest copy of news and sports up in the OPSUL passageway. I heard the CO's hotline to Control whoop once, then heard the OOD say "Aye, aye, Sir," and call for the messenger of the watch. The messenger headed back a few moments later. I stopped him outside Nucleonics.

"What's up?" I asked.

"Just got word from Pearl. We're going back through the Sea of O and into the northern Sea of Japan. The Akula's there. We're supposed to try to follow her. So we got to rig for ultra quiet."

"What!? We're going back there? Shit! I thought twice was enough. What are they trying to do, get us caught? Damn it!" The problem was, in ultra quiet, I couldn't even slam the door or bang on the counter; I could only sit there and swear to myself.

My thoughts were really mixed. On the one hand, I had a pretty fair degree of confidence that we could penetrate the Soviet sonar line again and not get caught. But I also knew from the last time how easy it was to make a mistake and I just didn't feel like pushing our luck any further. The bottom line is that I had just had a bad feeling about this mission from the start and it was starting to seem as though we were really asking for trouble. I just felt uncomfortable trying to get into and out of the Sea of Okhotsk one more time in an old, beat up boat. But feelings of unease are not sufficient reason to not follow orders and, in any case, I couldn't do a damned thing about them anyways. So I swore to myself some more, rigged my lab for ultra quiet, and headed for my rack.

This time, we were in Ultra Quiet for nearly 20 hours, my longest stint ever. In fact, in this single mission, I'd spent more time in Ultra Quiet than in the previous three years on *Plunger* put together. I read, slept, used the head when I had to, and had a few quiet and tasteless meals, and listened. I listened for the pinging of foreign sonars, for the thrumming of nearby propellers (we were making another shallow transit), and for the sound of one of my shipmates dropping or slamming something that might give us away. In the engineering spaces, people were sitting and talking quietly, reading tech manuals, or just thinking and listening on their own. Silent, tense, and worried, we made our way back into the Sea of O.

Once in, we rigged for modified Ultra Quiet for our transit through, then had another, briefer stint in Ultra Quiet again as we crept between Sakhalin and the Japanese island of Hokkaido, through the Soya Kaikyo, into the northern Sea of Japan. Once there, we cleared baffles, then came to PD to copy some radio traffic.

For the next two days, we cruised back and forth near the strait. Apparently the Akula had left Petropavlosk and, instead of cutting through the Sea of Okhotsk as they'd done the last time, took a longer way around to Vladivostock. We were now waiting for them to return to Petr, counting on their taking a shorter route to return. And sure enough, on the third day, we got word the Akula had left Vlad and was thought to be heading our way. We went to Ultra Quiet again and continued waiting.

Six hours later, sonar reported a submerged contact that did not match any of our sound profiles of Soviet submarines. We set the fire control tracking party, and I headed to Control to man the time bearing plot. Since the submarine was pretty clearly submerged and sounded as though it was travelling with a surface escort, we didn't expect to use the scope at all. Now, to me, a submarine travelling with a surface escort seemed a bit stupid because it gave away the boat's position. Kind of like crawling through the bush, stalking an enemy soldier with bright orange helium balloons tied to your belt. But the Soviets did things differently. For all I knew, the Akula was out on sea trials and these were the safety vessels. Or maybe we weren't supposed to know about the Akula traveling beneath these ships. But we did, and they made our target a lot easier to follow.

It took us awhile to be sure we even had the Akula. It's one thing for Sonar to say they had an unknown submerged contact, but it's something else entirely for them to say for sure that the unidentified contact is, in reality, the Soviet's most advanced submarine, for which we had virtually no acoustic intelligence. Kind of like blindfolding yourself, going into your front yard, and saying "That must be a Mercedes because it just doesn't sound like the neighbor's Volkswagon." Eventually, however, Sonar and the CO both felt confident we really had the Akula, and we started drawing closer.

This was ticklish. We were no longer in Ultra Quiet and we were outside what we thought was their best passive sonar range. But, still, with another submarine, two skimmers, and a hydrophone line approaching, and we needed to be careful. As we drew closer, we maintained a continuous flow of data, we plotted positions and calculated distance, and our fire control solution firmed up. But, due to the lousy acoustics in that piece of water, we just didn't have a really good bearing and, without that, our range information was still somewhat suspect. What we needed was a good, solid bearing; something we could really hand our hat on.

A half hour later, the Akula obliged us. "Control, Sonar. Transient. Relative bearing 285." Someone on the Akula had dropped a wrench or slammed a door. We were in business. If this were war, we could shoot based solely on the information we had. This being peacetime, we moved closer, more confident we wouldn't be caught.

Submarine tactics call for patience. Over the next five hours we closed a total of 6 miles on the Akula, from 26,000 yards to 14,000. In the next four hours, we closed to 10,000 yards, and decided to stay there. In Sonar, tapes were running, recording all the sounds we could pick up for later analysis. After this mission, any boat in our fleet would know what the Akula sounded like and could ID it even without advance intelligence.

As we approached the straits again, we closed still more on the Akula and, more importantly, on her escorts. Skimmers make a lot of noise; we were betting that, even at our higher speed, their din would mask our noise and we could slip through undetected. It worked and, once inside the Sea of O, we backed off a bit, opening our range somewhat.

The next passage, the Straits of La Peruse again, was simply too tight to pass at the same speed as the Akula. Sonar reported her coming to the surface a few miles from the entrance to the straits and we fell back, rigging again for Ultra Quiet. Even with the noise from the surface ships, it was just too risky to go through at any speed at all, so we let her go. We didn't need to follow her any further; this mission was complete. We'd found her, trailed her, and taped her. Without getting caught.

Profiles of a small selection of Soviet war machines

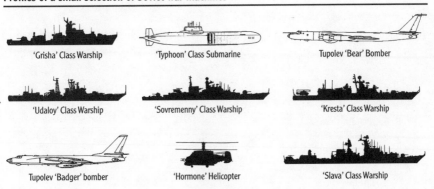

'Grisha' Class Warship   'Typhoon' Class Submarine   Tupolev 'Bear' Bomber

'Udaloy' Class Warship   'Sovremenny' Class Warship   'Kresta' Class Warship

Tupolev 'Badger' bomber   'Hormone' Helicopter   'Slava' Class Warship

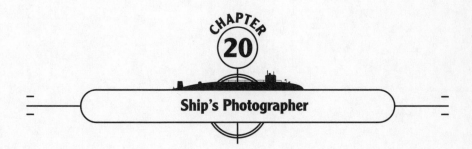

Ship's Photographer

I MANAGED TO FINISH my daily routine after we secured from tracking the Akula and then caught a few hours of sleep before waking to take care of the next day's routine. I made it to sleep around 6, only to be woken by the messenger at 8:30. "Karam – OOD wants you in Control ASAP. They found a Delta IV on the surface and want some pictures of it."

"Who's the OOD?" I asked groggily, trying desperately to feel alert. I was hoping it was someone who could take a decent picture, giving me a chance to wake up a little.

"The Navigator."

"Shit." The Nav was a nice guy, but he was a lousy photographer. He wore contacts that apparently didn't correct his vision completely, so what he thought was in focus usually turned out to be pretty fuzzy. Too fuzzy, at least, for any decent intelligence. I had no choice but to wake up quickly. I rolled over and looked at the messenger. "Go get the photo officer up, too. How long ago did we find the Delta?"

"About five minutes ago. And I already woke him."

"Good. I'll be there in a few minutes." The messenger vanished and I lay still for a moment, collecting my thoughts. The camera was always kept in Control, along with the adapter for the scope. Unlike newer boats, we didn't have an integral camera. Instead, we had a Nikon F-3 that clipped to an adapter. We'd remove the eyepiece on the scope and attach the camera. So that was in Control, but I'd have to stop by the Wardroom to grab a few rolls of film. And, as long as I was in the Wardroom, I'd check on the photo officer, kicking him out of the rack if necessary. We really had to get to Control to get the camera out of the Nav's hands. I rolled out of the rack, put on my poopy suit, and headed aft, towards the Wardroom.

There, I found the photo officer already loading up on film. Mr. Huggins was the best officer I had ever worked with. A graduate of the Naval Academy, he'd been selected to continue directly on for graduate work before reporting to the Fleet. He was smart, had a ton of common sense, was personable, and liked Jimmy Buffet. We worked well together and enjoyed each other's company. Too bad he was an officer. We headed on up to Control, joking about what the Nav was probably up to.

The Nav was really a nice guy and he, too, was pretty smart. Usually in a pretty good mood, the only thing he really lacked was the ability to really critique himself. These photos, for example. I had lost track of the number of times I'd talked with him about taking photos and the importance of good focus, even suggesting he turn the scope over to someone with good vision or that he might consider wearing glasses instead of contacts. But, every time, he happily put the camera on the scope and started snapping pictures, contacts and all. And, every time, they came out blurry. And, of course, bracketing the exposures just didn't happen. But who was I to interfere with his fun.

This time he'd had less than ten minutes of film to waste, but he'd still gone through an entire roll. Mr. Huggins and I sailed into Control. "What've you got, Nav?" Mr. Huggins asked.

"Delta IV on the surface. About 1500 yards away. I've got a roll taken already."

"Well, why don't we take a few more, just to have some insurance shots?" Huggins suggested. I reloaded the camera with Surveillance 400 film. This was specially made for us by Kodak. It was supposed to have grain as good as that in 100 ASA film with the speed of 400 ASA film. We joked that it actually had the grain of 400 speed film and the speed of 100 ASA but, in reality, it was OK. We got the bearing to the Delta from the Nav and raised the scope until it was less than a foot beneath the water. "Ready, Karam?"

"You bet, Sir!"

"Let's go." I raised the scope the rest of the way with Huggins on the camera. His job was to focus the scope and keep it on the target. My job was to raise and lower the scope, change exposure settings, and take the shots. The scope raised and Huggins searched for a second. He moved the scope through wider arcs and finally settled on a bearing nearly 20 degrees to the port. He pulled back and said "Down scope." He looked at the Nav. "We should have asked about relative motion, Nav. Our movement and theirs moved them about 20 degrees. But we've got them now." He looked at me. "OK, Karam, let's try it again. Up scope."

I raised the scope again, moving it slightly to port. This time, almost immediately, Mr. Huggins started talking. "There it is. Delta IV, all right. Centered in the cross hairs. Let me move the scope a tad. OK, shoot!"

I had already the camera for a 1 f-stop overexposure. I snapped three shots, the motor drive advancing the film after each. I called out "That's three at plus one!" and reduced the exposure to the normal setting. Three more shots. "Three at zero!" I stopped down again to one f-stop underexposed and shot another three. "Three at minus one!" I was lowering the scope even as I spoke. Huggins looked at the Nav.

"What was our scope exposure time?"

The Nav looked at his watch. "Ten seconds."

Huggins looked at me. "We're slowing down. Want to try again?" I nodded and prepared to raise the scope again. We ran through another set. "Scope exposure time?"

"Seven seconds."

Huggins grinned. "That's more like it. One more time? How about you take this set, just to make sure the focus is right?" We practiced this, too. Either of us could do either job pretty well. I usually deferred to letting Mr. Huggins take the scope because, as an officer, he had more chance to use it and could use it better. But I did what I could when we played with the surface fleet at home, so I was at least competent. I took my spot on the scope.

"Where's the target, Sir?"

"Horizon should be about halfway up, target centered in the crosshairs when we put the scope down. Relative motion should put it a little to the port and we have a gentle sea, so it's not moving up and down much. It's close."

"Great! We at the right bearing? Up scope." The scope came up with the Delta a little to the port side of the crosshairs. It was huge! It couldn't be any more than a half mile away. I twisted the left hand grip to zoom out, finding that the scope was already on low power. I couldn't believe the Nav had the scope up this close to a Soviet boat. He was either confident or clueless.

"Right on the money, Sir. Shoot!" Three shots. I twisted the hand grip on the right of the scope gently, compensating for the roll of the boat. Twisting the hand grip tilted the mirror slightly up and down, making the target image move in the opposite direction. At the same time, we were moving past the Delta, so I had to try to smoothly pan the scope to keep the target in one of the quadrants of the field of view. Centering it in the crosshairs looked nice, but the crosshairs themselves could cover important details or could be mistaken for linear details, so we tried to keep them off whatever we were photographing. So Mr. Huggins shot and bracketed and shot again while I panned and tilted. As soon as he took the last shot, he twisted the control ring and the scope dropped.

We shot one more series of the Delta IV and, just as we were taking the camera off the scope, the CO came in. We'd been in Control for about five minutes at this point. The Old Man walked up to the Nav. "So what've you got, Nav?" he asked.

"Sir. We have a Delta IV on the surface about 1500 yards away." Huggins and I looked at each other and shrugged. We both knew it was a lot closer than that. "It's ahead of us and relative motion is taking it to port."

"Mind if I take a look?" He went to the scope. I moved to take position as Periscope Assistant, out of habit more than anything. The CO looked at me and smiled. "I still remember how to put up a periscope, Karam." I told him the bearing should be close since we'd just stopped taking pictures. He put up the scope, turning slightly to port as it came up. He looked for about two seconds and put down the scope, turning to the Dive as soon as it was down. "Take us to 150 feet. Course, 090." This was about 45 degree from our current course and away from the Delta.

"How far away are they, Nav?"

"I figured about 1500 yards, Sir."

"Try about 1000. And are we in front of them or behind them?"

"Well, pretty much in front of them. But they're heading across our bow, so they're not going to hit us or anything."

"When you drive, do you pay more attention in front of your car or behind it?"

"Uh, in front."

"So they're coming towards us, a half mile away, and you're sitting here taking pictures? They have people in the bridge, looking this way with binoculars. Thank God we're going slowly enough that the scope isn't leaving a wake! What in the hell were you thinking of? I hope we at least got some good photos." He turned to look at Huggins and I. "I want to see those as soon as they're ready."

Mr. Huggins and I took good photos, but where we really stood out was in our processing time. Doing everything manually, we'd got to the point that we could develop a roll of film and print the four or five photos that were worth anything in less than an hour. It would have been faster, except that there were some steps that specified a certain amount of time. Even there, we had experimented to try to find out which waiting times were important and which could be shortened. We had heard from chiefs, other officers, the CO and the XO that we were the fastest and best photo team in the Pacific submarine fleet. Skimmers had full-time photographers, so they didn't count. I took both rolls of film and headed to the head while Huggins stowed the camera and set up Nucleonics as a photo lab.

I kept my developing chemicals by the head and always had gallon bottles of developer and fixer ready to go. I put the film, a can opener, take-up reels, and the developing tank into a light-tight changing bag, zipping it up. I then put my arms into the arm holes and started feeling around. Everything had to be done by feel until the film was safely within the developing tanks, otherwise the film would be ruined. Luckily, I'd done this for a few hundred rolls of film and it went pretty smoothly.

First, I organized the objects in the bag. Film in the middle at the far end. Reels on the left side in the corner furthest from the armholes. Developing tanks in the right corner. I felt around for the can opener, finding it beneath a fold of cloth. Using it, I popped the end off one roll of film and gently, without touching the film, took it from the canister. Before putting the film in the bag, I'd already cut off the leader because that just got in the way. The reel was just a thick piece of stainless steel wire wound into a spiral track. Two of these tracks were joined to a central shaft with openings to hold the end of the film. Working by touch, I stuck the end of the film into an opening in the shaft and then, bowing the film slightly with my finger, I wound it onto the track, starting from the center. Every so often, I'd run into a slight snag and couldn't tell how the film was winding. Each time, I'd back up until I was sure everything was right, then would start forward again. The potential problem was that, if the film wasn't wound right, two pieces from adjacent tracks might press against each other. This, in turn, would keep developer from reaching that part of the film, ruining whatever images might be on that part of the film. The Navy was spending a lot of money to put us on station, taking these pictures. I didn't want to ruin them.

Finishing the first roll in about five minutes, I wound the second in just another three. I put the film spools into the developing tank, popped the lid on, pulled my arms out of the bag, and looked at my watch. Fifteen minutes since we left Control. I poured some developer into the tank through a light-proof opening at the top of the tank, popped the cap on, and started agitating the canister. A slow turn to stir the chemicals and a sharp tap against the palm of my hand to dislodge any air bubbles that might mar the film. Wait a few seconds, another slow turn, and another tap. According to the Kodak black and white darkroom data guide, I had to keep this up for 8 minutes since the chemicals were at ambient temperature, about 70 degrees. I'd found I could shorten this by up to a minute, but image quality might suffer a little if the exposure was marginal, so I went the full time. Next came continuous agitation in a water bath to remove all the developer, then four minutes in the fixer, another short rinse, and the developing was done. Normally we were supposed to make sure that the temperature of all these liquids was the same; luckily, black and white film is pretty forgiving. I'd stick a thermometer into the chemicals to make sure they were at ambient, then I'd just hold my hand under the water to make sure it felt about right. So far I'd had no problems. But there was no way I'd get away with that using color film. I emptied the last water out of the developing tank and headed for Nucleonics. Elapsed time, about 30 minutes.

In the Nuke Lab, Mr. Huggins had set up the enlarger, mixed the developer and fixer for the paper, got out the grain magnifier, and had the photographic paper in its light safe. The safe light was on and a roll of duct tape was sitting on the counter. I stepped into the lab, shut the door, and slipped a piece of rope between the door handle and a latch welded to the wall as a lock. Then, I opened up the developing tank and took both reels out. This was the first test.

We unspooled the first roll of film, taping one end to a pipe that ran across the forward end of Nucleonics. We clipped a weight to the bottom end and took a quick look at the film. No green spots, indicating film sticking together during developing, no apparent air bubbles, and we could see the image of the Delta IV quite nicely. Not too dark, not too light. The second roll was much the same. Both rolls hung beneath a ventilation duct to dry most rapidly and, while they dried, we turned off both normal and safe lights and grabbed the roll of duct tape.

Around the margins of the door light was streaming in. Mr. Huggins tore strips of tape two to three feet long and I slapped it up around the edges of the door. Within a few minutes, the door was tight enough for our purposes. We'd found through more experimentation that we could tolerate some light leaks provided they didn't shine directly on the photo paper. So we always made sure that the enlarger was away from the worst offenders, and tried to tape up the rest as best we could. This time, we did a pretty good job.

We turned the lights back on and looked at the film again. Still a little wet, so I put a tape into the walkman clone we had set up in Nucleonics. We both agreed on Jimmy Buffet, despite other musical disagreements, so Jimmy played the official photo team music. I had stopped by the messdecks on the way up, grabbing two cups of crushed ice. Reaching under the counter, I pulled out two cans of soda and we each poured a glass. We looked at the film again. Dry. Time to start working. The clock showed nearly 45 minutes since leaving Control. Our goal was to have photos in the CO's hands within an hour. Part of it was showing off, part was to give him the chance to go back and take some more shots if these didn't turn out. Mostly, though, we were showing off. Most boats took four hours or more.

When we first started, we always did a formal test print. We'd take a sheet of photographic paper and expose it in strips. Four or five successive strips at about five seconds each. This would, theoretically, show us what the "perfect" exposure should be. Every shot was supposed to be done this way. We took a shortcut. I had read an article suggesting we adjust the brightness of the image to something that looked like a 15 second exposure brightness. One day, just for the hell of it, we tried it. And it worked! Surprised the hell out of both of us. So, for the first shot, we set everything for what should have been a 10 second exposure (15 was a little too long, given the motion of the boat). We did a quick test print from the roll we'd shot (we could tell which one had had shots bracketed) at ten seconds, developed it, and it looked decent. A little tweak on the exposure and we entered production mode.

I took the first frame and put it into the enlarger. I focused by eye, then put the grain magnifier on the enlarger stand. Looking at the images of the photographic grains, I focused on them to make them as sharp as possible. Turning the enlarger off, we made sure the timer was set for ten seconds, slid some paper into place, and exposed the picture. When the enlarger shut off, I slid the paper out and handed it to Mr. Huggins. He put it into the developer while I moved to the next photo. Focus was already set, so I put another piece of paper on the stand, exposed again, and handed another picture to Huggins. We did another five, one from each series of bracketed shots, and then stopped to look at the results. Three were pretty good, two were acceptable, and one really sucked. We went back and blew up some of the better shots, trying others in the same grouping. When we had a dozen photos that were developed and in fixer, we stopped and transferred them to the Nucleonics sink, rinsing them off as completely as possible. Elapsed time, 57 minutes.

After a few minutes of rinsing, we took some photos out and hung them up to start drying. We decided on three of them to show the CO and Huggins headed out with them. While he was out, I started printing some of the Nav's shots. Huggins was back in five minutes with a huge grin. "Did you see these, Karam? Look at this!" He looked to make sure there was no undeveloped paper out, then turned on the lights. "Look at this! This is great! We're less than a thousand yards from this thing – look – you can count the people in the bridge, you can see the camouflage pattern on their scope, you can even see the anechoic tile topside! Is this cool or what?"

I looked at the pictures. I had to admit we'd done a pretty good job. You can get better pictures from a P-3 (an ASW plane), but not of an unsuspecting boat. Planes have a way of advertising their presence and people act differently when they know they're being watched. These photos showed us what the Soviets did when they thought they were all alone. I pulled out a few of the Nav's photos and showed them to Huggins. "Well, here's the other batch. Good thing we took another roll."

He looked at them. Most were out of focus. In some, the crosshairs were right on the sail. Aesthetically pleasing, not what we wanted for intel because they hid some scopes or antennae. In others, the boat was partially out of the picture, and so forth. All in all, it was a good thing we'd taken our roll of film, too. We printed some more from our roll, then printed the best few from the Nav's roll, and hung them up to dry while we started cleaning up the lab. Just a few minutes into that, there was a knock on the door.

"Yeah?" I said.

"Karam, this is the CO. There's a display in Sonar you need to get a picture of right away. It's from the Delta."

"Aye, Sir. I'll be right there." I grabbed the Nikon and put our zoom on it. Ripping the tape off from around the lab door, I sprinted out of the lab, ran down to the Wardroom to grab some Polaroid slide film, and hustled back up to Sonar. I managed to get a roll of shots of the screen, then returned to Nucleonics. Mr. Huggins was looking a little nonplussed.

"While you were gone, the CO stuck his head in," Mr. Huggins said.

"Oh, shit." I replied. Nucleonics was considered a part of the Engineering spaces. There was a strict prohibition on food, drink, books (unless they were plant manuals), or music in all Engineering spaces. I looked at Huggins. "What did he say?" I asked.

"He looked around a minute, then nodded and said 'Nice setup you have here.' And then he just left. Not another word."

We both shrugged, locked the door again, and went back to work. Since we knew we had some good shots, we made 5x7s and 8x10s of many of them, enlarging some as far as possible to see how much detail we could get out of them. We knew that the film would be eventually gone over by people with better equipment than us, probably computer-enhanced and whatever else they did to it, but we wanted to give the CO the best photos we could, both from a sense of personal pride and to give him something to show the people he'd be briefing when we pulled into Pearl and returned to San Diego at the end of the mission. All in all, we spent a few more hours printing pictures, got the last of them hung up to dry, and called it a day for the darkroom. Now, I just had to develop the Polaroid slides from Sonar, but this was pretty easy. For that, we had a snazzy Polaroid slide processor – we just rolled the film in along with a chemical pack, let it sit for a few minutes, then rolled it back out. The rest was automatic. Looking at the strip of slides, it looked as though some had turned out, making me feel good. When shooting a computer screen I usually tried to underexpose at least two f-stops and bracket extensively. On this roll, the first attempt, at –2 was right on the money. I mounted the best three into slide frames and gave them to Mr. Huggins. "Here you go, Sir. I think this'll do it." I was starting to get pretty tired at this point. I had been up for over a day with only a few hours sleep and, with the adrenaline rush gone, I was starting to drag.

I gave all the photos and slides to Mr. Huggins. He got out the classification stamps, stamped the backs of all the photos "Top Secret" with a secondary classification, and marked the slides. From this point on, I wasn't allowed to look at any of them since I had only a Secret clearance. If you ask me, it was pretty stupid since I'd already taken, developed, and printed so many of the photos, but rules are rules, I guess. My clearance was insufficient, so, once officially classified, I couldn't look at the things anymore. But, at this point, I just didn't care too much.

Huggins then took the rolls of film and wrote all the relevant information on the film leader. Roll number, date, time, number of exposures, classification level. The roll was never cut, mainly so we couldn't cut up several rolls of film, take some photos out to sell to spies, and still assemble a seemingly-complete roll from the remaining frames. After labeling, the film was slipped into a plastic sleeve for protection, rolled up, and placed into an empty plastic film canister. Then the negatives, photos, and slides were all bundled up and Mr. Huggins took them to the Wardroom, never again to be seen by anyone with less than a Top Secret + clearance. I locked up the lab and returned to the rack.

A few days later, we went through the same drill, just a little later in the day. And the next day, we had two photo sessions. Originally planned as a primarily sonar operation, this spec op was rapidly turning into a photo shoot. But the Soviets kept putting subs on the surface or doing interesting things with surface ships and who were we to turn down a nice photo op. We had debated the amount of film to bring with us because space was so short. Mr. Huggins and I had held out for more film and chemicals, figuring we'd regret running out more than we'd regret coming back with unused supplies. I was starting to be glad we'd gone that route. The next test of supplies would come when we started working on the post-mission slide show. But that wouldn't be for another few weeks or so.

Over the next week or so we took nearly 20 rolls of film. We didn't actually take 720 photos, although we did take quite a few. But even a roll with only a few shots was developed immediately, just to see what we got. In that time we got some beautiful shots of one of the Soviets' space tracking ships with what looked to be a few huge golf balls on latticeworks on top of the ship. We also came across several ocean-going tugs apparently maneuvering synchronously. After laughing for a while at the "dancing tugs", as we dubbed them, we decided to take some shots just for the hell of it. I don't know if any valuable intel came from the dancing tugs, but we at least found some amusement in it.

At the same time, we also managed to get a few nice shots of Kamchatka and some of the mountains and volcanoes on it. All this time Sonar had been reporting the odd seismic sounds, like a giant underground belly rumbling. Some of our coastal shots showed us why – with nearly 20 feet of scope out of the water we could see a fair distance and the mountains were tall enough to be seen for many miles. The volcanoes were especially striking – one in particular reminded me of Mount Fuji in its perfect symmetry; a white, perfect cone standing above its neighbors with a small wisp of steam or cloud marking the very peak. To either side, lesser mountains and volcanoes were visible, but none so perfect. That one was blown up to 8x10 and hung in the Wardroom for the rest of the mission. It was no Ansel Adams shot, but it was a beautiful scene. I wish I could have kept a copy.

The best photo opportunity of the mission came a few days later, however, and I didn't get a chance to play at all. During our normal message traffic, we got word that the Soviets were going to be conducting a missile shoot in our area, and we were to take a look. A missile shoot is test-firing or a missile exercise. The missile could be a anything from a submarine-launched ballistic missile to a much smaller surface-to-air missile designed to shoot down one of our aircraft. I wasn't sure what kind this was to be, but we were to try to observe it and get as much information as possible on it. Of course, we first had to get to the area and work our way past the ships, planes, subs, and helos trying to make sure their security was maintained.

We did manage to get into the vicinity of the shoot, closing to within a few thousand yards of the ship that was to be shooting. It really didn't seem that difficult getting in; they had only a few support ships in the area, not many planes in the air, and they just didn't seem too concerned. There was a submarine to keep an eye on, and a few helos were up looking, but just not all that bad. This either meant that they weren't doing anything very important, they were certain that nobody knew of this exercise, or that they didn't know we were in the area. Whatever it was, I was glad.

We arrived a few hours before the scheduled time, so we hung around taking photos, getting fire control solutions on their ships, and monitoring whatever we could. I got a few looks through the scope, but not many because everyone else wanted a look, and they all had a better excuse. Finally, about 15 minutes before the scheduled time, the skipper ordered the video camera hooked up to the scope. This would record the missile shoot for future analysis by some intelligence people somewhere.

I never got to look through the scope, and we had no ability to play the images in real time in Control. What I saw was the CO making regular periscope observations, leaving the scope up for only a few seconds at a time. When the time was right, he put the scope up, switched on the video recorder, and left it up for what seemed much too long a period of time.

Later, watching the tapes, I had the chance to see what the skipper had seen. There was a large warship steaming through the water, throwing up a little bow wave, but not much. Beside her were two other, smaller warships, and a helo was in the air a little ways back and on the far side. Suddenly, the after end of the large ship was covered with thick billows of white smoke, and a slender missile rose abruptly from the center of the clouds. It seemed almost indecisive at first, or perhaps uncertain, but after a half second, it suddenly accelerated away and up into the sky. I could only see the missile itself for a second, but the flame from its engine and its exhaust remained visible for much longer. After going for a few miles on a shallow trajectory, it suddenly nosed up, gaining altitude rapidly. It then started changing course, apparently tracking something higher up, trying to close for the kill. A few miles up and a few miles away, it nosed up even further, going into a nearly vertical climb. Two seconds later, there was a bright flash and a cloud of smoke. Then, water closed over the scope.

As soon as the CO lowered the scope, he ordered the Dive to take us down to 300 feet and clear the area. We had our tape, this part of our mission was over, and it was time to get on with the next tasks.

CHAPTER 21

Standing Watch

THE MONTH WAS COMING TO AN END and most of my ELTs still had to draw their proficiency reactor coolant samples. We agreed that the best way to do it was for me to take the midwatch on AMSLL for three days while those three ELTs drew their samples, then I'd stand a midwatch ERS so the last could pick up his. At the same time, this would give me my proficiencies at AMSLL and ERS, both of which I still needed. For me, it would also be nice to be able to eat with the oncoming watchstanders rather than waiting for the second seating.

Standing watch in AMSLL on a submarine at low speeds and low reactor power towards the tail end of a spec op is pretty boring. Keeping the generator chemistry steady during high-speed transits or right after pulling on station is interesting because things are constantly changing. But, by now the generators had settled out, so the chemistry stayed almost constant for weeks at a time. Right now, we hadn't added chemicals for over four weeks, hadn't blown down since the chloride casualty, and the generators were happy. Chemistry was near the top of the allowable band, but not so close as to worry us. So we certainly did not need to add and we might last another few weeks before having to blow down. We were trying to push the blowdowns back as far as possible because they were so noisy. We (the ELTs) did our part by purging as much water as possible during every sample, helping to dilute chemistry each time.

We had to sample each generator every six hours, an hour after each chem add, and an hour after each blowdown. We also had to sample our condensate system every eight hours. At low power, this meant a total of three samples, each of which took about 15 minutes if we were taking our time. In addition to sampling, we had to take logs on our equipment every hour. That took another two minutes. On the midwatch, we had additional duties. We switched the running pumps to equalize pump run time, we took a sample of the chemicals used in the after CO_2 scrubber, and a few other things. That took up to an hour, but usually much less. And, at least once each watch, we'd try to pump the bilges down, but (if our drain system was working properly), that took only another ten or fifteen minutes. This left a lot of time with not much to do. And, as I mentioned earlier, we weren't allowed to take anything on watch that was not directly related to nuclear power. We were also not allowed to eat on watch (although beverages were allowed). In their quest to keep us forever vigilant, Naval Reactors even dictated how many seats we could have on each watch station, where they were permitted to be located, and how comfortable they could be. Any seat that was deemed to well-cushioned was forbidden because we might accidentally fall asleep.

Of course, anyone desperately tired is going to fall asleep regardless of the comfort level and locations of his seats. I had dozed off once in the after escape trunk while in port. The escape trunk is a steel sphere about five feet across (I'm nearly 6'4" tall) and the shore power cables ran through it, further reducing the space. But we were in port in the Philippines and I was dead tired from having had about three or four hours of sleep in the past two days. I was stationed in the escape trunk just in case some Filipinos decided to burst onto the base, past the Marine guards, storm the pier (past some more Marines) and try to board our boat through the after escape trunk. My feeling was that this watch was cutting into my sleeping time and I was supposed to have the 0400-0800 shutdown roving watch that I didn't dare sleep through. Plus, the next day was to be quite busy, with a reactor compartment entry scheduled and a lot of support work. I also felt pretty sure that any rabid crowd storming the submarine would probably wake me up when they rushed through the hatch and, being unarmed, I was not likely to stop them. So I curled my back up against the warm shore power cables, put my feet against the walls of the escape trunk, and dozed for most of three hours. That left me still tired, but able to get through the next day with no mistakes; mistakes that I probably would have made had I not had that additional sleep.

My feeling was that if Naval Reactors didn't want us to sleep on watch the answer was to give us enough time to be rested. Instead, they kept us on a short "day" and filled our off-watch time with maintenance, training, drills, and whatever else they thought necessary. Now, don't get me wrong. All of these things are necessary. Drills helped us train for possible problems, and proved their worth several times. Training helped remind us of important information about the plant or the ship. Maintenance helped keep everything running smoothly and gave us a regular schedule to look for incipient problems. What was not necessary was the frequency or the timing of these activities. For example, many days we would have training on the morning watch and drills on the afternoon watch. Convenient for the officers and chiefs, most of whom were on four-section duty (i.e. normal "days") but murder on the rest of us. A person standing the midwatch would come off watch and have two hours until training started. If he chose to try to sleep, he'd miss breakfast and would only get a few hours down, anyhow. So chances were that he'd stay up for breakfast, maybe try to shower, and get back in time for training. First, departmental training for an hour or two, then divisional training for an hour.

That would leave us with about two hours until drills started. Same dilemma as before, but for a more tired person. Drills would go on for most of a watch. The drill team would brief right after the meal, and then the drills would go down. Lots of running around, wearing EABs or other masks (sucking rubber, as we called it) and general work coupled with "Where in the world did they come up with THIS bullshit scenario?" The other possibility with drills on a boat our age was that the boat would throw us a curve and start running its own casualties on us. This happened a lot and, sometimes, we'd keep score. While more fun than the set pieces run by the drill team, it was also more trying because things were really going wrong. But it kept life interesting. Drills would end about an hour before dinner and, just after dinner, it was time to stand the next watch. By the time the watch was over, the person would have been up for over 24 hours straight, 24 hours of high activity. It was not uncommon at the end of all this for someone to end up in their rack and "fail open", not be able to get to sleep because of the excessive fatigue and adrenaline.

Other days, other ways of keeping us awake. Reviewing paperwork for upcoming audits or Squadron inspection. Preventative maintenance, often described as "take apart a piece of equipment that's working fine, find out why it's working, and break it while reassembling it" had its place, just as periodic oil changes and checkups for a car do. But the scheduling of the maintenance often left something to be desired. In general, it seemed that very little consideration was given to making sure we were able to stay rested, a mistake in my opinion. Tired people make mistakes, they fall asleep when they're not supposed to, and they frequently exercise poor judgement because they just can't think critically about complex problems. Many people don't understand this because most people have never been really tired. Pulling an all-nighter in college or in high school can be tiring. But pulling five or six in a row, combined with hard and tedious work and, at most, a few hours of sleep here and there leaves you not only physically and mentally exhausted, but exhausted to the point where you see the world through a fog. I could usually go up to about 30 hours without sleep, but after that I'd start to have problems. I might do whatever anyone told me because I just didn't care enough to argue and lacked the energy to think about whether or not they were giving me stupid orders. Or I might decide I wouldn't do anything until I really understood it and waste a lot of time trying to remember exactly what was happening. Either way was bad. The only thing I have read that seems to approximate this state of weariness is what is experienced by high-altitude climbers working without oxygen, although they have a much harder predicament than we did.

And this takes us back to my proficiency watches. I had a six-hour watch on AMSLL with about an hours and a half's worth of work, no comfortable place to sit, nothing to read except for the reactor plant manual (RPM), and nobody to talk to. I spent the first hour working on my journal, doing the midwatch routine, then took a set of logs. The next hour, I popped my head up to AMSUL, saw it was someone I got along with, and we talked for nearly a half hour. After that, the EWS came around reviewing logs, so we talked for awhile, finishing that hour. The third hour, I sampled the port steam generator and condensate. That took a half hour, and I broke down and read part of the RPM for the rest of the hour. The fourth hour, I practiced writing left-handed, figuring it might come in handy some day. Like, if I ever broke my right arm. That kept me busy for nearly an hour, and I took logs again.

During this time, too, the ERS came to visit. I caught him at the foot of the ladder and asked my standard question for admission to AMSLL. "Hang on a minute. Before you set foot on my watchstation – who's the most beautiful woman in the known universe?"

He looked at me quizzically. "Huh?" he asked intelligently.

"You heard me. Before I'll let you on my watchstation, you've got to tell me who the most beautiful woman in the world is."

"You've got to be kidding." I shook my head. "OK, fine, I'll play your silly game. Brooke Shields."

"Good guess, but wrong."

"Kim Bassinger."

"Better guess, but still wrong."

Finally, about five or six tries later, he got it. "Michelle Pfeiffer?"

"Bingo! You may enter AMSLL."

The history of this went back a few years. On my first WestPac, we had the movie *Into the Night* in our video library. I wanted to watch it because Jeff Goldblum was in it; I'd enjoyed him in *Buckaroo Banzai* and wanted to see another of his movies. At that time I hadn't even heard of Michelle Pfeiffer. I quickly forgot about Jeff Goldblum, though (although he did a great job in the movie) and became enchanted with Michelle Pfeiffer. The next night, just by happenstance, we watched *Ladyhawk*, another movie with her in it, and I was hooked. From that point on I'd insist that anyone trying to enter my watchstation correctly identify Michelle Pfeiffer as the most beautiful woman in the known universe before they were allowed in. I even wrote her a fan letter at one point, offering to take her on a tour of a slightly dilapidated fast-attack submarine if she ever found herself in San Diego. Unfortunately, the letter was returned a few weeks later – I wasn't quite sure where to send it and guessed wrong. But such is life. And, lest you wonder, I was not an incipient celebrity stalker, just an ordinary sailor with a little too much time to fill. In any event, the ERS was granted entry to AMSLL, checked whatever he came to check on, and left again.

The fifth hour, I pumped bilges, which was actually pretty entertaining. Our drain system worked according to some laws of physics and engineering that interacted only passingly with those in our universe. Or, to put in another way, sometimes we could pump bilges and sometimes we couldn't. This time, when I opened the valves to pump my after bilge, water flowed in rather than out. I pointed this out to the person manning the drain station and we worked on it for awhile before we could finally get water out of the after bilge. By this time, it was threatening to overflow the deckplates which, given the general smell from the bilge, I didn't want to have to clean up. From there, I went to pump the forward bilge, having similar problems. Finally, after almost 45 minutes of coaxing, we got the bilges pumped down. A pain the neck, but it passed most of another hour. The last hour of the watch I was asked to light off two oxygen candles (we were still a little short on oxygen), I sampled the starboard generator, and tidied up the secondary sample sink. Little things like refilling all the reagent bottles, cleaning all the glassware, organizing things, and so forth. The, I sat around and waited for about 30 minutes for the morning watch to arrive. After turnover and watch relief, I grabbed some breakfast, finished up the rest of my daily routine (mostly just the radiation and contamination surveys) and went to sleep.

The next day was pretty much the same except that I brought my dirty laundry to wash in the sample sink. This wasn't really allowed, but I hadn't had a chance to do laundry the last time my division was up for laundry and I was running out of clean socks and underwear. So, when I filled the 2 ½ gallon sample sink for a steam generator sample, I didn't drain the water and mixed some detergent in. It took about a half hour to wash everything, another fifteen to rinse in condensate and wring the water out, and then I draped the wet clothes over pipes, ventilation ducts, on the ladders to AMSUL, and wherever else I could find room. The EWS and EOOW, during their tours, didn't even bat an eye. It had been one of the few nice things about standing the watch that we had the opportunity to do our laundry and, at least, it kept us awake. Aside from the excitement of doing laundry, this watch was much like the last, including the troubles pumping the bilges. And the next day was much of the same, as was the next. But, by the end of it all, my left-handed writing was easier to read than my normal writing. You take what you can get, I guess.

This should not be taken to mean that we spent all of our on-watch time just spacing out. I can't speak for anyone other than myself, but I just didn't trust the plant very much. It may have been a bit anthropomorphic of me, but I just didn't trust it. I always tried to teach my students to respect the plant, and I tried to do that myself. I spent a lot of the watch trying to figure out what could possibly go wrong and how I would handle it. I'd fight casualties in my mind, walking myself mentally through my actions, trying to figure out what could possibly go wrong. If I couldn't figure it out, I'd go to the RPM or would talk with the EWS when he came around on his tour. But you couldn't spend a solid six hours doing this.

Probably the biggest reason I respected the plant was because I didn't consider myself to be outstanding at standing watch. I was pretty good at it and I was a good ELT, but I had no instinct for machinery the way some people do. And, fundamentally, it just didn't interest me enough to become an outstanding watchstander. I think it's possible to be good at something regardless of your feelings towards it, but to really excel, you've got to be fascinated by it. And I wasn't.

In many ways, standing watch was being at sea in a microcosm. Very long periods of boredom that we both welcomed and cursed. The good part about it was that it meant nothing was going wrong. The bad, that we had nothing to do. And, when something did happen to relieve the monotony, it was either the synthetic excitement of drills or a real casualty that might end up hurting someone. So we cursed the boredom and the routine, all the while knowing that the only thing worse would be to have it alleviated.

CHAPTER

22

Rub-a-dub-dub; Clean up the Sub

The last few weeks on station were upon us and the spec op was winding down. Although the Soviets kept us busy, our minds were already on going home and our mission became a job and an annoyance, but no longer something exciting. As with so many other transitions, the change was not noticeable. With me, I suddenly realized that I didn't care much whether or not we found any more targets to take photos of. The mission was almost over. It was time to wrap up and get on with everything else we had to do before we could go home. I wanted to talk to my parents and sister, feel the sun, take a shower that had no water limit, breathe fresh air, taste fresh food, see real live women, see colors other than gray, white, black, and red, and do all the other things that were impossible at sea. This is not to suggest that we did our jobs with less diligence or attention, we were just starting to think about returning to the world and we were letting it mean something to us again.

We received our orders and pulled off station during our eighth week at sea and our seventh week on station. We were ordered to Adak, where we would take on a team of five Squadron "riders". Then, without pulling in or bringing on supplies or mail, we were to go back out to sea and head for Pearl Harbor, drilling all way. A week later, we'd pull into Pearl, take on another group of riders and some supplies, then head out again for our annual Operational Reactor Safeguards Examination, or ORSE. ORSE would be an intensive three-day audit of our paperwork, knowledge, and abilities to safely run our reactor plant. We had one each year and it was the biggest pain in the ass any of us could imagine. Normally, a boat would take from two to four weeks to do an "ORSE workup", complete with additional training and drill sessions. We had a little more than a week. On the other hand, failing ORSE would mean not being allowed to go to sea until we upgraded. So the worst they could do to us was to lock us up in Hawaii for a few weeks. We felt it was a no-lose situation.

It took us about two days to creep off-station to the point that we could start making noise again. Then, we started catching up on all the missed maintenance and other activities. We blew down both steam generators for the first time in two months to clean them out. Next, we shifted our main coolant pumps to fast speed and knocked a lot of corrosion loose from the insides of the pipes. The technical term for this was "crud" (really, that's what we called it) and any activity that routinely knocked a lot of crud into the reactor coolant was called a crudburst. A lot of crud was not much, perhaps a few tenths of a part per million. But, because crud was fairly radioactive, we had to try to reduce levels as much as possible by maximizing the flow rate through our reactor coolant purification system. This time, we were put us into what we called a "crudburst cleanup" that lasted about a week (normally crudbursts could be cleaned up by filtration through our reactor water purifier in less than a day). We also ran the mains up to a flank bell, did some noisy maintenance, and, in general, just returned to normal operations. Like someone stretching after a long stint at a desk, we were getting the kinks out, both of ourselves and the boat.

Around this same time, things started getting busier again. Mr. Huggins and I were spending three or four hours a day working on the Captain's slide show for our mission debrief. My ORSE watchstation was ELT, so I retained that watch for the transit, but most of the rest of the watchbill was bounced around to get people standing their ORSE watches in their prospective ORSE watch section. We were training every other day and running drills daily, along with field days every other day to clean up the boat. At one point, we even started painting, something that brought complaints from nearly everyone. Our atmosphere controls were so tight that we weren't even allowed to bring shaving cream or shoe polish onboard; we felt that painting should have been out of the question and was only being done to make the boat, and the CO, look good for the ORSE board. In any event, our oxygen levels were still low, CO_2 was still high, and the painting stopped after only a day. My day rapidly became four to five hours for the daily routine, four hours for the slide briefing, six hours for drills, three hours for training, three or four hours to review the last year's worth of logs for errors, an hour or so for meals and personal hygiene, and, on a good day, three or four hours to sleep. During the week transit to Adak I averaged four hours of sleep daily, never more than two hours at a time. My particular peeve, though, was field day. Not just at ORSE time, but any time.

Field day was an intensive, all-hands effort to clean the entire boat. It usually lasted for 2 or 3 hours, but would sometimes be extended under extenuating circumstances. Like, if the CO didn't think we were doing a good enough job or getting ready for a big inspection or for any other reason that seemed appropriate. And, sometimes, we'd get nailed with "after-watch cleanup", a sort of mini-field day just for the off-going watch section. We normally cleaned up our watch station towards the end of our watch anyhow, but sometimes the powers-that-be thought that more needed to be done.

My objections to field day were almost too numerous to mention. But I'll try. First and foremost, I resented anything that cut into sleeping time, and field day certainly did that. Most of us nukes got so little chance to sleep that we lived on coffee. To arbitrarily take away a block of sleep time to clean up really irked me. I was also irritated because the work was just menial. By this time, I had been in the Navy for nearly 8 years and was relatively senior. Any nuke did things that very few others on the boat could do, but any idiot could wield a scrub pad, paper towels, or dustpan. To me, it made sense to let us do the things we had trained to do and that nobody else could even attempt while letting the junior people with no skills take care of the cleanup. And field day was dirty and smelly and a lot of other unpleasant adjectives.

It also rankled that, while we lowly enlisted men were busily scrubbing lube oil out of the bilges, the officers and chiefs were walking around pointing out places we'd missed. With the chiefs, I could handle it to some extent; they'd already paid their dues with years of their own field days. But, given that the officers were never going to do any of this dirty work at any time, they could have had the decency to not rub our noses in the fact. Especially the junior officers. It didn't bother me that the CO, XO, and Eng inspected our work; they had earned that right by years of service, responsibility, rank, and everything else that went into being a senior officer. What bothered me was having somebody right out of the Academy with no time on submarines telling me how to clean my particular part of the engineroom or chewing us out for not working hard enough. Especially when we were all tired and under-caffeinated. But, this was the Navy and if I held my breath waiting for complete fairness, I'd be a long time without air. So, like most of us enlisted men, I did as much cleaning as I needed to to stay out of trouble and very little more.

The pre-ORSE field days were particularly bad. They lasted longer because we were trying to impress the ORSE board. The post-field day inspections were more serious and more thorough. And we had more of them. On *Plunger*, even the chiefs were tasked with getting dirty during pre-ORSE field days and it was not unusual to see them cleaning (albeit in more convenient and less grimy spots) alongside the lesser enlisted men. The officers may have made their beds, but not much else that I was aware of. In fact, to the best of my knowledge, the officers didn't even do their own laundry, the cooks washed it for them on the midwatch. But I digress....

Each of us were assigned a particular part of the boat to clean up. All of my division (RL Div, or reactor laboratory division) and M-Div (the nuclear machinists mates) were assigned to the Engineroom, RC Div (reactor controls) cleaned up AMSUL, and E-Div (the electricians) cleaned up in AMSLL. The coners had their own field day areas, too, but I really didn't pay much attention to them. Within our designated space, each person had his own special part of heaven to keep clean. On this underway, I was assigned to the starboard side of the condensate bay in ERLL. Another of my ELTs had the port side, two more were assigned to the next space back (the ASW, or auxiliary sea water bay) and the remaining ELT was assigned to the lube oil bay. This was irksome, too. Typically, the more senior personnel were assigned to ERUL. My division was really top-heavy with four first-class petty officers, but we ended up cleaning in ERLL in some of the worst areas. But such was life.

Today being our first Friday since going off-station, we had a field day. At 8 AM sharp the lights went on in the berthing compartment for the first time in over two months, the General Alarm sounded (all 21 gongs), and an MC announcement was made, letting one and all know that field day had arrived and we were all invited to join in the fun. All of us in the forward nine-man groaned, tried to steal a few more minutes of sleep, then gave in to the inevitable. I rolled out of my rack, dressed slowly, made up my rack, and wandered aft, stopping to fill a coffee cup on the way. The goal was to arrive at your field day area just before a search party was sent after you. I was too quick this time; people were still milling about smartly when I showed up. I guess you just have to practice your vices to stay in top form. We listened to the obligatory pep talk about getting ready for ORSE and the reminder that we'd really had it easy for the past two months. This, of course, made us all feel much better about our upcoming battle with dirt and grime and, cheered, we armed ourselves for battle with the forces of grime.

We ELTs moseyed on down to our assigned areas and decided that we should really discuss a game plan for dealing with our area while we drank our coffee. Looking through the hatch into the main sea water bay (immediately forward of the condensate bay), we could see the crew there following the same strategy. Our planning session lasted about 30 minutes, about the same length of time it took for the first junior officer to come by. We put on a show of cleaning for him and then decided to do a quick cleanup on everything that was easily inspected. That took another half hour or so, after which we reconvened our tactical session. After another half hour or so we returned to cleaning, this time going after some of the less obvious areas. A few minutes after we started this, the CO wandered into the condensate bay. I was in the bilge, a few feet below the deck level, squatting down to clean beneath the condenser. I straightened up to greet the CO as he entered. "Morning, Sir."

"Good morning, Karam. How's everything going?" Now that was a rhetorical question if I ever heard one.

"Everything's great, Sir!" I answered enthusiastically. The CO looked at me warily. I'd been on the boat for over three years now, and he'd been here for almost two. He knew that I was sometimes not quite serious.

"It is?" he replied.

"You bet, Sir! Look at it this way. We all know that cleanliness is next to Godliness, right?"

"Uh, yes."

"And the Commies are atheistic assholes, right, Sir?"

"Well, yeah...."

"Then, the way I look at it, that means that cleanliness is next to Truth, Justice, and the American Way of Life. So I'm proud to be doing my part to help keep the Engineroom safe from the scourge of Communism. What could be better than that, Sir?" The CO gave me a concerned look, muttered something, and went forward into the MSW bay.

We kept at it for another few hours, alternating between cleaning when officers or chiefs came by and talking the rest of the time. Joe was really tired, so he climbed outboard the port condenser, wedged himself into a corner where, from a distance it'd look like he was going after a hard-to-reach spot, and went to sleep for nearly an hour. I was able to catch almost half an hour of sleep myself, but it wasn't nearly enough. Finally, we heard the MC announcement "All hands, secure from field day." We threw away our paper towels, put away our cleaning supplies, and headed forward. We did this two more times on the way to Adak, gradually getting the engineering spaces to point where the CO, XO, Eng, and the nuke chiefs approved. Just in time to take on the Squadron riders for our ORSE workup.

Luckily, our slide briefing was done. We had some problems with the slide developer and our Pola Blue film (Polaroid high-contrast blue and white slide film), but we ended up getting all the photos we needed with, literally, the last shots on the last roll of film. We still had some computer graphics to take care of, but the hard part, the copy stand work, was finished.

The slide brief was another exercise in security classifications. The quartermasters had made a number of charts showing ship's movements, relative positions, and so forth for a number of the events we had witnessed or participated in. These were carefully done, drawn, and lettering added. We put them on the copy stand, made sure the lighting was good, framed and shot the photos, and developed the film. As soon as the CO agreed that the slides were acceptable, the charts were stamped "Top Secret" and, as with the photos, I was no longer allowed to see them. But, in any event, we'd put together nearly 100 slides for the CO to choose from and now, with the exception of last-minute changes to some of the computer graphics (for which we simply photographed the computer screen), it was up to him. If there was one person onboard getting less sleep than I at this time it was the Old Man. He was finishing up a spec op, getting ready for an ORSE, preparing his mission debriefing and slide show, and doing all the other things that being skipper entailed. On the other hand, he was also paid a lot more than any of the rest of us, but he definitely earned it.

We swung into Adak's harbor and, just as we had done over two months earlier, took a small boat alongside. The last time we were transferring a chief off, this time we were taking on six Squadron riders. They were called "riders" because they just rode along with us. They didn't stand watch or do maintenance or anything else to help with our daily routine. Their job was to cram three weeks' worth of ORSE preparation into a week-long transit from Adak to Pearl. They had planned on meeting us in Hawaii, riding us for a week after our arrival and before the ORSE board arrived. The CO insisted they meet us in Adak instead because it would shave three or four days off our at-sea time by drilling before we got to Pearl. Although this gave us less time overall to prepare for ORSE, the skipper correctly assumed we were tired and ready to go home. And, although I don't think he anticipated this, when we found out what he'd done and why, it made us much more willing to try to do well for him, to show him our appreciation. If he'd come out and said "This is what I'm doing for you, now this is what I want you to do for me," we probably would have responded with overwhelming apathy. But, by just trying to help us out and not saying anything, we figured he was genuinely interested in us and we responded in kind.

The biggest disappointment with the personnel transfer in Adak was that no mail came on with the riders. This really irritated us all. Squadron had known for several weeks that we were pulling into Adak, plenty of time to send our mail with us. We'd all been out of touch for weeks, looking forward to the first letters from home when we got to Adak. To show up and have no mail was a real blow to morale and caused no small amount of bitterness among the crew. It didn't last long, however, because the riders got to work almost immediately with training, drills, tests, interviews, and paperwork audits. That kept at least the nukes too busy to fret about anything else.

We were also happy to know that Greg was now OK. For the last month or so the Doc had been dosing him with antibiotics and we all followed his case pretty closely. He'd been seen up and about a few times, but never for more than an hour or so, and many of us were concerned. Pulling in to Adak, he was one of the first off the boat, where he was taken to the base hospital. We were told that, within a few hours his appendix had been removed and he was in the recovery room. Of course, by that time, we were already underwater again, heading south, and getting ready for our upcoming inspection.

We had a number of inspections each year and, based in large part on these, the Squadron would choose one boat as the most battle-ready. Everyone on that boat would then get a purple ribbon to wear on their uniform; the "Battle E" award. It may not sound like much, but it was hardly a trivial award and winning the Battle "E" looked great on the service record of a skipper who was trying to advance. So we worked our asses off to do well on our inspections. In addition to the ORSE, we had the SMI (Supply and Materials Inspection) that looked at our stores and cooks; the TRE (Tactical Readiness Examination), primarily for the weaponeers, but everyone got to play somewhat; another inspection for our damage control (sorry, can't remember the acronym for that one); and others. The two biggies were the TRE and ORSE and, of those, ORSE was arguably the more difficult because anything dealing with Naval Reactors was a pain in the neck. One reason was that failing an ORSE would get the boat tied up at the pier, unable to go to sea until we improved our performance. And, of course, a boat at the pier can't do much to help fight bad guys. So we (and most other nuclear-powered ships) spent a fair amount of time preparing for ORSE each year.

Personally, I thought that the ORSE preps were ridiculous. In my opinion, the purpose of the inspection was to see if you were able to operate safely. The best way to do that was to see how you operated every day, not how you operated for three days after a month of intensive effort to make everything look good. Every training session we had was based on giving answers to questions ORSE had asked the previous year. Every drill set we ran was based on drills the ORSE board had run on boats the previous year. I can't remember more than a handful of drills run during my time onboard *Plunger* that didn't come directly from notes of other ORSE inspections. This was a shame because the real casualties we had usually didn't follow the ORSE scenarios and my guess was that, if we ever went into battle, the battle damage wouldn't follow the ORSE playbook, either. My concern was that the Navy was falling back into the same trap it had been in at the start of World War II, when every ship looked great on paper but few could actually fight effectively. Unless, of course, we sent the TRE and ORSE scenarios to the Soviets.

ORSE prep was just no fun any way you looked at it. We ran two drill sets daily for nearly a week along with training, interviews, and field days. Whenever we weren't working on that, we were reviewing our paperwork to look for errors or inconsistencies. For my part, I had to dig out the previous year's worth of our logs and go through every one of them, checking calculations, log entries, surveys, and everything else. Then I reviewed all of our other paperwork. Radioactive material tags and logs, reactor compartment entry logs, reactor plant and steam plant water chemistry graphs, radiation dosimetry records, radiological surveys, chemical inventory records, chemical expiration dates, procedures. Every single one had to be checked to make sure that it met the requirements, was correct, and was consistent with all other related records. I hated it, partly because it was incredibly boring and partly because it served no real purpose. But mine was not to reason why.

If we hadn't been so tired, some of the drill sets might actually have been fun. Each drill set was planned in pretty good detail before starting. The CO, XO, and Eng would assemble in the Wardroom with a selection of people from all nuke ratings. They would have already selected a series of drills designed to test whatever they thought was necessary. At the start of this ORSE workup, the drills were all pretty simple ones because we hadn't drilled in nearly two months. As the week went on, the drills became increasingly complex and close together. But more on that in a little while.

During the briefing, the Eng would go over the drills, one at a time. For each one, each drill team member would have an assignment and instructions. For example, I might be assigned to AMSLL during a loss of feed pump drill and told what to do, what to NOT let the watchstander do, and what to tell him if he asked for indications. Some drills were more real than others. For the loss of feed pump, for example, I would actually reach over and turn off the pump at the appointed time. Steam generator levels would start to drop and, if the watch didn't start another one up in a timely manner, we could boil a generator dry. That was another function, to start another feed pump if generator level got too low, before we could actually hurt the plant. And, if the watchstander was trying to figure out what happened, I was told what to tell him. For example "You smell an acrid odor," which would suggest that the pump had shorted out electrically. Other casualties were entirely imaginary because, for example, we really didn't want to start a fire. For that, I'd hold up a sign that said something like "Acrid odor" and, as time went on, would hold up other signs like "You are having trouble breathing" and, if the watchstander didn't put on an EAB at that point "You are dead." This is what we reviewed at the briefings.

After the briefing, the drill team would wander back to the engineering spaces and disperse as planned, waiting for word to start the drill set. When we were on watch, this was our sign to get ready. Most of us would look for a drill team member on our watchstation under the assumption that they couldn't really run a drill unless they were there to initiate it and to take notes on our performance. So, if no drill team members were on our watchstation, we'd relax a bit. In my opinion, this was another mistake, but one that I never figured out how to rectify. With a limited number of people, you can't put drill team members everywhere all the time. But, on the other hand, you don't usually have a heads-up before a real casualty. Basically, it just made things a bit easier for us.

We ran a lot of drills. Reactor scrams were one of the favorites and they came in several flavors. We almost never got lucky enough to have a simple scram. Too bad, too, because we could go from scramming out to being back at full power in much less than a half hour. On the other hand, a complicated scram, one for which we couldn't meet the criteria for a rapid recovery, might take a few hours to recover from, forcing us to rig for reduced electrical (that is, turning off everything electrical except what was absolutely necessary), come up to PD to snorkel on the emergency diesel generator, and a number of other actions. During a fast scram recovery, we'd hardly know the reactor was down without listening to the MC. During a delayed scram, however, lights, air conditioning, and other non-essential loads would be turned off. AC may seem like a luxury, but temperatures all over the boat would rise to over 90 degrees within fifteen or twenty minutes and, in the engineroom, it would get up to 120 degrees all over and 140 or so near the mains and the turbine generators. It was about the only place onboard hotter than the reactor compartment (during initial RC entries, temperature was usually over 135 degrees and we'd have to enter in heavy canvas anti-contamination clothing).

One of the most miserable drills I played in was a delayed scram during which we had to turn the turbine generators by hand to keep the rotors from bowing. Five of us took turns with a huge wrench on the shaft, manually keeping the two-ton rotor turning in 140 degree heat. We took five-minute shifts, after which we'd go into the relative cool (only 95 degrees) of AMSUL to gulp down a quart or so of ice water and try to rest until our next shift. This went on for nearly an hour. My glasses were so encrusted with salt from dried sweat that I could barely see and we all soaked our clothes completely through to the point where we could wring them out.

Each drill set usually contained at least one scenario that called for donning EABs (or, as we called it, sucking rubber). This could be a fire, a reactor coolant leak, or anything else that seemed to call for masks. Sucking rubber was something else that just, well, sucked. The masks were hard to get to fit correctly and impossible to be comfortable in. Talking was difficult, especially talking on the phones. For me, with my glasses, it was doubly difficult because my glasses made it difficult to get a good seal on the mask. But, without my glasses, I couldn't see at all. So my options were simulated suffocation if caught or real blindness without my glasses. I usually chose to wear the things and risk someone checking the seal on my mask.

One of the interesting things about the masks was the buddy connection. This was a connection at the belt clip where someone else could plug into your hose and pull their own air from the manifold. Most manifolds had only six jacks, so this allowed more people to use a single manifold if they needed. It also gave more range on the hoses – the hoses were only ten or fifteen feet long, so you had to stay within that distance of a manifold. However, jacking into someone else's buddy connection let you double that range. However, this could give rise to other problems.

I remember one time in particular when I was involved in a "daisy chain" going down the OPSML passageway right outside the messdecks. A line of about ten people were all jacked into the buddy connection of the person ahead of them when the guy at the very front of the line decided it was time to move. He unplugged himself, not realizing that this also cut off the air to everyone plugged into behind him. Ten people felt their facemasks suck in as they tried to inhale. After five seconds or so, I lifted my mask up (since it was only a drill and not real toxic gas in the air and yelled "Plug yourself back in, you idiot!" A second later air was restored and everyone went back to breathing.

Another time, my division officer was plugged into my connection during a fire drill. He decided it was time to move out and took off. Without unplugging. He was short but powerful and dragged me ten feet or so before realizing his mistake. Yet another time, one of our junior M-Div'ers needed to go down a ladder, but didn't have enough line to make it. The normal action would be to hyperventilate a few seconds, unplug, and walk briskly to the next manifold to plug in again. Since the manifolds weren't too far apart, this was not much of a problem and, in fact, you could go the length of the boat like this once you learned where the manifolds were. This guy, however, decided to plug into his own buddy connection and nearly passed out before realizing that, without the air pressure on the line, he wouldn't get any air at all.

My favorite EAB story, though, is the one in the diesel generator room. During another drill, a group of mechanics gathered in the diesel space to try to figure out why it wasn't starting. They were daisy-chained around the diesel, going clockwise from the manifold. One guy decided to take a better look at a part of the diesel, so he unplugged from the manifold and plugged into the buddy connection on the guy next to him. Instantly, everyone lost air – the guy who'd unplugged was the only one plugged in, so he'd just completed an EAB daisy chain around the diesel. I'm sure it happened on other boats, but this was the only one I ever experienced myself.

At their best, drills could be valuable training tools and, sometimes, could even be fun if looked at as a contest between the watch section and the drill team. At their worst, drills interrupted much-needed sleep with repetitive, boring, and unrealistic scenarios. (And then, of course, there was the guy who'd walk around with an electric drill saying "This is only a drill.") Most drill sets were somewhere in between these extremes.

Afterwards, there was the critique. Immediately after the drill set was finished (perhaps 4-8 drills, depending on their complexity) the drill team would gather again to compare notes. Any problems were discussed in detail as well as any departures from the plans. This would usually take things up to the next meal (normally dinner since drills were usually run on the afternoon watch), so after the meal, the Eng would go over the drills and observations with the watch section.

Between all the ORSE preparations, the trip to Pearl seemed to take forever. I was already sleep-deprived from the previous week's worth of photographic work and this made things almost intolerable. I was drinking anywhere from 20-25 cups of coffee daily just to stay awake, and there were times I'd doze off while standing up in Nucleonics reviewing logs and other paperwork. And I wasn't alone. Wherever you looked, you'd see both nukes and coners dragging around the boat. It was worse for nukes because this was our inspection, but the coners had to play on a lot of the drills, so drill sets ate into their sleep time, too.

During this time, too, beards were coming off and we were lining up for haircuts. Our CO didn't care what we looked like at sea, provided we were squared away when we pulled in. After over two months at sea, most of us, myself included, had pretty good beards and decidedly shaggy hair. Unlike skimmers, we had no real barber shop and no trained ship's barbers. What we had instead were two guys, a cook and a chief nuke. The cook had been through a whole week's worth of training in how to give haircuts. The chief had no training, he just liked giving haircuts. It was a tough choice to make.

I eventually decided to schedule a time with the chief. No particular reason except that the last haircut I'd had from the cook had left me less than impressed. Of course, it wasn't helped by the fact that we'd been in Shaft Alley, on the surface, in rough seas with the boat taking 15 degree rolls and jumping up and down a few feet at a time. That haircut was short enough that I was allowed to leave the boat to get to the base barber. He had to just about shave my head to keep me from looking ludicrous. So we live and learn.

This time, we were at the Doc's station. The chief, wielding the clippers with a fiendish grin, was just finishing with the previous person when I wandered in. I gave the current victim a careful look. The chief stopped and looked at me. "Inspecting my work, Karam?"

"Just making sure I want to put my good looks at your mercy, Chief," I replied. "Looking at this, I'm not too sure." Actually, the haircut looked pretty good, but the person on the stool didn't know that.

"Yeah, I know," the chief replied. "But I think I can fix it. I just need to take another half inch off over here and then shorten up this sideburn a little. That ought to do it."

I looked critically at the guy. He was starting to look a bit worried. "Well, Chief, you're both lucky, I think."

"What makes you say that?"

"This guy's so damned ugly to begin with, the worst you can do will still be an improvement. If he's lucky, you'll butcher his hair badly enough that nobody'll look at his face. By the way, you missed a spot there. See that tuft of hair here?"

"Good catch! Yeah, good point, Andy. I just keep telling my customers that the difference between a bad haircut and a good one is about three weeks."

"But Chief, we pull in in less than a week."

"So he'll have a few weeks to go. Could be worse. Besides, you get what you pay for."

The chief's "customer" was now looking a bit more worried. I told him he didn't look any worse than before, which really didn't cheer him up any. He looked at me. "If this is so bad, how come you're still waiting here?"

"Because the chief likes me enough to open his eyes when he cuts my hair. Besides, I like to live life on the edge."

The chief finished up and gave the guy a mirror. Relieved is a good way to describe his expression. He left and I took his place. "How would you like it, Andy?"

"Legal. Short enough to get me off the boat when we pull in. Nothing fancy."

"Good enough. Mohawk it is!" He started trimming. Fifteen minutes and a lot of hair later, he stopped. "Beard, too, Andy?"

"You bet, Chief!" He put on the shortest trimmers and attacked my beard. Five minutes later I took a quick look in the mirror, thanked him for not making me look too bad, and went to the head to take care of the beard stubble with my razor. I'd had better haircuts, but I'd had many worse, too. This one would do.

Two days out of Pearl, the CO decided enough was enough. He gave us two days with minimal training and only what paperwork we could audit while on-watch. He realized that it'd be better to have a rested crew than one with a little more training. It was the best thing he could have done for us. I don't know about anyone else, but I slept for over twelve hours, stood six hours of watch, then slept another 15 hours. When I woke, we were getting ready to set the Maneuvering Watch and pull into port.

CHAPTER 23

ORSE

For the third time this underway, we set the Maneuvering Watch, pulled into port, and didn't tie up to the pier. Instead, we did another small boat transfer in the harbor, brought on some supplies along with the ORSE board, and, again, no mail. My last Family-Gram had come in nearly a month earlier, so I was a long time between any contacts with home, but it was worse for some others. As before, I popped up topside as soon as we opened the weapons' shipping hatch. Unlike other times, however, this time nobody else went up until after I had read all of the wipes and cleared them. The XO was concerned that the ORSE board might be watching us and seeing how long it was between my appearance and that of the deck crew. Since we're within sight of the pier, maybe this degree of caution is warranted. I just shrug to myself and do my job. At this point, I could really care less. I just want to get these jokers on, play their silly games, and finish this underway.

After we take on the ORSE board, several large packages of stores are brought onboard, too. Fresh milk, fresh fruit and vegetables, snow crab legs, lettuce, and other ambrosia, the likes of which we haven't seen for two months. Fresh eggs are passed down the hatch along with orange juice. Mouths watering, we are strictly enjoined not to sample anything. This isn't for us, although we'll get to partake. If it weren't for the ORSE board, though, we'd be lucky to take on a loaf of bread. This is to help make the ORSE board's stay as pleasant as possible under the assumption that they'll treat us better if they're well-fed with good food. Luckily, on a submarine, everyone eats the same food, all cooked in the same galley. In order to spoil the ORSE board, they've got to feed us well, too. We eat this well once each year, during ORSE. After taking the food on, we offload the riders and some of their equipment. They'll pick up the rest of their gear when we pull back in two days from now.

We turn around and head back out to sea, carrying the ORSE board. All sorts of anti-military activists talk about submarines carrying "deadly cargo", referring to nuclear weapons. In our opinion, the cargo we now carried was far deadlier than any nuclear weapons. At least the weapons didn't steal our sleep and equanimity.

We took the ORSE team onboard at about 10 AM and, after a short briefing in the Wardroom, they started in on us by 11. First came observed evolutions. They watched each division perform some standard mainte-nance, then they watched watch sections perform evolutions. For RL Div, they had Louis read a dosimeter and Mackin draw and analyze a reactor coolant sample. Rather, they watched me watch Louis and Mackin, taking notes the whole time. First of all, they wanted to see if he did anything incorrect that I missed while monitoring him. Secondly, they wanted to make sure our most junior ELT was capable of drawing a reactor coolant sample and analyzing it correctly. It put me in somewhat of an awkward situation. Any time I saw Mackin do something less than perfectly I had to debate noting it in my comments. If I didn't note it and the ORSE member noticed, it was a comment against me and Mackin both. If I noted something that the ORSE member missed, then it was a comment against us that would otherwise have been avoided. I decided just to assume they missed nothing and wrote everything down.

It was the most painstaking primary coolant sample I've ever seen drawn. We'd been practicing for a month; I'd set up a rotation to monitor every ELT drawing a primary with the Eng, CO, and CRA all filling in, too as monitors. But it's nothing like working in front of the all-knowing ORSE board. I was worried about Mackin, too. We were all kind of blasé about the ORSE by this point, but he had never drawn a particularly good monitored primary sample and I was dreading this one. He surprised me. Although the sample took nearly twice as long as any other he'd done, he made all of his time requirements and drew as close to a flawless sample as any I'd seen or done myself. Same thing with the dosimeter read – Louis did a bang-up job. Things were starting off well for RL Div.

Apparently, based on word from others, it was going well for the other divisions, too. A few years earlier, we had fried one of the nuclear instru-ments (which monitored the reactor) during ORSE. They had us repair the instrument at sea, which necessitated surfacing, shutting down the reactor, replacing the instrument electronics, testing it, then starting up again. So we spent eight hours on the surface, sweltering because the AC was down while the ROs repaired their gear. They did a good job, but it was a no-win situation. Anytime you take on something that complex under close scru-tiny you're going to make some mistakes and, even if you catch them, correct them, and move on, ORSE only seemed to note the errors. The highest praise they gave on any drill, interview, or evolution was "no dis-crepancies noted" – not exactly high praise. Or, another way to put it, their job was not to document what you did well, just to hammer you for what you didn't do perfectly. So far this ORSE, it sounded as though we had a lot of "no comments" taking place.

There was one minor comment during Mackin's primary. For one sample, we were to draw exactly 250 ml of reactor water into a sample bottle. After the sample was drawn, the ORSE board member asked why we hadn't marked the 250 ml level line on the bottle. Thinking quickly, I pointed to the painted radiation symbol on the side of the bottle and told him that the exact top of the painted part had been measured and found to be 250 ml on the button. He looked skeptical, but made a brief note on his clipboard and didn't press any further. Later that evening, Brian told me that the ORSE team member had returned to the lab, graduated cylinder in hand, to test this assertion. In five trials, that bottle had come out to 250 ml on the nose every time. It was the only sample bottle in our lab that was even close. According to Brian, the ORSE team member just scowled, wrote in his notebook again, and left.

After the observed evolutions came interviews to test our level of knowledge. These were fairly specific for your qualifications. There were separate sessions for each specialty rating, EOOW, EWS, and ELT. This meant I could be interviewed as a mechanical operator, as an ELT, or as an EWS and there was no way of knowing in advance which it'd be. For the interviews, we were paired off with someone else, but my partner held the same quals I did, so that was no help, either. Finally, when we were called in, we found we were being quizzed as ELTs, a big relief.

The interviews were in what we called a "screw your buddy" format. I was asked a question and, after I answered, my partner was asked "Do you agree with that?" or something similar. This was another dilemma. Of course the ORSE board knew the correct answer, but we were reluctant to sit there and say "No, Sir, he's a complete idiot." On the other hand, if you didn't shoot down your partner, you could both be disqualified. Most of the time I went with a qualified approach. "Well, Sir, he got a lot of it, but he forgot to mention…." The thing was, you never knew what they were going to ask or in what sequence. Once they asked me to calculate how radioactive the reactor coolant would be with a small leak of air into the reactor plant. That was followed with something so trivially easy that I almost muffed it. The best thing about the interviews was that they were strictly limited to 20 minutes and the questions were scripted. Having scripted questions made it easier for them to grade, but it was also limiting. It is remarkably easy, with only a few questions, to home in on weak areas. Once you locate a few, you can make just about anyone look and feel like a complete moron by hammering away at the weak areas and ignoring everything else. And, after 15 minutes of wrong answers or "I don't know" answers, you start to sound, feel, and appear like a fairly significant bonehead. And, if you partner is hesitant to cut you loose, he begins to look incompetent, too. Having had experience on both sides of the table, I can confirm this from personal experience.

Luckily, this interview was in areas of water chemistry and radiological controls, our bread and butter. We were both comfortable with standing EWS, myself somewhat more so since I was senior and had qualified the watch a year before Louis had, but we both felt more comfortable with what we did day in and day out.

The interviews took place in the various staterooms. Ours was in the XO's stateroom. Present were the two of us, one of the JOs, as a representative of the boat, one of the Squadron riders, and the ORSE board member. It made for a somewhat cramped stateroom, but we managed. We were all introduced and the rules were read to us. We were assured that everything would be fair and impartial and that this was just to make sure that everyone standing watch on a nuclear power plant was qualified and competent to do so, including basic knowledge of the plant. And then the interview began.

Petty Officer Karam, can you tell us about reactor plant water chemistry addition chemicals? Which ones do we add and why? Can you write down the kinetics equations for us? What happens when reactor power increases to these parameters? How about you? Do you agree with Petty Officer Karam? Did he make any mistakes or forget anything? I see. OK, your turn. You're steaming along fat, dumb, and happy and all of a sudden you get a radiation alarm on this instrument here. What do you do? Why? Petty Officer Karam, do you agree? Back to you, if your instrument reads this, what does it tell you? What do you do next? Why? Petty Officer Karam, is this correct? Has he left anything out? What's wrong with the plant? Next question. Petty Officer Karam, you draw a steam generator sample and you get these results. Are these normal? What's abnormal about them? What could cause this? Petty Officer Scott, write down the chemical equations for our steam generator addition chemicals and how they help protect the steam generators. Is that correct, Petty Officer Karam? Back to our last question. With those chemistry results, what do you think's happening? Why? Do you agree with that, Petty Officer Scott? Did Karam forget anything? Can you draw a diagram of the reactor coolant sampling system, showing all of the valves and including the apparatus inside the sample sink? Is that correct, Petty Officer Karam? Did he leave anything out?

And that's pretty much how it went for exactly 20 minutes. At the designated time, the Squadron representative cut off the answer in progress, noting time had expired. We were thanked for our time, ushered out, and the next group ushered in. We looked at each other, shrugged, and went to the messdecks for the written exam. The written exam was along the same lines as the oral interview, but without the "buddy-screwing" aspect. I was given the EWS exam which included about 15 questions of varying degrees of complexity. Draw a schematic of the ship's electrical system. Describe the seven immediate actions for a reactor scram. List the pressures at which the reactor plant pressure relief valves lift and provide a detailed derivation of how those numbers were derived by the engineers. Draw a schematic of the reactor protection system electronics. Describe the workings of the control rod drive mechanisms. And so on. Some of the questions were pretty simple, others were devilishly hard. I fell back on illegibility. My handwriting is pretty bad at its best; for tests like this I just wrote as poorly as I could on the questions I was clueless about, making sure that all diagrams were correct and that I had the occasional legible key words in the answer to each question. This and the approach that "it's better to be generally right than specifically wrong" was my ORSE exam-taking philosophy. I don't know if it helped or hurt, but it couldn't be any worse than putting down a completely legible and completely wrong answer. And I would pray to the God of partial credit.

The interviews were completed during the evening watch of the first day. I'm not sure if the ORSE team slept or not during their time onboard. If so, it must have been in shifts because activities were scheduled during the midwatch, too. Our drill team stood the midwatch on all watch stations so the rest of us were able to get a good night's sleep. I told Mackin to draw the primary quickly and save the rest of the routine for later in the day. I don't know if he did or not, but the best I could do was advise. I wasn't about to hold his hand. I went to sleep about 10, slept soundly, and woke at 5 AM, feeling pretty refreshed.

No matter what else they did, the drills were what defined ORSE for me. As I mentioned earlier, during drills, things are really being done to the boat. The reactor is shut down and must be brought up again. Feed pumps are tripped and must be restarted. And so on. At every step there is the possibility of something unexpected going legitimately wrong that we'll have to deal with. And, no matter how much you try to anticipate and error-trap these things, the plant is more complex and more mischievous than the person and the plant would usually try to have fun with us. Add to that a team of highly knowledgeable people paid to do nothing except catch you in mistakes and you have an interesting situation, especially in a boat destined for the scrap yard after this underway. In any event, I was in the first drill section, so I ate quickly and relieved the watch. I wanted some time to prepare myself, running through some likely scenarios and making sure my watchstation was in good shape. Louis had done well – both steam generators were in good shape, AMSLL was the cleanest I'd seen it in months, and all of our reagent bottles were topped off with the sampling glassware spotless. Louis went forward to eat and prepare to run drills. I felt a bit sorry for him, too – we had had some arguments recently, but he was as tired as I'd been earlier and had a full day of running drills and debriefing ahead of him, followed by another midwatch. By the time this was done, he'd have been up for over 36 hours with only two or three hours' sleep. But that wasn't my concern right now; I had to stand a good watch and get ready for drills. Starting in about 45 minutes, after the drill monitors ate and briefed the first drill set.

Almost to the minute drill monitors appeared in AMSLL. Three of them, including a member of the ORSE board. This was a giveaway. They'd never waste someone from ORSE on a watchstation where nothing was going to happen. The phone rang. "AMSLL, Maneuvering. Man the coolant discharge station."

"Man the coolant discharge station, aye." The EWS came down the ladder and told me we were going to be discharging some coolant to the retention tanks. I opened a storage locker and took out a plastic bag containing a pair of thin cotton gloves, a pair of anti-contamination rubber gloves (they looked like orange dishwashing gloves), some swipes, and some paper towels. I set up the contamination monitor next to me, put on both sets of gloves, and set up to operate primary plant valves. The precautions were necessary because reactor coolant flowed through these valves at high pressure and could leak out. While the radioactivity levels were not dangerous, we still tried to be careful. One of my instructors years ago had told me "Think of it as dog piss, Karam. It's not going to hurt you, you just don't want to get it on yourself and, if you do, you just need to wash your hands off." As I set up at the discharge station, one of the drill monitors whispered to me "If the valve starts to leak, don't try to close it again, open it all the way."

That told me the rest that I needed to know. I had been certain that the drill was going to be some sort of simulated leak of reactor coolant – we were done with observed evolutions, so this was just to set up a drill. At the discharge station, the most likely drill would be a leak along the valve stem as soon as it was opened, just as a household faucet will leak along the valve stem until you tighten the washers. In this case, the valve was a type that felt the pressure on top of the valve seat, so simply closing the valve again would do nothing. The only way to isolate a leak was to fully open it, putting the valve on its back seat to take pressure off the packing. That would be the first part of it for me. I was also going to get wet because of the simulated reactor coolant spraying on me.

As usual, valve operating instructions were relayed from Maneuvering. They wasted little time because the third valve of nine that were to be operated was the one that "leaked". No sooner had I cracked the valve off its seat did the drill monitor whip out a spray bottle and start spraying me from the vicinity of the valve. All valve operations were reported in real time to the EWS, so I was already talking. "Opening the valve. It's off its closed seat and...Chief! Valve is leaking! Moderate water spray. Putting the valve on its backseat! Valve fully open and backseated. Water spray stopped. The leak is stopped. Repeat, the leak is stopped." I turned to look at him. "Engineering Watch Supervisor. While operating the last valve, a spray of water was emitted from the valve stem. In this valve, pressure is on the top of the disk, so I opened the valve fully to stop the flow of water. The valve is fully open and the leak is stopped. However, I am contaminated as is the entire discharge station, the pumps behind me, and any deck that looks wet. Recommend a watch relief for AMSLL and the spill response team."

The EWS had been relaying everything to Maneuvering as I reported it. Immediately word went out "Spill at the discharge station. Spill at the discharge station. Muster the spill response team in Machinery Space Lower Level. Contaminated man in Machinery Space Lower Level. Muster the decontamination party in the Wardroom."

My participation as a contaminated man put us at both an advantage and a disadvantage. The good part is that, as the senior-most ELT onboard, I was in an ideal position to make sure no mistakes were made in the immediate spill response. I made sure that spill boundaries were properly established, gave detailed instructions to the EWS and the spill response team, and even cleaned up some of worst of the spill since I was already "contaminated." I then supervised myself being dressed in anti-contamination clothing (also called "anti-Cs"), in this case to keep me from contaminating the rest of the boat, and moved to a clean area to let the spill team in. After a few minutes, I received instructions to go forward to the decon area.

This is where we were at a disadvantage. My normal assignment with heavily-contaminated personnel was at the decon station. Since I was contaminated, we were short one ELT and our most junior man was taking my place for decon. Luckily, I could still help out. I climbed the ladder to AMSUL and headed forward. Starting in the tunnel, the deck was lined with yellow plastic to help contain any contamination. I followed the yellow brick road to the hatch just outside the storekeepers area. The hatch was lifted and latched; the person ahead of me lifted the chain for me and I descended the ladder. Behind me was an ELT, surveying my path to make sure I didn't contaminate the boat.

I descended into a world of yellow plastic. At the Doc's station, the deck and bulkheads were covered with taped yellow plastic. The yellow plastic continued through the wardroom, where a yellow sheet reached from floor to ceiling between me and the table, and down to the last stateroom, just before the officer's head. A yellow and magenta rope was strung across the doorway and, behind it, squatted Mackin and the Doc. Both were wearing anti-C gloves and Mackin held a geiger counter. I stopped, the ORSE member behind me a few paces. I turned to look at the Doc and Mackin and reported what had happened.

"I was operating primary plant valves at the discharge station when one of them started leaking. I received a moderate spray of water in my face and chest and a heavier spray on my arms and hands. I would consider my whole body to be potentially contaminated."

Mackin and the Doc looked at me. The Doc had a survey map with a human figure on it. He'd use this to record any results Mackin read off. Mackin said "OK, first you need to take off the anti-Cs. Remember, you're contaminated and the inside of the anti-Cs are contaminated, too. So, when you take them off, keep the inside part on the inside." I carefully removed the hood, leaving it hanging down my back by it's velcro attachment. In a real spill, you didn't want to pull it off because this could make it snap, spreading contamination. Next, I loosened the drawstring at my neck and started shrugging off the heavy, yellow canvas. I tried to minimize my contact with the material to minimize the chance to contaminate anything. When my arms were free, I started to roll up the coverall to further contain the "contamination", finally getting it completely off and dropping it into a plastic bag taped to the wall behind me. I stopped and Mackin surveyed me.

The drill monitor held up a card, telling Mackin what the meter was reading as he surveyed my right arm. Mackin turned to the Doc and told him I had high levels of contamination on my right arm which the Doc, in turn, relayed over the phones to Control and Maneuvering. Mackin completed the survey with no more hot spots, then had me remove my gloves and shoe covers. My "contaminated" shoes had been left at the discharge station along with my "contaminated" pants, shirt, and undershirt. This left me standing in my underpants. Following normal procedures, I had started to remove them, too, but was stopped by the ORSE team member. He was glad we knew this was the right thing to do, but apparently had no more desire than I to have me parading around the submarine naked. Probably the only time my mother's constant injunctions to "always wear clean underwear, just in case you're in an accident" ever bore fruit. Or, at least, fruit of the loom. In any event, I was on one side of the rope in my shorts with "contamination" on my right arm with Mackin and the Doc on the other, talking me through the decon. The first step, a simple wash with soap and warm water. To be truthful, I had had skin contamination on several occasions and, every time, this was sufficient to decontaminate me. This time, however, ORSE wanted to see more. So we went through a few iterations and then he started quizzing the Doc and Mackin about further decon. Mackin made a few errors, so I noted that I usually filled that role and offered up what our procedures called for. But, all in all, they both did a great job and I only had to involve myself a few times. We finished up, they tore down the yellow plastic, and I headed back aft, still in my skivvies, to get dressed and resume my watch. One drill down, two to go. For our section. Then two more sections to go.

The other two drills for our section were pretty straightforward. One involved only the electricians and the other was in the engineroom. In both cases, my only involvement was to log the periodic announcements in the comment section of my logs. And then we were done. We ate and, as the off-going watch constituted the casualty assistance team, we were required to stay in the Crew's Mess for the next drill set.

Lunch ended, the mess cranks cleaned up the messdecks, and the off-going watch section gathered to wait. Conversation was desultory; we talked to relieve the tension, but there was no use talking about anything of any importance since we were bound to be interrupted soon. The last drill set had given us our radiological drill; we still had some sort of major reactor controls drill and a ship's casualty coming. In the past, the reactor controls drill served primarily to cause us to scram out and put us into a delayed scram recovery while the ship's drill would undoubtedly be a fire of flooding casualty. We assumed there would be one major and one minor drill per drill set with another two or three less involved drills rounding things out.

We didn't wait long. Within five minutes of the drill team going aft I heard the control rods slide in and thump against the bottom of the reactor. This was the first time I'd actually heard the rods in a scram and I spent a second wondering if that was what it really was. Then the MC announcement "Reactor scram, reactor scram. Muster all off-watch reactor operators in Machinery Space Upper Level. Casualty Assistance Team lay to the engineering spaces."

One of the assembled CAT members said "Well, I guess that's us." We headed aft, the first person placing the tunnel doors on their open latch and the last shutting them.

As we were heading aft, the boat took about a 15 degree up-angle. This told us that we were looking at a long time until recovering from the scram. If we met certain conditions, we could start recovering the reactor immediately and, before too long, would be steaming again. Heading up meant that we'd have to run the diesel, something we wouldn't have to do in a fast recovery scenario. So someone had already decided this was going to take awhile. And, sure enough, before we all filed through the tunnel, another MC announcement came. "The cause of the reactor scram cannot be immediately determined. Scram recovery will be delayed. Rig ship for reduced electrical."

This was important for several reasons. First, the heat of the reactor heated water in the primary plant which, in turn, boiled water in the steam generators that turned the turbines. We could continue to spin the turbines, using up stored heat in the primary plant but, without the reactor to add heat, we'd just cool down the primary. Eventually it would cool down to boiling, at which point it would make no more steam. The more steam we used, the faster the primary would cool down and the less time we had. The cooldown stressed the primary, too, so we had to limit the cooldown rate and the lowest temperature we reached. To help in this, we used the main engines just enough to get to PD and we took the turbine generators off-line. This put all of the electrical load on the battery until we could get the diesel generator up and running. So, to conserve the battery, we rigged for reduced electrical. We HAD to run our main coolant pumps, some lube oil pumps, and some other vital electrical loads. Everything else, including air conditioning, some lighting, unnecessary pumps, and any other electrical load that wasn't absolutely necessary was shut down. Throughout the boat, temperatures started to rise, reaching 90 degrees everywhere within ten minutes and peaking out at over 140 in parts of the engineroom.

Each member of the CAT had his own assigned responsibility. Mine was to go to AMSLL and man the charging station, ready to add water to the reactor plant to compensate for the water shrinking as it cooled. I manned a headset, ran through the procedure with the EWS, and stood by to charge. On the other side of AMSLL, at the discharge station (miraculously recovered from the earlier spill drill) stood the discharge station watch. If I had to charge water due to cooldown, he'd have to discharge the same amount as we heated back up. I stood there, a copy of the procedures open next to me, watching the pressurizer water level gauge and waiting for an order to charge.

Instead, the order came down to charge as necessary to maintain pressurizer water level in a given band. If it dropped too low, I'd inform Maneuvering I was about to charge, give them a second to stop me, and then go ahead and add water. When I reached the top of the given band, I'd stop and again inform Maneuvering. Pressurizer level dropped rapidly at first and then, as electrical and steam loads were secured, more slowly. This meant people were doing their jobs well and quickly. With luck we might not have to charge.

Luck wasn't with us on this one, though. To reach PD we had to run the mains a little more than planned, cooling down the reactor plant and dropping pressurizer level below the setpoint. I informed the EWS and passed the word that I was going to start charging. One valve operation and two switches lined us up to add water to the primary, started the charging booster pump, and the charging pump. A few minutes later, I stopped the pumps, closed the isolation valve, and reported to Maneuvering again. Fifteen minutes later I repeated these actions. And, after that, I heard the MC announcement "Prepare to snorkel!" and felt the sudden drop in pressure as the diesel started up.

The rest of the CAT and watch section had it considerably harder. In AMSUL, sweating electronic technicians were methodically going through all of their trouble-shooting procedures, trying to find the cause of the reactor scram. Nothing they tried would convince the drill monitor to acknowledge that they had found the cause of the scram, so they kept at it. In the engineroom, some mechanics were jacking over the port turbine generator by hand, sweating as I had done a few years earlier. Others were checking the rig for reduced electrical because we were still drawing more amps than the diesel could supply, draining our battery slowly but surely. This is why the initial cooldown rate was so good; the EO picked up a lot of load on the battery, saving heat in the primary but taking more out of the battery than was desired. With luck, we'd be able to get the electrical loads down to less than the diesel put out so we could start a battery charge. Without it, we might have to look at a more severe cutback in electrical power use. But, at least we made it PD and the diesel started up the first time. Sometimes it took several tries to get it running, each one sucking more life from the battery. The downside to having a reactor was that we weren't designed to run without it. Once it was gone, if we couldn't get it back quickly, we had only a small battery and diesel to take care of us. All in all, though, I'd rather go to sea on a nuke boat than on a diesel-electric submarine. Right now, though, it was a moot point. We were on a nuke boat with the reactor down and we were all sweating our asses off.

The next drill came with the reactor down. This surprised the hell out of all of us. Normally you didn't run drills simultaneously. On the other hand, this way was a lot more realistic. All I know is that, about 45 minutes into the scram, we had a low pressure alarm at the discharge of the running main lube oil pump. This got our attention. One of our nightmare scenarios was a main lube oil fire because they were a bitch to put out (or to simulate putting out) and they were dangerous. And the way most drills led into a lube oil fire was usually through a low pressure alarm. The watchstander would go to the lube oil bay, see a spray of oil onto an electrical panel, and everything would simulate bursting into flame. From there, things got very hot and messy. The last thing we wanted was to have to fight a lube oil fire during a delayed scram recovery.

Luckily, this was more of a feint on the part of the drill team. The ERLL watch and just about every other off-duty mechanic rushed to the scene, only to find a perfectly-running system. The scenario was a malfunctioning pressure switch, probably either to see if we'd freak out and over-react. I guess we did all right. And, five minutes later, word was passed that the cause of the scram had been found and corrected. Five minutes after that, we started the reactor startup and, within another hour, we were securing from reduced electrical and back deep. The discharge station secured discharge, we cleaned up, and headed forward. The remaining drill didn't require the CAT, so we secured and went to eat dinner.

For the third drill set, as an on-coming watchstander, I was assigned to the Backup Response Team. The CAT was first to the scene, wearing normal clothes and carrying whatever equipment they could bring to the scene. The BRT was the cavalry. We took a few minutes more to dress out in appropriate clothing and showed up bringing the rest of the equipment. If the CAT couldn't get things under control, the BRT was the best and last we could throw at a casualty. If the BRT couldn't handle it, things were pretty serious. Normally we'd probably be in the rack and it could take several minutes to muster and dress everyone. However, this being ORSE, we were "pre-staged" in the torpedo room, out of sight of the ORSE board, and already dressed out in our flame-resistant coveralls with our OBAs on and everything else ready to go. If we had a flooding drill, we'd strip off the fire-fighting ensemble quickly and respond to the flooding. For a fire, we'd wait a fashionable amount of time (so it didn't seem as though we were pre-staged) and would then respond to the fire, dragging fire hoses, extinguishers, and every other piece of damage control gear with us that might help out. For a major steam leak, we'd put on silver steam suits and respond and, for anything else, we'd show up in normal uniforms with appropriate gear. As before, we sat and idly chatted, waiting to be called.

This time we waited almost three hours. First there was a relatively easy electrical drill, then came a chloride casualty. I had to strip off the fire-fighting gear to respond for that, but it ran about like our real chloride casualty two months earlier. We sailed through it, returned forward and, no sooner had I donned my fire-fighting gear again, did we hear the gongs of the General Alarm and the announcement "Steam leak in the Machinery Space. Steam leak in the Machinery Space." We tensed. Two minutes later, another announcement. "There is an unisolable leak from the port main steam header in the Machinery Space. Muster the Backup Response Team in the Reactor Compartment Tunnel." We got our gear and headed aft.

In any potentially serious casualty such as this one all watertight doors and ventilation ducts were shut immediately. The premise was that by so doing we would confine the fire or flooding to a single compartment, giving the rest of the boat a better chance of survival. Only necessary people who were adequately dressed were sent into the affected compartment. In this case, for a steam leak that could not be isolated by shutting the main steam stops, procedure called for the watchstander to abandon his watch station if at all possible. In a drill, a drill team member would take over the watch to make sure nothing went wrong. In real life, a steam leak was nothing to trifle with; the steam would kill the watchstander pretty quickly. Either way, the watchstation would be unmanned. One way, we'd be short-handed, too. It was assumed that the AMSLL watch would be trapped in lower level by the steam. His actions were to dive into the bilge and stay there until the casualty was over. If possible, he was to grab an EAB and plug it in, time permitting. The theory was that the steam would condense in the cooler, lower level bilges, hopefully leaving some air for the watchstander to breathe and not boiling him alive. I should point out, too, that this steam was not the white fluffy stuff coming out of a kettle. Rather, it was a very hot, invisible gas as hot as an oven that could strip the flesh from a man's bones in seconds and could displace all of the air in minutes, leaving nothing to breathe except steam. Putting the watch in the bilge with an EAB was better than nothing, but a real steam leak in the AMS was the one scenario that worried me the most, if only because of my relative helplessness.

We mustered in the tunnel, the watchsection EWS manning the phones and taking charge of the BRT. As on the CAT, we each had our assignments. Mine was to put on a steam suit and enter the space as soon as we could see steam condensing. This would mean that temperatures had dropped to less than boiling in AMSUL. I started putting on the steam suit.

The steam suit was one of those big, bulky silver things with an aluminized faceplate and rubber hose coming out of the headpiece that made me look like a poorly-done alien in a cheap movie from the 1950s. It was one size fits all, so I was a better choice than one of the really small guys. We wanted to send a mechanic into the space because a steam leak is fundamentally a mechanical problem. An AMSLL watchstander was important, too, because we had to drain the steam generator feeding the leak in order to stop it. This was done at the steam generator blowdown station in AMSLL. Best to have someone familiar with the space and the valves.

The scenario ran like this. Somehow or other, a steam leak was detected in the AMS. The first action is to shut the nearest isolation valve, in this case the main steam stop. If this doesn't stop the leak, it's unisolable and there's nothing to keep it from filling the space with steam. The generators held several hundred gallons of water, all of it at over 400 degrees. We had to drain this water out of the steam generator before it all flashed to steam. Hence, my imitation of a cheap alien. Unfortunately, the steam suit was not ergonomically designed. I suppose keeping me alive was an important ergonomic point, but it was hard to work in. I had very little range of motion, no peripheral vision, couldn't see my feet, and was about twice my normal size. For breathing, I was dependent on an EAB line, but at least it plugged directly into the hood so I didn't have to suck rubber. The suit was so clumsy that a drill monitor was assigned just to watch me and to keep me from falling down a ladder or hatch.

The decision was made to send me into the space before the steam started to condense. The rest of the BRT backed out of the tunnel and I (and my safety monitor) opened the after tunnel door. I ducked and stepped up and, a few minutes later, made it onto the AMSUL platform. Turning awkwardly, I shut the tunnel door, then turned again and started down the ladder, taking excruciating care to not fall. I made it to the bottom of the ladder, turned to the right just past Instrument Alley, and headed down the ladder to AMSLL. At the bottom of the ladder I did a quick search and found the watchstander crouched in the bilge behind the feed station. He had been allowed to live by the drill team and was wearing his EAB with a set of headphones on. I could see him talking, presumably announcing that I had entered AMSLL. I waved at him, then headed for the blowdown station.

It took some more negotiating to reach the blowdown station, but I made it in a reasonable amount of time. It was impossible to conduct normal voice communications; the steam suit prohibited putting on a headset or using a handset and, in any case, the noise of the air rushing into the hood would have drowned out anything that was said. But this was known. I heard a very slow, loud, and distinct MC announcement "A person from the Backup Response Team has entered the Machinery Space and manned the blowdown station. Blowdown station, Maneuvering, prepare to drain the port steam generator." The assumption in a case like this was that I would be able to competently carry out the orders in a reasonable amount of time, with Maneuvering monitoring what instruments they could to verify my progress. In this case they didn't have valve indications, so all they could do would be to make sure the right steam generator level started to drop.

From there, Maneuvering walked me through the entire procedure valve by valve. It was just like any other blowdown except that none of the orders were repeated back. That sped things up, but the steam suit hampered me enough to more than compensate. We lined up all the valves, did a token blowdown (just enough to show a drop in water level), and Maneuvering announced the successful draining of the port steam generator. A few minutes later we secured from the drill, I took off the damned steam suit, and headed forward. We secured from ORSE drills at 10:30 and called it a day. The at-sea portion of our ORSE was over. We turned and headed back to port. For my part, I felt I had done neither particularly well nor poorly. In general, I supposed I did more right than wrong, but others had done more and had worked harder. I was just glad to have finished my final ORSE drill set. All that remained was the paperwork audit. And, for that, I needed a full night's sleep.

I woke at 5, showered quickly, ate, and went to my lab to wait for the inevitable summons to the Wardroom. It came at 6:15. Or, rather, at 0615.

The Wardroom had been taken over by the ORSE board. The table was filled with paperwork, the seats filled with people. At the near end of the table was the CRA, a stack of our logs, an ORSE member, and the sole empty seat. My seat. I was still in the process of lowering myself into the chair when the questions started. "Petty Officer Karam, what can you tell us about this set of logs?" I looked at them, ordinary reactor water chemistry logs from an in-port period.

"I'm not sure what you mean, Sir. These are shutdown logs. Doesn't look like much happened and water chemistry was in spec."

"But here," he said, pulling out some other logs "your stores records show receipt of a hydrogen meter. Why isn't this logged in your comments section and the receipt surveys performed?"

"It was a new meter, Sir. Since it hadn't been previously used, it was uncontaminated and no surveys were required. That's why we didn't log it in."

"But isn't it part of your analytical equipment?"

"Yes, Sir. I guess I didn't realize we had to log receipt of uncontaminated analytical gear."

He wrote something down on his clipboard and went on to the next earth-shattering item. "OK, what about this, Petty Officer Karam? It looks here as though, when you graphed primary water chemistry, you plotted a point incorrectly. See here, where the logs give a pH that's about 0.1 lower than what you've plotted? Why didn't you correct that?"

"Hmmm. You're right. We must have missed that. We'll correct that mistake right away. At least the sample was in spec."

And on and on for almost two hours. One nit-picking thing after another, none of them of any real importance. They were looking for something serious; evidence of falsifying records, missing samples, out-of-spec chemistry, misinterpretations of chemistry trends, procedural violations, and the like. What they found was a handful of minor discrepancies that added up to normal, honest mistakes that had been missed during log reviews. My guess would be that, if they had found no mistakes whatsoever, they would have felt that suspicious, evidence no doubt of tampering with the logs or falsifying them after the fact. From my perspective, I was happy. I could live with minor problems like not logging in receipt of a clean piece of equipment. I could not live with anything that suggested we didn't know how to do things safely, legally, and in compliance with the procedures and specifications. If this was the best they could come up with, we were on our way to a good grade in Chemistry and Radiological Controls.

Finally, the records review was over. In all, we'd taken about ten legitimate comments and a few others that could be argued. All minor. Just after leaving the Wardroom, we set the Maneuvering Watch again and pulled into port. This time, I was again the first person topside and I actually took a few minutes to sightsee while taking swipes. I hadn't paid much attention before, concentrating on doing a good job and assuming I was being watched. This time, I took in the sights and did a pretty cursory survey. We were already in the shipping channel, steaming towards the tug that would deliver the harbor pilot and take us in. This part of Hawaii, coming into Pearl Harbor, seemed pretty well-developed with buildings and roads down to the water and very little vegetation. Looking beyond the Navy base, I could see some of the lush vegetation I expected, but surprisingly little. Behind the base, I could see the terrain start to rise, but much was hidden by clouds and haze. But I really didn't care much. I was outside, feeling the breeze against my face and hearing the water against the side of the hull. I was smelling something other than submarine smell, there were things more than 30 feet in the distance, and I was seeing colors other than white, gray, black, or red. It was a wonderful treat for all my senses, more so because, this time, I actually got to leave the boat.

We tied up for the first time in ten weeks and the coners were gone almost before the brow came down. The nukes, of course, still had a few hours' of work to be done. Bring on shore power, shutdown the engineroom, shutdown the reactor plant, and so forth. This was one of the joys of being a nuke; like unwanted party guests we were always the first to show up and the last to leave. At least I wasn't in the duty section – they'd get to spend their first night in port onboard the boat standing watch.

Forward, the ORSE paperwork audit continued. A few more junior guys were assigned to the ORSE board, running log packages and other paperwork to them on demand. This part of the ORSE lasted until dinner, at which time the board left the boat and met to discuss their findings. These would be presented to the CO, XO, and Eng the next day with opportunity given to allow us to protest any findings we felt unwarranted. We'd correct what we could during their deliberations so that, when these findings were noted the Eng could respond that the problem had already been taken care of, and the rest we'd just take our lumps on. But I just didn't care.

By the time we were able to leave, mail had actually been delivered to the boat. The yeomen locked themselves into Control with the mailbags and forbade entry to anyone while they sorted mail. Since the Nuke Lab was the first space aft of Control, I hung out there, waiting for them to finish. As soon as they were done, I scooted into Control to pick up the mail for my division and took it back to the lab. News of this sort spread by telepathy or something similar. In the two minutes I was gone, the lab had filled with my division. I handed out the mail to everyone and, with the exception of the duty ELT, they vanished. As did I. I packed my civilian clothes into my backpack, grabbed my dirty laundry, and headed for the barracks to check into a room. In spite of the recent chances to sleep, I was still dead tired, grimy, and out of touch with the world. I desperately wanted to get away from the boat, make some phone calls, read mail, and just relax.

CHAPTER 24

Pearl

I HAD READ AND HEARD A LOT ABOUT PEARL HARBOR and Hawaii from fellow sailors, tourists, geology texts, Michener's book, and any number of other sources. Although I am not a big fan of the tropics, I was really looking forward to seeing what I could. Right now, though, I didn't care a bit about any of that. I made a beeline for the barracks office to get a room assignment. Submariners are lucky in this; we got to stay in barracks in whichever ports we pulled into and, if barracks weren't available, we'd stay in hotels. Skimmers just had too many people – when they pulled into port, even their home port, they still lived onboard the ship. No respite at all unless they wanted to pick up the tab themselves. The barracks were usually just like college dormitories for quasi-adults, but they were a lot better than staying on the boat. And, at least, we could make an attempt to choose our roommates.

It was about a ten-minute walk to the barracks. The walk was great. Just being ashore was great – I could have been run down by a car and loved it, just by virtue of having the opportunity to be ashore to get hit. I got all checked in at the admin desk and headed for my room. Once there, I did my normal first-day-in-an-exotic-foreign-port routine. First, I took a long, hot shower, luxuriating in the sensation of high-pressure water with no time limits. I spent nearly half an hour just standing under the water, feeling it running over me and washing away over two months of accumulated grime and stink. After that, laundry and mail. I bought a small detergent box in the laundry room, grabbed a washer, and started my first load. While that was running, I sat on the washer and started reading my mail. First, the letters from my mother, father, and sister. Next, letters from friends and relatives. After that, a quick look at the magazines and newspapers, just to get a taste of what was waiting, and then on to bills. My first deployment, I'd written checks that I left with a cousin to mail on specific dates to pay bills. He made all the payments, but the Navy forgot to pay me, so while we were at sea, checks started bouncing. It took months to straighten out and my credit didn't recover until a few years after my discharge. So I looked at my bills to make sure it hadn't happened again. The Navy was quick to reclaim money we were overpaid and glacially slow to pay us money due so, if there had been a mistake, I wanted to jump on it right away. This time, good luck. They'd passed up an opportunity to mess with me. Relieved, I found an empty drier, started a second load of laundry in my washer, and went back to my mail.

Three hours later I was clean, had fresh laundry, had caught up with most of the mail, and (thanks to a subscription to the Washington Post National Weekly Edition), was pretty well caught up with world and national events, too. As always, it was gratifying to find out that the world hadn't fallen apart due to my temporary lack of participation. I'd also managed to call both parents, my sister, and my best friends, talking to each of them for ten or fifteen minutes, catching up on events and letting them know we hadn't run into any trouble. Or, at least, not into any trouble that couldn't be recovered from. I'd call again before we left, to talk a little more and to hear the voices I really cared about; this time was just a "Yes, I'm back, alive, and unhurt, and so are you" call. But important to everyone.

Next on the list was real food. Or, at least, a reasonable facsimile thereof. I headed for the base McDonalds. I know it's not gourmet, but also wasn't Navy cooking, and even my heartburn would be a nice change from the predictable stomach upset due to boat food. And, after McDonalds, I headed back to the barracks, stopping on the way for a bag of chips and some beer. I had no intention of getting drunk and, in any event, was too tired to really do so, but it had been a long time between beers and I was ready to sit down, relax, have a beer, and turn the TV on. In short, I was more than ready to vegetate. I had two beers and was asleep by 8:30.

I didn't have duty until our third day in port, so I was able to sleep in the next morning, not waking until around 9. I woke up groggy, but another long shower and a few cups of coffee with breakfast took care of that. My roommate had shown up sometime while I was sleeping; we discussed a game plan over breakfast. We decided to see some of the sights around the Navy base first, then to see what we could on the island. We'd be there for a week, so we had the luxury of taking a few days to rest up and figure out what we really wanted to do. One of the guys in my division had rented a car; he was staying in a hotel in Honolulu, but offered to provide some transportation if we wanted. On the other hand, after a few WestPac deployments, we were all pretty good at figuring out local mass transit, and here, everything was in English.

Our first stop was to gather some information on base. Based on that, we decided we really wanted to visit the Arizona Memorial, the Bowfin Memorial, walk down Tin Can Alley, visit Ford's Island, and drive around the island a bit. We also decided to be somewhat typical tourists and go to a luau later in the week, just for the experience.

Rather than go into exhaustive detail about each of these, it's probably best just to say that our stay was as it should have been; a chance to rest, relax, and get back in touch with the world after so much time locked up, making holes in the water. We had a ship's picnic one day, spent some time on the beach, saw some of the sights, made a lot of phone calls, shopped, and stood our duty days.

I will say that I was much more impressed and moved by the Arizona Memorial than I had ever expected. Like the Vietnam Veteran's Memorial in DC, the power of the memorial was as much in what it represented as in the simplicity of design. The elegance of the memorial itself was uplifting, but there was no disguising the somber nature of what it memorialized. I spent a lot of time reflecting on the sailors who were still onboard her, profoundly grateful that neither I nor any friends of mine had suffered a similar fate. And, hopefully, never would.

In counterpoint to the Arizona Memorial was the Bowfin Museum. The Bowfin, a WWII diesel-electric boat, had been restored and placed on display as a museum. Walking through the Bowfin and lingering among the displays reminded me of what I had been fortunate enough to have missed. The *Plunger* was not roomy, but alongside the Bowfin, it seemed palatial and luxuriously appointed. I tried to imagine what her crews, my predecessors, had gone through. Depth charging, crash dives, evasion, sinking enemy ships, air foul with diesel fumes, and all the other risks and hardships of war. We had our moments, but comparatively speaking, we were pampered and safe. Some aspects of submarining haven't changed much in the past 50 years, but many have. I was thankful that I had not had to go to war and I felt a tremendous sense of respect for those who'd fought in this vessel, and all the others like her.

The other thing during our visit that particularly impressed me was the Naval base itself. I do not know if my shipmates were similarly affected, but to me, there seemed an aura about Pearl Harbor that was impossible to dispel. This was the heart and the home of the Pacific Fleet, where our orders came from, where our high commanders lived. The President, of course was our commander-in-chief and the Chief of Naval Operations lived in DC, but, for all practical purposes, this is where our daily, monthly, and yearly operations were planned and controlled. And not just us, but the whole of the Pacific Fleet. The history of Pearl Harbor just added to this feeling, as did walking along Battleship Row and Tin Can Alley, where the destroyers tied up when in port. I suppose the feeling might have been oppressive under some circumstances, but I was out in the fresh air, rested, and just didn't care about much else.

I also found out during our stay in Pearl that we Nukes owed the CO a big thanks. It turns out he had the option of pulling into Maui, the CO's preference. Maui would have been more relaxing than Pearl, but they had no shore power available. That would have forced us to tie up in the harbor with reactor critical so we could turn the turbine generators and make our own electrical power. And that would have required the nukes to stand steaming watches. The CO decided that, after an ORSE, he wasn't about to put us through that, so he put us first. We tied up in Pearl in four-section duty (one duty day out of every four) instead of being port-and-starboard (standing 12 hours of watch each day, every other day) in Maui. I discovered this only accidentally, and I doubt that many other nukes realized it at all.

I stood EDPO on my sole duty day in Pearl. There were enough watch-standers that the EDPOs (the shut-down equivalents of EWS) could go seven section for duty. My duty day was right in the middle of the in-port period, so I only got three days at a time away from the boat, but I could live with that. We were not in a maintenance mode, we were just trying to fix enough to get us back home safely. So the duty day went by pretty smoothly with a lot of time spent topside, drinking in the sun, sights, and smells of shore. I still had to make the 3 AM tour of the engineering spaces (supervisory tours were required every three hours, alternating between the EDO and EDPO and there was no way you'd find an officer waking up in the middle of the night), but that took only 15 minutes or so and I dropped back off to sleep. I spent most of the day catching up on my magazine and newspaper reading in Nucleonics since there were no evolutions taking place aside from normal duty day routine. The oncoming duty section relieved us at 0800 and I was gone by 0815 to continue R&R.

We left Pearl after a week. I still was no fan of the tropics, but I would have enjoyed a week ashore just about anywhere. I had enjoyed myself, I was rested, and I was ready to get back to San Diego. This time I was not in the startup section, so I checked out of the barracks in the morning, showed up at 0730 for quarters, and we pulled out at noon on the last leg of our final spec op.

CHAPTER 25

The Trip Home - Trim Party

We untied from the pier precisely at noon, cast off the tug as soon as we could, then submerged and headed home. Six days to San Diego. Then, two weeks until our home-port change. Once in Mare Island, I had less than six months left in the Navy. I had been counting the days left for over four years already; now I was down to 170 days to go. And after that, college, grad school, hopefully a research and teaching position somewhere, and, I sincerely hoped, someone else to care about and share life with.

It was time to stand another proficiency watch as EWS, so I headed aft after lunch the day after we pulled out. Arriving in the Engineroom, I happened to look up and saw Tim, a 20 year-old guy who'd joined us in Pearl. Looking up at Tim was a bit unusual since he was over a foot shorter than I am. This time, however, he was taped to the underside of the handwheel of one of the large steam valves, looking straight down about seven feet to the deck. His expression was somewhere between concerned and bemused; it looked like he'd been up there long enough to realize the tape was strong enough to hold him, but not yet long enough to feel comfortable. Nobody else was around. "Hi, Tim. How's it going?"

"Uh, not bad, I guess."

"Well, that's good. Working on your quals? When do you think you'll be ready to start standing watch?"

"I'm kind of working on ERLL. That's sort of what got me up here. I missed a question they thought was too easy. I'm supposed to be thinking about it."

"OK. Well, good luck. You ought to be able to finish the checkout by the end of the watch." I went on back and continued my pre-watch tour. I managed to not find the on-watch ERS or ERUL, so I didn't have to ask about how Tim ended up taped to the valve and, by the time I relieved the watch, he was down. I supposed he'd been taken down since I hadn't heard any thumps and there was no blood on the deck.

About an hour into the watch, I saw about 10 people in ERUL, heading back towards Shaft Alley, the furthest aft you can go. A few seconds later,

I heard the valves on the after trim tank open. As soon as they opened, the people standing in Shaft Alley headed forward. A few minutes later, we had a slight down-angle and I heard the after trim tank isolation valves open again.

This time, over a dozen people came rushing aft, again cramming into Shaft Alley. By the time they were all there, we had about a ten degree up-angle. Again, when the trim tank valves opened, they rushed forward again. This time, we wound up at about 13 degrees down-angle and reached 15 degrees up when they showed up in Shaft Alley again.

What was happening was a trim party. Ten people in shaft alley puts about 2000 pounds of extra weight as far aft in the boat as you can get. To balance the sub, the COW had to shift 2000 pounds of water to the forward trim tank. As soon as the valves opened, the people in Shaft Alley knew that the water was moving, but they could move faster. Rushing to the Bow Compartment and picking up a few more people, we were suddenly about 4500 pounds heavy forward, pushing the bow down, and forcing the COW to move water aft again. And it continued, each time forcing the COW to move more water and each time putting us at a greater angle.

After 15 minutes of this, we had nearly 30 people running back and forth, laughing and joking. The boat was going through angles up to about 35 degrees up and down, we were taking nearly 400 foot depth excursions, and the COW and Dive were fighting to keep us in any semblance of trim and on depth. Finally, the CO came over the loudspeaker as everyone was crowded into Shaft Alley again. "Attention all hands. I'd like to remind you that trim parties are strictly unauthorized. All off-watch personnel are to return to their racks immediately." The trim tank valves opened again. Everyone laughed, someone said "Well, I guess we just need to follow orders, don't we?" and everyone rushed forward along with the water to obey the captain.

The rest of the trip home was pretty uneventful. We were through with our ORSE, we were done keeping the world safe for democracy, and the Mighty *Plunger* was nearly done, period. The CO and Eng decided to not run any drills on us, letting us rest, so we had six days to just do our jobs. If every underway was like this one, I might have been tempted to stay in the Navy, but I knew this was a rare treat.

I stood AMSLL on the trip home, to let Louis stand underway ELT for a break. We'd left our riders at Pearl, so we had plenty of rack space and I kept my own rack. Most of my off-watch time was spent polishing our slide brief with the photo officer and working on the program for our upcoming decommissioning ceremony. On-watch, I was kept moderately busy with our steam generator water chemistry, but we weren't moving with any-where the urgency of our transit west, so even this wasn't too bad. I spent much of my time thinking about post-Navy plans; what college I'd go to, what I wanted to study, and how I'd pay for it. Without the pressure of the past few months and with no training or drills to cut into our sleep time, it was a surprisingly enjoyable underway.

Two nights before pulling in the midnight movie was exceptionally well-attended. The married guys were starting to think about seeing their families again, wondering what they'd find when they met their children and wives again. The single guys were looking forward to seeing their girlfriends, getting their cars back, getting drunk, or some combination of the above. In short, we had "channel fever." Our last night out was much the same. Tempers started to flare a little bit as we all anticipated returning home after over two months with nothing more than a few phone calls and letters for contact with those we cared about. Even I was having trouble sleeping, unusual for me.

We surfaced at 6 AM. The bridge crew ascended the sail and, as we approached land, the topside detail lined up outside of Nucleonics, ready to go topside for line-handling. They'd be the ones to take us alongside the tug and tie us up to the pier. As Maneuvering Watch ELT, I was to be the first up, to make sure there was no radioactive contamination topside before anyone else went up. I found a life vest, a harness and safety line, and put on my deck shoes, got my gear (a clipboard with a map of the boat and a bunch of smear wipes), and waited in the Nuke Lab. At 10:30, the order came down to open the weapons shipping hatch and go topside.

I was up the ladder almost before the hatch was secured on its latch with the COB right behind me. Nobody could be topside without an escort and, as the senior enlisted man onboard, the COB allowed himself the privilege of walking with my beneath the California sun. As always, I stepped onto the after deck and stopped for a moment, taking in the view. Looking for landmarks, I saw the Point Loma lighthouse, the rocky bluffs falling to the sea, North Island, and the ships and subs tied up at the sub base. Pleasure craft filled the harbor, nimbly weaving around the commercial and warships entering and leaving port. The air was dry and warm and the sun felt perfect. I drank it in for a minute, every sense vying for attention, before remembering my job. Looking ahead of us, I could see the tug waiting for us a mile or so in the distance. I took a dozen or so wipes, dashed down to my lab, and counted them. No contamination, of course, so I gave the line handlers permission to go topside.

Five minutes later, I was topside again, camera in hand to document our last return to home port. We were just taking on the lines from the tug, making it fast to the cleats on our deck while the harbor pilot stepped from the upper platform onto our fairwater plane. We continued steaming down the channel and, as we turned the last corner, we could see our tender with a big sign welcoming us home. On the pier was a crowd, the families, friends, and other important people of many of us onboard. As we turned to come up to the pier, we could hear shouts and see wives, girlfriends, and children searching the topside crew for their own sailor. For our part, everyone topside was doing the same, looking for anyone they knew and waving if they saw someone. We finally tied up to the pier and the brow was lowered onto the top of the boat, connecting us to the pier.

If we'd been coming back from a WestPac deployment, we'd not have been allowed to leave until Customs had visited. This time, however, we hadn't stopped in any non-US territories (and Soviet waters didn't count for Customs), so we could leave right away. As soon as the brow was down, most of the Coners rushed topside and across to the pier, searching, hugging, kissing. I was right behind them, taking pictures of men holding sons and daughters, kissing wives, and simply looking at their loved ones. Over the next week, I'd develop and print them, giving copies to the people in them. Right now, as always, I was moved nearly to tears by the sight of so many who were so happy and so fortunate to be part of these reunions. The Engineer, holding his son, born while we were dodging Soviet ASW forces and seeing him now for the first time. The photo officer, holding his daughter in the air while both smiled ecstatically. Lumpy, trying to hold his entire family at once. The Sonar Chief, squatting down and re-introducing himself to his two-year-old daughter. And everyone else, except, of course, for the nukes on watch.

I finished taking pictures and returned my attention to work. Shore power cables were still being lowered by crane while the phone, water, and waste connections were being secured to the hull connections. I went back to my lab, took off my topside gear, changed shoes, and hurried back to AMSLL. There, Louis gave me an aggravated look. "Nice of you to show up, Andy. We're getting ready to feed the generators for hot standby." I apologized for tarrying upstairs and asked where we were. Mackin had already sampled both steam generators, Brian was on the feed station, and Louis had the watch. Nobody really liked measuring and mixing chemicals, so I calculated the chem add, ran it to Maneuvering for approval, and returned to AMSLL to mix them up. This was another case for creative chemistry. The chem add I'd had approved would take us to near the bottom of our specification band, but not near enough for me. I knew that the chemical concentrations would rise steadily for the first week back and I also knew that we had a large margin of error below the low spec. So, while I calculated a chem add that would leave us low in the band, but with a comfortable margin of error, I mixed a chem add that would take us to exactly the bottom of the band. If we ended up out of spec low after feeding generators, we'd log something at the low end, knowing it'd come back pretty quickly. By doing this, we might be able to make it until the next working day before having to blow down, rather than forcing the duty section to do a blowdown at midnight or later. This was also something that

I never explicitly mentioned to anyone; everyone in my division suspected I calculated adds this way, just as I suspected that everyone else did, too. But none of us ever admitted as much to anyone else, just so we'd never know for sure. That degree of doubt, we felt, would protect the others from complicity if the short chem add was ever discovered.

In any event, while shore power was connected, the engineroom was being shut down. First, the mains and, after we lined up shore power, the turbine generators. As this was happening, we were adding chemicals and feeding the generators to hot standby, adding water to raise water level to just below the steam dryers to help protect the steam generators from corrosion and to give us water for the next startup. With the generators filled and the engineroom shut down, the main steam stops were closed, the feed pump secured, and the engineering duty section relieved the engineering watch section. The off-watch nukes scrambled off the boat to a pier deserted except for their families, patiently waiting for their fathers, husbands, and lovers. We were all home now.

CHAPTER 26

Epilogue

ONE OF THE BETTER SUMMARIES I have read about what it's like to be on a submarine is also one of the funniest. I was given a copy that was obviously copied from a copy and I am afraid that the original was probably written by the great wit, Anon Y. Mous and modified by many intermediaries (myself included). It's worth including here.

How to Simulate Submarine Life at Home

1. Surround yourself with people that you don't like.
2. Close all windows and doors tightly, shut all curtains, and seal any openings to the outside world.
3. Unplug all radios and televisions to completely cut yourself off from the news, football games, Saturday Night Live, the Muppet Show, and any other recent news or entertainment.
4. Monitor all operating household appliances hourly. If an appliance is not in use, log as "secured".
5. Do not flush toilets for the first two days to simulate the smell of blowing sanitary tanks and venting inboard, then flush daily.
6. Wear only approved coveralls or Navy uniform.
7. Have blind barber cut hair periodically with lawn shears.
8. Live on an 18 hour day (as opposed to a 24 hour day) to maximize body confusion.
9. Listen to the same cassette repeatedly until it becomes intolerable. At this point play one that is merely nauseating.
10. Set very loud alarm to go off just as sleep hits. For variety have optional settings such as "Man battle stations", "Fire", "Flooding in the Basement", and so on.
11. Prepare food with a blindfold to simulate real submarine cooking. Remove blindfold and attempt to feed to dog. Break out peanut butter, tuna, or other smuggled food supplies and a vitamin.
12. Cut bed in half and enclose all but one side using a small casket for reference size. When not in bed, make up blankets properly in case anyone who cares passes by and can see in the dark.

13. Periodically, for excitement, open the main power breaker and run around the house yelling "Reactor Scram!" until sweating profusely. When finished, restore power and announce that the scram drill is over.

14. Purchase a snorkel and mask and periodically wear them, pretending to be in a smoke-filled room with no way out. For variety, hook up and pressurize a garden hose.

15. To prepare for any eventuality, constantly study wiring diagrams and operating instruction for various household appliances (stove, toaster, refrigerator, can opener, etc.) At specified intervals (weekly, monthly, etc.) tear an item apart in case it was going to break and reassemble.

16. Paint everything navy gray (no substitutes), off-white, or black.

17. To ensure a clean and happy environment, every Friday set the alarm on loud for a short but hated drill sound and get up, armed with only a bucket, sponge, and green scrub pad to clean one spot repeatedly, even if already spotless. Prepare discrepancy list when finished.

18. Daily, after normal programming hours, plug in TV and watch one movie. Ensure that the movie:

Is at least five years old

Is bad enough to require a seat belt in order to watch in its entirety

Has been seen often by all present.

19. As no doctor will be available, stockpile bandaids, aspirin, and actifed. These have been shown to cure everything. Practice surgery, dentistry, or other surgical procedures on pets as required. Document all procedures performed.

20. When commencing this simulation, lock out family, friends, and anything of any meaning. Tests will run at least two months.

We returned to San Diego after nearly three months away, ten weeks of which were spent on our last spec op. Less than one week after our return we held the decommissioning ceremony for the *Plunger*, duly reported in the San Diego and the Sub Base newspapers. About two weeks after our return, we put out to sea for the last time, headed north to the Mare Island Naval Shipyard, where the *Plunger* would go into drydock to be dismantled. Ironically, this drydock was only a few hundred feet from the site where *Plunger* had been built 28 years earlier.

The time between returning home and moving was frantic. As an enlisted man with less than six months left in the Navy I was not entitled to have the Navy pay for moving my belongings to Vallejo. I also had to ride the boat up, by the luck of the draw. This left me about a week to load as much as I could into the boat, persuade one friend to drive my car north for me, and persuade another friend to stick the rest of my things in with his family's.

On the other hand, I had it better than the married guys. When we found out how little time we had until our home port change we were at sea with no way to communicate with home. Many of the married crew asked

"How are we supposed to find a place to live, arrange for movers, and do everything else we need to do?" The response, "Your wives will manage." Some wives did manage quite well, others didn't manage at all. There were a number of guys who ended up separated from their families for weeks or months because of this, flying from San Francisco to San Diego every few weeks to visit wives and children. Another complicating factor in this was that all crew members were absolutely required to be present for the decommissioning ceremony, which was right in the middle of the little time available for planning this move. No allowance seemed to have been made for families in all of this, the Navy apparently assuming that Navy families were as subject to orders as the sailors themselves. So I was doubly upset. Angry that I was forced to move with no assistance from the Navy and angry that my married division members and friends were unable to offer more than sympathy to their wives and families during this short-notice upheaval.

The trip to Mare Island was mercifully short. Taking only the bare minimum crew with us, we were standing watches "port and starboard" (on watch for six hours and off for six) for the three day trip. I was underway ELT again, as well as helping round out the Engineering watchbill. Of this trip, my fondest memory is that of being called to the bridge with my camera. I ascended the ladder and asked what was up. We were getting ready to pass beneath the Golden Gate, the CO told me, and he thought I'd appreciate the chance to photograph it. I stood on the port fairwater plane for most of the next hour as we approached and then passed beneath the bridge that signified home to so many troops and sailors for so many years. In the harbor, I turned and photographed the bridge, our stern, and our wake. The CO had spent many years here on previous commands and took the opportunity to play tour guide, showing us Alcatraz, Treasure Island, the waterfront, and other sights as the OOD steered us through San Francisco bay and toward San Pablo Bay.

Going below, I took my Maneuvering watch for the last time in AMSLL. As we pulled into San Pablo Bay, we took on our pilot who guided us up the river to our berth. Misjudging the river currents, he let the bow get into the current and the boat swung the wrong way across the river, going through a mud bank. By the time this was taken care of, we had sucked mud into many of our seawater systems, shutting them down and ruining heat transfer. High temperature alarms started going off, main condenser vacuum dropped like a rock, and we scrammed the reactor. So the Mighty *Plunger*'s last shutdown was ignominious, to say the least. But, perhaps better to have some excitement than having just one last routine shutdown.

In Mare Island, we spent a few months getting the boat ready for drydock, then were pulled in. Wooden keel blocks up to eight feet tall had been laid out in the drydock basin. We were pulled in, positioned over the blocks, the drydock door shut, and the water pumped out. We settled into the keel blocks and began decommissioning. In the months that followed, the *Plunger* was slowly dismantled. Holes appeared in the hull, allowing removal of many of the large pieces of equipment. Electronics, computers, pumps, even racks disappeared. The reactor refueling plug was removed and the reactor defuelled, the spent core to be sent for disposal in Idaho. Although I have never seen an organ harvest performed on an accident victim, it must feel similar.

I had mixed feelings during this time. On the one hand, I was happy that I would never again be under water longer than I could hold my breath. And I was looking forward to leaving the Navy less than six months after we docked in Mare Island. But I was sorry to see the *Plunger* go. During this last underway, while I was researching its history and that of its predecessors, I came to understand more that we had been graced with a good ship, and that this ship was now being ripped apart. I am not sure what it is that makes a ship good or bad. Certainly, the care with which the *Plunger* was designed and built helped, because it's hard for a vessel to be good if it's always broken or awaiting repair. But there must be more than just good engineering and construction or every well-built boat would excel, and that simply was not the case. However, it was difficult for me to place all responsibility on the crew because the crew changes so frequently. How can one outstanding crew in the 1960s influence another crew in the 1980s, especially when many of the latter might not have even been alive when the boat was built?

I came to believe that early crews set a high standard because they had a good boat and a good skipper. They excelled and, by so doing, future crews came to expect that *Plunger* would do well. And so it did. At the time of decommissioning, *Plunger* was the most decorated warship in San Diego and the most honored submarine in the Pacific Fleet. I could almost imagine what it must have been like to have been on the *Plunger* when she was the best and most modern submarine in the world, eagerly taking on challenges and missions and doing well at them all. Even in her old age, nearly obsolete, somewhat cranky, and scarred, she still seemed willing to do whatever we asked of her, and then some. So, although my years on *Plunger* were not the best I have ever had, there is something about them, and about *Plunger* that I miss.

Before leaving for Mare Island, a team of vultures came aboard, inspecting and cataloging all our equipment to see what could be recycled into spare parts or into other submarines of our class. But, thanks to a number of events, the 594 class submarines weren't to be used for much longer. The fate of the *Plunger* would be to be gutted, defueled, and towed to Puget Sound. Once there, she would be tied up and left to rust.

My last few months on active duty mostly consisted of winding down. I was really looking forward to getting out of the Navy but, at the same time, was understandably nervous about my ability to earn a living while going to school. I toyed with the idea of staying in, if only because of the job security, but the Navy ultimately forced my hand. I was just ready to move on. At one point I offered to re-enlist for three years and to waive my next shore duty assignment if I were assigned to Operation Deep Freeze, the Navy team that staffed the US Antarctic research stations. I was flatly told that nukes were not eligible for this duty. When I pointed out that I'd leave the Navy if I didn't get the duty I was told it made no difference. I also offered to stay in if I could cross-rate to another, non-nuclear specialty, but was not permitted to do that, either. This stance really irritated me. From my viewpoint, no matter what happened, the nuclear power program was going to lose me because I was ready for a change. But, given that, I had given the Navy two chances to keep a relatively senior enlisted man with a very good service record and proven abilities. To me, it just didn't make any sense, but it made my decision to leave the service much easier.

Although there was much about the Navy that I disliked, I have to admit that there was a lot of good mixed in with the bad. I had joined the Navy because I realized I needed some self-discipline, a direction in life, and the chance to earn some money for college. In one form or another, I found all these and much more. I have no doubt that my life would be much different had I not joined the Navy, and I think that it is much richer for the time I spent there and the things I learned and did. And my post-Navy life is vastly different than would have been the case otherwise, again most of the differences being for the better. I have absolutely no doubt that, had I not joined the Navy, I would not have the discipline I learned, primarily mental, and I would very likely not have had the patience to stick with my educational and professional goals to achieve things that are so important to me. I also know that I would not have my current job, profession, or family had I not joined the Navy. So I got an incredible amount out of the experience. This is not to take away from the things I disliked, but, rather, to put them in a more complete context. The work was hard, the learning curve was often brutally steep, and the life we led was not an easy one. But these qualities also gave me a lot of pride in what I did, pride I still feel when I tell others what I used to do or when I meet other ex-Navy Nukes and swap sea stories. I know for a fact that I was able to complete my undergraduate degree, a master's degree, and will be able to finish my Ph.D., in spite of working full time and having a family, because of the discipline I learned in the Navy, and because I had no choice but to learn to carefully budget my time and to make the most of every waking hour.

There's another way to view this my decision to leave the Navy. Naval Reactors (or, as we called them, NR) made an exact science out of running nuclear reactors. We went through an exceptionally rigorous training program that crammed into our poor little heads the rough equivalent of a few years of education in nuclear engineering in six months, followed by an equally arduous six months of prototype training. The technical manuals, operating and emergency procedures were refined exquisitely, and virtually nothing was left to chance. Unfortunately, this left virtually no room for individuality, improvisation, creativity, or many of the other characteristics I valued the most. After six years, I had done virtually everything I could as an enlisted man. To retire from the Navy would have meant 14 more years of the same. That was simply too much for me. I'm not rebellious by nature, but neither am I a conformist, and I was giving up too much to stay in the Navy. Running nuclear power plants had become boring, without any new challenges and no way to really do anything unique, so it was time to go. NR had done a wonderful job of taking an incredibly complex and sophisticated job and making it doable by motivated individuals with determination and intelligence. But I wanted more variety in my job, and more freedom.

Around the time I was to get out, the RadCon shop at the Mare Island Naval Shipyard sent someone down to talk with some of us "short-timers" about working for them. I thought about it very seriously for over a month. I figured that, working for them with a lot of overtime, in just a year or two I could save up a fair amount of money to use to help pay for college. I was worried about being able to pay for school because, although I had saved some money, it was looking less and less impressive and I was growing increasingly uncertain about my ability to find a decent job on the outside. Talking with my father about it one evening, he suggested I should just take my chances with finding a job at school. His point was that expenses usually increase to match your income and that my thoughts of setting money aside for college would probably come to naught. That being the case, better to start sooner and finish more quickly. Thinking about it, I realized he was right, and I decided to return to Ohio State to finish my undergraduate degree.

I returned to college, completing a Bachelor's and then a Master's degree in Geology. At the same time, I was trying to catch up with my life. For a number of reasons, I had felt my life to be on hold the entire eight years I spent in the Navy. I wasn't going to school, I wasn't dating (or at least not much and with one exception not seriously), and I wasn't pursuing any particular career. I was just marking time until I could get out and get on with the rest of my life. Once out, I felt that I had to make up for lost time. At heart, I was an academic, and I longed to return to the university environment, preferably for the rest of my life.

The last thing I wanted to do after leaving the Navy was to have anything to do with nuclear reactors or with radiation. I wasn't scared of either; in fact, my feelings were quite to the contrary. I realized that nuclear reactors can be made inherently safe, can be operated safely, and that the levels of radiation I was exposed to were without risk. I was just burned out on nuclear power and I really didn't know of any way to continue working with radiation safety that didn't involve reactors. And, like many of my fellow sailors, I had not saved much money for my post-Navy life. On reflection, I really wished I had had the foresight to have spoken with a financial planner while I was in the Navy, but I barely knew that such people existed. The Navy didn't talk to us about financial planning. I ended up with about $3000 in the bank and $8100 through an educational assistance program, the latter only dished out in $225 monthly increments, not nearly enough to pay for tuition, let alone living expenses. And, if I didn't take a full course load, the amount was reduced even further. Once I understood how that program worked (and how the local Veteran's office didn't work) I realized that the benefits I'd counted on to help me make the transition to civilian life were not nearly as nice as I thought I'd been promised. I understand that the benefits are much better now, but I joined up at the wrong time. So, for my first post-Navy year, I worked nights at a local copy shop, running copies for students.

The single most humorous incident from my year at Kinko's came shortly after I started. I was working during the day for training and the assistant manager came up to me. "So, Andy, how are you doing with all this pressure?" he asked.

I looked at him, genuinely puzzled. "What pressure?"

He gestured at the lines of people standing at the counter, the stacks of materials to be copied, and the backlog of items waiting to be bound. "All this stuff that has to be done, all the people waiting. That pressure."

I looked around and looked at him again. "Mike, no matter what I do, nobody can be killed and the most expensive thing I can possibly break doesn't even cost a hundred thousand dollars. So where's the pressure?"

He gave me a blank, non-comprehending look. I tried again. "Look, I spent the last four years on a submarine. If I screwed up, I could help sink a boat worth a few hundred million dollars and kill up to 150 people. I helped to run a nuclear reactor fueled with highly enriched uranium, and I spent more time off the coast of Russia than San Diego. So tell me, where's the pressure here?" He walked off, shaking his head.

In trying to catch up with where I felt I should have been I made mistakes, of course. I left Kinko's and got back into radiation safety, called health physics in the civilian world. The jobs worked out all right, although it was difficult working full time and taking a full course load. Nevertheless, I finished up in four years with grades good enough to enter graduate school. And, in many ways, I pushed myself too hard in my efforts to "catch up", the only thing saving me being my learned ability to work long hours with little sleep.

I was luckier than many of my shipmates in that I entered a field in which my Navy training helped. Some of my shipmates were in specialties that gave them no marketable job skills. I felt that, in many ways, the Navy recruiters misrepresented the ease with which Navy job skills would translate to the civilian world. Or, as one of our torpedomen commented "My recruiter told me that I'd learn good job skills in the Navy. And I guess that's right. If I can just find a civilian ship that's armed with Mark 48 torpedoes. Otherwise, I haven't learned a damned thing that'll help me get out of here." Luckily, the number of fields in which this is true is limited, and all of the nuclear power rates were very valuable outside the Navy.

Although I didn't realize it at the time, within my first year out of the Navy the Berlin Wall would fall, followed by the Soviet Union. Three years after my last spec op off the coast of Russia, I found myself at a professional meeting listening to a speaker from the Russian Ministry of Atomic Energy asking for help in dismantling and disposing of nuclear weapons. After his talk, I went to him and told him that, not too long before, I had been on a submarine, worried about being caught by his navy. He looked at me a long while, started to smile, and then laughed long and hard. "Let us hope this does not happen again," he finally said.

Appendices

Appendix A: A detailed tour of the Plunger

Topside

SITTING AT THE PIER, the first thing you notice is that the boat is completely black and low in the water. The only relief from black (besides seagull droppings) is small white depth markings on the hull. With the boat in the water, you see the number 26 at the waterline and the numbers stop at 30 on the hull. This means that the hull is 30 feet in diameter, 26 feet of which are beneath the water. The top of the boat is round because the hull is roughly cylindrical in shape, the better with which to cut through the water silently and efficiently. Rising above the main deck at the front of the boat is a black sail with what appear to be wings at the sides. The sail, what was called a conning tower in earlier diesel boats, is about 12 feet tall, perhaps three or four feet thick, and is shaped like a teardrop when seen from above. This contains two periscopes, a radio mast, a radar mast, the snorkel mast, and a cockpit from which the boat is navigated when on the surface. Right now we can see a periscope raised another 20 feet or so above the top of the sail for maintenance. It's about as big around as an average man's upper arm and is painted in mottled shades of gray for camouflage against the sea. The "wings" coming off the sail are the fairwater planes (sometimes called the sail planes) and the analogy to wings is not entirely inappropriate. They jut out nearly 10 feet on either side of the sail and taper from about three feet wide at the tips to perhaps six or seven feet wide where they attach to the sail. Their purpose is to help maintain the proper depth and angle on the boat when submerged.

Immediately aft of the sail is an open hatch, the weapons shipping hatch. When loading or offloading weapons, we lower them vertically through this hatch and into the torpedo room three decks directly below. Twenty five inches in diameter, this is also the primary way for people and supplies to enter or leave the boat. Right now, we're loading stores for the extended underway period coming up. Three months' of supplies for 150 people is a lot, and there is a line of sailors running from the pier to the boat, food and other gear being passed from sailor to sailor until it disappears down the hatch, eventually to be stored somewhere.

The one major exception to the hull's smooth curvature is a small half-tube running the length of the hull on the port side (the left side of the boat when facing forward). This half-tube is about a foot across, perhaps three or four inches in height, and is almost far enough down the curve of the hull to make it possible to lose one's footing if careless or on a slippery deck. This is the housing for our towed array sonar. It emerges from the hull a few feet forward of the sail and runs horizontally to about 80 feet aft of the sail (about halfway between the sail and the rudder). There, it veers smoothly down the hull, disappearing beneath the waters of San Diego harbor after another 20 feet or so. Not far past where the towed array fairing vanishes, the rest of the hull narrows and slopes down beneath the water as well and, perhaps 20 feet further aft, the rudder rises abruptly, black and square.

We need to cross the brow to get from the pier to the top of the boat, stopping to salute the flag and the topside watch and requesting permission from the topside watch to come aboard. Permission is automatic for crew members. Visitors require either permission from the Officer of the Day, the Captain (also called the skipper, the CO, or the Old Man), or they will be escorted the whole time they're onboard. Receiving permission to come aboard, we go forward from the brow to the weapons shipping hatch. The hatch itself is black and round, giving the impression of complete solidity. As well it should. This hatch, and the rest of the hull will be called upon to hold back our most constant enemy, the sea and all the pressure it can bring to bear. If this hatch fails in this, neither the boat nor the crew is likely to return to port and neither the Navy nor our families are likely to ever know why.

Directly beneath the hatch is a stainless steel ladder nearly ten feet tall. It is set up so that we turn to face inboard (towards the centerline of the boat) with our backs to the sea. There's a rail to hold onto until we drop down far enough to be stable, and we start to climb down the ladder. The hatch we go through is 25 inches in diameter. That's the upper size limit to what can enter the boat in one piece. Anything larger must be dismantled or needs to go in through a hole cut in the hull and welded shut afterwards.

At the bottom of the ladder we find ourselves in the upper level of the Operations Compartment. We call it OPSUL, for OPS compartment Upper Level. We are in a passageway about three feet wide that runs aft (to our right) about 80 feet or so, ending in a massive watertight door that leads into the engineering spaces. That door is at the forward end of a tunnel through the reactor compartment and it's posted with a radiation warning sign when the reactor is running. In port, we keep the reactor shutdown, so the sign is covered with red naugehyde right now. The pas-

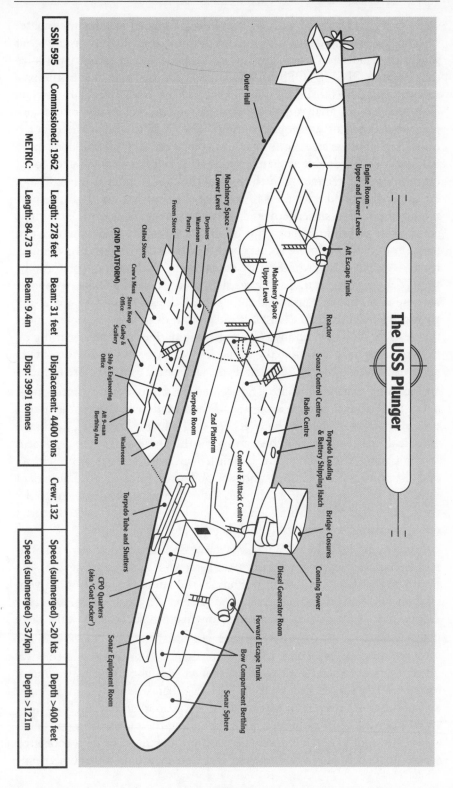

The USS Plunger

Outer Hull

Engine Room - Upper and Lower Levels

Aft Escape Trunk

Machinery Space - Lower Level

Machinery Space - Upper Level

Frozen Stores

Drystores

Wardroom

Pantry

(2ND PLATFORM)

Chilled Stores

Crew's Mess

Store Keep Office

Galley & Scullery

Ship & Engineering Office

Aft 9-man Berthing Area

Washrooms

Torpedo Room

2nd Platform

Reactor

Sonar Control Centre

Radio Centre

Torpedo Loading & Battery Shipping Hatch

Control & Attack Centre

Bridge Closures

Conning Tower

Torpedo Tube and Shutters

Diesel Generator Room

CPO Quarters (aka 'Goat Locker')

Forward Escape Trunk

Bow Compartment Berthing

Sonar Equipment Room

Sonar Sphere

SSN 595	Commissioned: 1962	Length: 278 feet	Beam: 31 feet	Displacement: 4400 tons	Crew: 132	Speed (submerged) >20 kts	Depth >400 feet
METRIC:	Length: 84.73 m	Beam: 9.4m	Disp: 3991 tonnes		Speed (submerged) >37kph	Depth >121m

sageway itself is paneled with light-colored simulated woodgrained material and has a medium blue linoleum on the floor. Immediately on the other side of the ladder is a steep stairway, also called a ladder in Navy parlance that leads to OPSML (OPS Middle Level). On the other side of the passageway from us is a sliding door leading to the Nucleonics lab, my lab. This is where we analyze reactor coolant samples, keep most of our supplies, and hold our divisional training. The basic theme of the décor is utilitarian stainless steel with blue linoleum accents. The total floor space is about that of a double-wide telephone booth with a stainless steel counter running for 7 feet along the far side of the room (about four feet away). At the forward and after ends of the space (to the left and right, respectively) are other counters covered with equipment. Beneath the counters are drawers and sliding doors; this is our storage space. And, when we can fit them in, we have more lockers and bookshelves. We don't have much room so we put things wherever we can fit them. Although uncomfortable, most of the guys in my division have slept on the Nuke Lab floor or counter at some time. I always preferred the counter; the stainless steel was colder than the linoleum, but at least I could stretch out, my work jacket under my head for a pillow and my olive green submariner's sweater warding off the chill. My joke was that the Nuke Lab was spacious enough to fit six people standing or could sleep three, provided they were all close friends.

One thing that's immediately noticeable is the profusion of pipes, ducts, valves, electronics, storage lockers, and the like all over the boat. There is no ceiling in most spaces, the overhead is filled with hydraulic, fluid, and electrical lines, valves, switches, and so forth. There are no tables, except in the Crew's Mess. We sit on bench lockers with storage space within, and all counters have cabinets and storage lockers underneath. Equipment is packed into the submarine the way my father packed suitcases into the trunk of our car for vacation. There is simply no room for space that isn't doing anything, so every cubic inch is utilized in some manner.

Going back into the OPSUL passageway and turning left (aft) takes us past Sonar and Supply on the starboard side (left as we're facing aft) and Radio on the port side. Just aft of Radio is the fan room, home of our ventilation fans and filters. Just forward of Radio is a small space, normally empty, that is filled with electronics for missions such as the one we're about to start.

Continuing aft, we come to the watertight door, a massive steel oval about four feet tall and less than three feet wide. Right now it's open, but at sea it's usually dogged shut by latching a lever beneath a latch on the right side of the door. In a pinch, we can also dog the door more securely by turning the central stainless steel wheel, expanding the mechanism on the aft side of the door to seal it securely beneath yet more latches. The door itself weighs several hundred pounds and is designed to take full submergence pressure if need be. We have four of them onboard, separating each of the five watertight compartments. In port, the door moves smoothly to open and shut; at sea, especially on or near the surface, the door can swing suddenly and dangerously shut and people have had bones broken by getting legs, arms, or hands caught between the watertight door and its frame.

The door leads into the reactor compartment tunnel, about ten feet across, slightly over six feet in height, passing through the top of the reactor compartment. Leaded glass windows allow a view of the reactor compartment and the equipment within. The tunnel is heavily shielded to reduce radiation levels when we're operating and, even at full power, radiation levels are completely safe in here. As we go aft through the tunnel, we descend four steps, passing between rows of reactor plant valves, some small water tanks, and through another watertight door at the after end of the tunnel. This leads to the Auxiliary Machinery Space, Upper Level (AMSUL).

Passing through this door, we are on a small platform about three feet square. To the left and right, a few steps takes us down to platforms leading off about 15 feet in either direction. To the port side is a stainless steel box about two feet across and three feet high. This is the reactor plant sampling station, called the primary sample sink. On both sides are more rows of valves, cylindrical heat exchangers used to cool the water that cools some reactor plant components, and other equipment. Going down another seven or eight steps takes us to Instrument Alley, some of the reactor plant instrument and control panels. Dull gray, chipped paint and a patina of wear makes them look like something out of a 1950s science fiction movie, reminding us that the *Plunger* was built in the early 1960s using technology of the previous decade. Leave it to the Navy to make a nuclear reactor look ordinary and boring.

Continuing aft down the passageway takes us past a double row of electrical switchboards, more large gray panels with circuit breakers that carry up to 1000 amps or so. Just outboard of this row of panels on the port side, we find a ladder leading down to AMSLL. This space, too, is filled with pipes, pumps, and equipment. More banks of stainless steel reactor plant valves are at the forward end of the space, immediately adjacent to the reactor compartment shield. Also forward is a stainless steel cabinet where we store chemicals used to reduce corrosion in the steam plant and boilers. Also in this area is another storage cabinet where we keep our analytical chemicals and reagents as well as our steam plant (secondary plant) sample sink. As we're facing forward, to our left (port side) are two refrigeration units, one running noisily, a few seawater pumps with brass, bronze, or monel (a copper-nickel alloy) fittings and pipes, and still more reactor plant valves. Directly across from the ladder is a carbon dioxide scrubber that helps to keep our atmosphere breathable. Just aft of the ladder and the scrubber is some electrical gear and, at the very back, is a small gaugeboard, a control panel, and four pumps, each about 8 feet tall. These are for adding high-pressure water to the steam generators (a nuclear power plant's equivalent of boilers). This is where I often stand watch, as do most of my division personnel.

Going back up the ladder and further aft, we come to the Engineroom Upper Level (ERUL). Passing through the door, we first see an air conditioning unit on the port side. Considered a luxury ashore, this is essential at sea. Without air conditioning, temperatures throughout the boat will rise into the 90s in a matter of minutes. At times, when we've lost AC at sea, temperatures in the Engineroom have been measured at more than 110 in the cooler areas and up to 140 in some places. ERUL is quiet now, with the engines shut down, and it's relatively cool because we're in cold iron conditions, no steam in the engineroom. In a few days, when we're moving across the Pacific at a flank bell, it'll be hot, sweaty, and so noisy that the watchstanders will have to wear ear plugs to avoid hearing damage.

Across from the AC unit is a small room, barely large enough to hold three panels and four watchstanders. This is Maneuvering, the control room for the reactor plant. The instruments here monitor all of the most important parameters needed to run the reactor, steam, and propulsion plants. The center panel, the reactor plant control panel (RPCP) is where the reactor is started up, controlled, and shut down. The first panel inside the door and boundary chain, the one with a large and a small wheel, is the steam plant control panel (SPCP), where the throttleman stands controlling the steam plant and the main engines. On the far side is the electric plant control panel (EPCP). Here, the electrical operator monitors, manages, and maintains the flow of electricity from the turbine generators throughout the boat. If we have any electrical problems, he is the one making sure we have lights, sonar, fire control, and our reactor plant running. Controlling as much power as a small city uses, the panel is laid out as a small-scale replica of the electrical plant engineering drawings to help him visualize the flow of energy through the boat. The rest of Maneuvering is covered with other monitoring and instrumentation panels. At the back, about two feet aft of the watchstanders at their panels, is a small raised bench seat. This is where the Engineering Officer of the Watch (EOOW) sits, supervising plant operations. And, right above the EOOW's head are two sets of switches, the Chicken Switches. If turned, these will instantly close large valves, stopping the flow of seawater through our cooling systems. Without the seawater, we can operate for only a few minutes, so this is not something done lightly. In fact, I never saw these switches used. In an emergency, however, if we're flooding, they go shut to stop the inflow of water and, hopefully, save our lives.

Leaving Maneuvering, we head aft again, past the port and starboard turbine generators that supply us with electricity, ending up at the main engine gaugeboard. Here, the ERUL watch can monitor the main turbines that move us through the water. Here, too, is a backup set of throttles, used for warming up the main engines and as a backup for the set in Maneuvering. There is a backup for almost everything. For whatever we have no backup for, we have some other way of cross-connecting, rigging, substituting, or doing without. Battle readiness is the name of the game, as we can't let minor problems keep us from fighting, hiding, or running.

Looking at ERUL from just outside of maneuvering the primary impression is that of a bewildering array of thick white pipes and valves. This is the steam system, carrying high-pressure and high-temperature steam from the boilers to the turbines. Steam is what makes turns the turbines, making electricity, propelling us through the water, making fresh water, for both ship and crew. Controlled, the steam is a useful tool. Uncontrolled, it can injure or kill in seconds. Looking around, some sort of pattern begins to emerge from the confusion. Pipes are marked, noting the system they belong to. Valves are color-coded by system, so a given pipe will have the same color valves everywhere. White for steam, green for seawater, blue for fresh water, yellow for lubricating oil (lube oil). Steam lines generally run into the tops of turbines and other things while blue lines, carrying condensed steam, come out of the bottoms. In all, there are over two thousand valves in the engineroom and several hundred pipes. I know some of them and I have enormous respect for those who know them all.

Both of the main propulsion turbines and the turbine generators are surprisingly small. Beneath thick white insulation, the actual turbine wheels are only three or four feet in diameter and the complete turbine assembly contains several turbine wheels packed into a space perhaps six feet long in the generators and ten feet long for the main engines. At the forward end of the generators is a large cubical electrical generator with thick cables coming out of it. At the after end of the mains are shafts that run into the main reduction gears. Turbines run most efficiently at high speeds while propellers run best at slow speeds. The reduction gears, the largest equipment in the engineroom, turn the high turbine speeds into slow propeller speeds. These, in turn, lead to the shaft, which runs through shaft alley and exits the boat through the shaft seals, mechanical devices that keep water from pouring in along the shaft. By the time we reach shaft alley, the boat has narrowed considerably and is now about 15 feet across. Coming down the starboard side, we have passed the engineroom head (bathroom) and the main hydraulic plant. We lift a small hatch set into the deck and descend a short ladder to ERLL.

If ERUL is steam, ERLL is water and oil. The after part of ERLL contains the lube oil system that keeps our reduction gears and main turbine bearings from chewing themselves up. The middle section contains our main condensers, huge cylinders with thousands of small tubes of seawater running through them, kept at a nearly perfect vacuum to get the most work out of the steam we possibly can. Steam exhausts from the main engines into the condensers, comes into contact with the cool tubes, and condenses to water that is pumped back into the steam generators. Less glamorous, dirtier, and less fun than ERUL, this is where the most junior mechanical watchstanders start off their sea-going careers. The forward part of ERLL contains the main seawater inlet valves and pumps, controlling the flow of cooling seawater through the condensers. These are the valves that will slam shut if the EOOW hits the chicken switches. Also in this area is our source of fresh water, an evaporator (evap) that can make, on a good day, 5000 gallons of fresh water from seawater. Beneath the deck are the reserve feed tanks, holding fresh water for addition to the steam plant to make up for the water lost through normal and abnormal operations. The valves in ERLL are all green, blue, and yellow and, if it's dirtier than ERUL, it's also cooler. There's a ladder just forward of the evap that returns us to ERUL, just outside Maneuvering. We climb this and head forward again, heading forward to see the other half of the boat.

Heading forward through OPSUL again, we go all the way forward, past Nucleonics, into Control. Control is where most of the important things happen. While we nukes would point out that, without us, there would be no propulsion, power, water, and undersea endurance, we're secondary. Without Control, we would have no purpose. In Control, watchstanders dive and drive, plot position and course, submerge and surface the boat, track targets, plan attacks, gather intelligence, coordinate damage control efforts, and do all the other things that go into making the submarine into an effective warship. Whether we're at battle stations, fighting a fire, or getting ready to surface, the Old Man comes here to find out what's happening and to orchestrate our efforts.

We enter Control through a small doorless doorway just forward of the ladder down to OPSML. Immediately to our right, in the overhead, is a gray locker about two feet square. This holds SINS, the Ship's Inertial Navigation System. When I was onboard the *Plunger*, in the few years just before GPS satellites went up, most of our navigation was done by tracking the forces on a bunch of small gyroscopes that spun incredibly quickly. The minute forces acting on them as we turned, accelerated, or slowed down the boat were translated into ship's position. Periodically, when a navigation satellite was in the sky, we'd come up to periscope depth (PD), put a radio mast up, and get an exact position. Further in that direction takes us behind some electronics panels and, turning a corner at the end of this instrument alley puts us on top of the seat for the Electronics Technician of the Watch (ETOW). Normally, the ETOW just maintains the electronics while, on a mission, he will man his console, helping to monitor foreign radio and radar signals. His primary function then is not intelligence-gathering so much as threat detection; he is the one to identify various radars, try to guess their distance, strength, and capabilities, and let the CO or OOD know what radars are up and what they can tell us. For example, a relatively low-frequency radar might not be able to see our scope, but if it's attached to a recon or anti-submarine warfare (ASW) plane, it tells us that someone's out and about who is trained to find and attack submarines. That's good information to have available.

Further forward from the ETOW station is the ballast control panel, a profusion of knobs and switches that controls the high pressure air, hydraulic, trim, and some emergency systems. The Chief of the Watch (COW) normally sits here, making sure the boat is balanced and close to neutral buoyancy. The BCP, like the ETOW station, runs forward and aft along the port side of Control. Turning to look inboard, we see the shining cylinders of two periscopes, one ahead of the other, taking the place of honor in the middle of Control. Just aft of the scopes is the Quartermaster of the Watch's (QMOW) station, a simple table with a chart, a light, and some drafting and measuring instruments. Although I often accused the QMOW of navigating us around the Pacific using a National Geographic map of the ocean floor, they did a pretty good job of keeping us on course and in our assigned areas.

Opposite the BCP, running forward and aft along the starboard side of Control is Fire Control, three consoles from which weapons can be checked, targeted, launched and, if necessary, guided following a launch. This is manned by the Fire Control Technician of the Watch (FTOW), whose job it is to track targets, predict their future positions, and, if necessary, launch the weapons to sink them. At the very front of Control is the Diving Officer's station, including the seats for the helmsman and stern planesman. These, usually the two most junior watchstanders on board, drive and dive the submarine, taking direction from the Diving Officer to keep us on course and at the ordered depth. Dive, the senior-most watch in Control (with the exception of the Officer of the Deck) rides herd on them from a seat between and just barely aft of their. All three seats come equipped with seat belts for, despite its size, the *Plunger* can maneuver rapidly at high speeds and, near the surface, we can take some heavy rolls.

Just inboard of these seats is a small door leading into a small dark area with a tube leading up. This leads to the bridge, a small cockpit at the top of the sail from which the boat is driven when on the surface. It's a long climb up through a narrow, dark tunnel, but at sea it's a great place to be. The few times I was able to be in the bridge at sea were memorable. A few watchstanders, one manning the phones, one scanning the sea for other ships, and the OOD making sure we didn't run into anything. If we're out of the harbor, we're probably making pretty good speed on the surface, so the forward deck will be completely underwater with the sea breaking against the front edge of the sail. Looking aft, part of the after deck is clear of water, but the waves curl up again partway down the hull. At even higher speeds, I have seen water covering the entire deck, making it look as though I was standing on a small steel island, alone in the sea. With the sun shining down or, even better, under the stars, it's a wonderful place to be. And, when I was lucky, there would be dolphins dancing with the ship and, perhaps, everyone else content to just enjoy the privilege of being on the surface in a submarine in the middle of the ocean. And, in port on holidays or Sundays spent on duty, I was known to take a book to the bridge when not on watch, curl up on the seat in the cockpit, and read, lost to the world.

Returning reluctantly down the ladder to Control, we go aft and take the ladder to OPSML. Directly ahead of the ladder at the bottom is the ship's office, where the yeomen keep track of all of our administrative details. Leave, promotions, correspondence courses, pay record entries, qualifications, and everything else for every crewman onboard; they're all handled here. The office is smaller than my lab with about as much floor space. There are two seats; in order for the person furthest from the door to come or go, the other must stop what he's doing, stand, and make room.

To the port side of the ladder is the Wardroom, Officer's country. Off limits to enlisted men on a surface ship, it's not quite as formally protected on a submarine. We can (and do) enter the Wardroom when necessary, but we try to steer clear. We hear rumors that concern us and make us try to minimize our exposure to the place. Things like their having napkin rings or having to eat fried chicken with knife and fork. And then there are all the other things that go into being "an officer and a gentleman" that we just want to avoid as much as possible.

The Wardroom (or, as it's sometimes called, the Weirdroom) has five stateroom, a head, and an eating area. The staterooms are nothing to write home about. The CO and XO have private staterooms, each with a rack, desk, washbasin, and chair. In addition, the CO's stateroom has a direct phone to Control and repeater gauges showing our depth, course, and speed. Both the CO's and XO's staterooms are about seven or eight feet long, about the same across, and tall enough to stand in. Two of the other three staterooms are the same size, but hold three officers each, and the last stateroom is barely large enough for the beds. In fact, if more than one person from that stateroom is dressing at any one time, someone will be in the passageway. Our boat has a dozen or so officers onboard at any one time; if there aren't sufficient staterooms available, the junior-most officer will have a bunk in one of the enlisted berthing compartments. Turning and heading aft along the wardroom passageway takes us to the dining area, consisting of a table that seats six, a long bench, and a TV set. A door on the inboard bulkhead takes us to what passes for sickbay on our boat.

Actually, we have no sickbay on the *Plunger*. Instead, we have a small corridor that connects the Wardroom and the Crew's Mess with our dry stores locker, our freeze box, and our chill box. A ladder goes up through a hatch to the OPSUL passageway and another ladder goes down to the Torpedo Room below. Sandwiched into all of this is a small desk, a bench seat, and some medical cabinets. This is where our corpsman, an enlisted man having specialized training at the Independent Duty School works. Diagnoses, prescriptions, injections, idle chatter, all take place here as the corpsman, universally called Doc, plies his trade. With a few exceptions, noted elsewhere in this narrative, the crew is pretty healthy, leaving the Doc with more administrative work than anything else. Better this than an emergency. Forward of the Doc's station is the Crew's Mess, a small room with four tables, a TV set, an ice cream machine, and a stereo system. Forward of the Crew's Mess, also called the Messdecks, a passageway leads past the stainless steel galley and scullery, past the Aft nine-man berthing area, to a watertight door. The Aft nine-man is on the starboard side of the passageway and, just past the ladder to OPSLL, is the crew's head, three stalls, a urinal, two showers (one of which almost never works), and three sinks. Continuing forward takes us into the bow compartment and two more berthing areas, the Forward nine-man lies at the end of a long (about 30 feet) passageway and the bow compartment berthing area lies to port. On the starboard side is the Chief's Quarters, also referred to as the Goat Locker, similar to the Wardroom, but set aside for Chief Petty Officers. We can go into the Wardroom whenever we want, but entry to the Goat Locker and sitting at the card table is only with the permission of a chief.

All of the berthing areas are similar in that they consist of tiers of bunks (also called "racks") stacked three high. Lit with only dim red lights at sea, they are brightly lit now, in port. Each rack is about 6 ½ feet long, 2 feet across, and there is barely enough room for a thin person to lie on their side. The forward nine-man has three sets of racks, as does the after nine-man. There are four sets of racks in the Goat Locker, 7 sets in the 21-man berthing area, and 7 sets in the bow compartment berthing. Add in the 11 racks in the Wardroom and another three along the top of the passageway to the forward nine-man and you come up with a total of 86 racks for a crew of 125. We'll be carrying an additional complement of nearly 20 riders during the upcoming op. So, in addition to the permanent racks, we put people in the torpedo room and we hot-rack. Not a lot of fun, but it's better than sleeping on the deck.

Beneath the decks in the forward berthing areas are the diesel generator room and the sonar equipment space. Diesel, the after-most compartment holds our emergency diesel generator. We can't go anywhere with it, unlike diesel-electric submarines, but we can use it for emergency power if necessary. It's big, painted some sort of metallic pea green color, and runs noisily, but well when we use it. The sonar equipment space, or SES, is chock full of electrical and electronic gear. I really have little idea what it all does, but

I would guess that this is what drives the sonar system, provides power to the hydrophones, and converts the results into something understandable and useful to our sonar technicians. The last space to visit is OPSLL, so we return to the ladder outside the head and descend.

The ladder deposits us in the 21-man berthing area. Directly in front of the ladder is another ladder that descends to the battery well, home of our lead acid storage battery. Not nearly as large as those on a diesel-electric submarine, this battery is an emergency power supply only. It has enough juice to keep us going until the diesel can come up or, if the diesel won't work, it may last long enough to let us get the reactor back up again and the turbine generators on-line. In spite of its limitations, there's enough stored energy there to blow out the side of the boat. And, if we get seawater into the battery well, we'll end up with chlorine gas being generated. That much chlorine would tend to be fatal, so we try to keep seawater out of the battery well. All in all, it's best just to treat it carefully.

There is nothing forward of the 21-man except for a watertight bulkhead. On the other side of the bulkhead is the diesel compartment. Aft is the torpedo room. Four torpedo tubes, two on each side, flank the 21-man, running forward and canted outboard at a slight angle to aim away from us when we shoot. The rest of the room is filled with torpedoes, harpoon missiles, and we sometimes would carry Subrocs, tactical nuclear subsurface-to-subsurface missiles. The weapons are on skids stacked two high and the empty skids all have mattresses on them. Continuing aft through the torpedo room we come to a small door leading in to Air Regen. This is home to our air compressors and some atmosphere controls equipment. It's small and, when the compressors are running, it can be noisy, dirty, and hot as well. All the way aft in the torpedo room is a ladder leading to a small hatch. We climb up and find ourselves at the Doc's station. Our tour is done.

There are some things that really stand out during this tour. One is the efficient use of space. Very few cubic inches are wasted on the *Plunger.* Everywhere you look is a storage locker, piping, electrical wiring, machinery, and so forth. And there is a feeling that everything has been done to a master plan; there is nothing ad hoc about this vessel. All open hatches have chains across them to keep crew from falling down the hole, and these chains clip onto hooks precisely far enough from the open hatch to make sure you can't step wrong. All hatches open and can be latched to keep them from falling on unsuspecting heads or fingers should the ship take a roll. Not coincidentally, this also minimizes the chance for noise. All electrical panels are designed to be splash-proof so that water spray will not cause an electrical fire. Everywhere you look, you see fire extinguishers, emergency breathing gear, fire hoses, and other damage control equipment so, no matter where you might be, you can fight whatever troubles might come your way. This also ensures that, no matter where a problem might be, it can't cut us off from the gear needed to take care of it. And you would have noticed technical manuals everywhere. The reactor plant manual, six copies of which are on the boat, fills up nearly 10 feet of shelving with multiple volumes giving the technical specifications of every piece of equipment in the engineering spaces as well as detailed instructions on how to perform every operation (also called evolutions) that are supposedly possible to perform. And every part of the boat is the same way. The submarine is literally operated "by the book" because failure to do so can lead to any number of bad things.

Something less obvious in this cursory tour is that all of our systems are duplicated wherever possible. We have two main engines, two turbine generators, two power supplies to most vital gear. In some places, we can even cross-connect important systems so, for example, we can run both main engines from a single steam generator. Like the damage control gear, this is another way to maximize our battle-readiness.

Appendix B: Glossary of terms and abbreviations

There are a number of terms and abbreviations that are unique to the Navy or to submarines. I have tried to use these terms because they reflect the way we talked, both to each other and about our jobs. In this glossary, I have tried to compile all the odd terms and acronyms used in this volume for your reference, in alphabetical order.

Each compartment was divided into two or three levels. These designations are added to the end of the compartment abbreviation. They are:

UL	Upper Level
ML	Middle Level
LL	Lower Level
	So, OPSML is the Operations Compartment, Middle Level and RCLL is the Lower Level of the Reactor Compartment.
AEA	Auxiliary Electrician Aft, roving watch that assists with electrical equipment all over the boat, particularly in the engineering spaces, stood by a nuclear-trained EM
AEF	Auxiliary Electrician Forward, roving watch that assists with interior communications equipment and some electrical equipment forward of the engineering spaces, stood by a non-nuclear trained EM or IC
AMS	Auxiliary Machinery Space, divided into two levels
AMSUL	stands watch in AMSUL, tends the reactor controls electronics stood by a nuclear-trained ET
AMSLL	stands watch in AMSLL, tends the steam generator feed systems and various reactor plant mechanical systems, maintains water chemistry on the steam generators, stood by a nuclear-trained MM (usually an ELT)
BC	Bow Compartment, divided into two levels
Blowdown Station	special watch stationed as needed to blow-down (remove water from) the steam generators, often stood by ERS, AMSLL, or other nuclear-trained MM
Charging Station	special watch stationed as needed to add water to the reactor plant, often stood by the ERS, AMSLL or other nuclear-trained MM

COW   Chief of the Watch, controls ship's trim, or balance, compressed air, and hydraulic systems, stood by a senior, non-nuclear enlisted man

DCPO   Duty Chief Petty Officer, in-port supervisory watch (enlisted), responsible for running the duty section, stood by a senior non-nuclear enlisted man

Discharge
Station   special watch stationed as needed to drain water from the reactor plant, often stood by the ERS, AMSLL, or other nuclear-trained MM

DOOW   Diving Officer of the Watch, supervises planesmen and COW to maintain ordered depth and course, stood by a senior non-nuclear enlisted man or a junior officer

EDPO   Engineering Duty Petty Officer, the shutdown equivalent of the EWS, stood by a senior nuclear-trained enlisted man

EDO   Engineering Duty Officer, the shutdown equivalent of EOOW, stood by a junior nuclear-trained officer

ELT   Engineering Laboratory Technician, responsible for maintaining reactor plant water chemistry and performing routine and special radiological controls, stood by a nuclear-trained MM who has attended additional training (14 weeks) at ELT school

EO   Electrical Operator, operates the electrical plant from the EPCP, stood by a senior nuclear-trained EM

EOOW   (usually pronounced "E-Ow") Engineering Officer of the Watch, supervises the overall operation of the engineering spaces, particularly in Maneuvering, stood by a nuclear-trained junior officer

EPCP   electric plant control panel, panel from which electric plant and associated equipment was monitored and operated

ER   Engineroom, divided into two levels

ERLL   stands watch in ERLL, tends the lube oil, seawater, condensate, and evaporator systems, stood by a nuclear-trained MM

ERS   Engineroom Supervisor, supervises ERUL and ERLL, assists as needed anywhere in the engineering spaces, stood by a senior nuclear-trained MM

ERUL   stands watch in ERUL, tends the turbines, stood by a nuclear-trained MM

EWS   (usually pronounced "E-Whiz") Engineering Watch Supervisor, the senior-most enlisted engineering watch, supervises operations in the engineering spaces, helps coordinate the actions of non-Maneuvering watchstanders, stood by a senior nuclear-trained enlisted man

Feed station   special watch stationed during certain evolutions, reactor plant start-up and shut-down, responsible for maintaining steam generator water levels in the program band, stood by any nuclear-trained MM

FRV (or feed
reg valves)   feedwater regulation valves, controlled by SGWLCP ("squiggle"), open and shut automatically to control feed water flow to the generators, maintaining steam generator water level at the desired level

ME ("mains")   main engines, turbines that turned the shaft, which turned the screw, pushing the boat through the water

MFP	main feed pumps, large pumps that took low-pressure water from the condensate system and raised pressure enough to add it to the steam generators
OOD	Officer of the Deck, operates the submarine, stood by department heads and junior officers who have graduated from EOOW
OPS	Operations Compartment, divided into three levels
RC	Reactor Compartment
RO	Reactor Operator, operates the reactor plant from the RPCP, stood by a senior nuclear-trained ET
RPCP	reactor plant control panel, panel from which reactor and associated equipment was monitored and operated
SDO	Ship's Duty Officer, in-port supervisory watch (officer), in-port equivalent of OOD, stood by junior officers who have graduated from EDO
SEO	Shutdown Electrical Operator, roving watch that monitors electrical systems when plant is shutdown in port, stood by a junior EM or ET
SG (called "generators")	steam generator, made steam for turbines by running hot reactor coolant through tubes, heating steam plant water to create steam
SGWLCP (called "squiggle")	steam generator water level control panel, automatically controlled water level in the steam generators to keep from flooding the moisture separators or boiling the generators dry
SPCP	steam plant control panel, panel from which throttles and steam plant were operated and maintained
SRO	Shutdown Reactor Operator, monitors shutdown reactor plant, stood by a senior nuclear-trained ET or EM
SRW	Shutdown Roving Watch, monitors mechanical systems when plant is shutdown in port, stood by a nuclear-trained MM
SSMG (or MG)	ship's service motor generator, converted AC power to DC and DC to AC for greater reliability of the electrical plant
SSTG (or TG)	ship's service turbine generator, provided electrical power to ship at sea
TH	Throttleman, operates the steam plant and throttles, stood by a junior EM or ET

Rates found on submarines

MM	Machinist Mate	**QM**	Quartermaster
EM	Electricians Mate	**YN**	Yeoman
ET	Electronics Technician	**RM**	Radioman
FT	Fire Control Technician	**TM**	Torpedoman
ST	Sonar Technician	**SK**	Storekeeper
HM	Corpsman	**MS**	Mess specialist
IC	Interior Communications Electrician		
ELT	Engineering Laboratory Technician (rated as an MM with additional training)		

Warfare designations

SS designates qualification in submarine warfare (called "ship's quals")
SW designates qualification in surface warfare

MILITARY RANKS

Enlisted

Grade	Abbreviation	Name (collar device showing rank)
E1	(SR)	Seaman (or Fireman) recruit (single slanted stripe)
E2	(SA)	Seaman (or Fireman) apprentice (two slanted stripes)
E3	(SN)	Seaman (or Fireman) (three slanted stripes)
E4	(PO3)	Petty Officer Third Class (single chevron under an eagle)
E5	(PO2)	Petty Officer Second Class (two chevrons under an eagle)
E6	(PO1)	Petty Officer First Class (three chevrons under an eagle)
E7	(CPO)	Chief Petty Officer (anchor)
E8	(SCPO)	Senior Chief Petty Officer (anchor with a single star)
E9	(MCPO)	Master Chief Petty Officer (anchor with a double star)

Rank and rate are usually combined by putting the rate first followed by the rank designation and the warfare specialty (if earned), so a first-class MM qualified in submarines would be MM1/SS and a master chief QM would be QMCM/SS.

Officers

Grade	Abbreviation	Name (collar device showing rank)
O1	(ENS)	Ensign (single gold bar)
O2	(LT JG)	Lieutenant Junior Grade (single silver bar)
O3	(LT)	Lieutenant (double silver bars)
O4	(LCDR)	Lieutenant Commander (gold oak leaf)
O5	(CDR)	Commander (silver oak leaf)
O6	(CAPT)	Captain (silver eagle)
O7		Commodore (1 star, wartime rank only)
O8	(RADM)	Rear Admiral (2 stars)
O9	(VADM)	Vice Admiral (3 stars)
O10	(ADM)	Admiral (4 stars)

Appendix C: Working around radiation and nuclear reactors

I SUPPOSE one thing that I ought to discuss somewhat is the fact that I was working around a nuclear reactor, some nuclear weapons, and with radiation on a continual basis. And, in fact, I continue to work with radiation and radioactivity, more than ten years later. It's probably a good idea, too, to explain why this didn't particularly worry me or my shipmates much, especially given the increasingly vocal paranoia and uninformed panic-mongering spread by anti-nuclear activists.

To start with, I should state up front that I am neither for nor against nuclear power. I am in favor of the military use of nuclear reactors because they serve a very specific purpose for which there is not now any viable substitute. Specifically, we need to have submarines that can operate unde-tected near potentially hostile parts of the world for long periods of time. The only way to do this is to put a nuclear reactor in a submarine. As far as the commercial nuke plants go, data from the US EPA seems to show that they put less radioactivity into the environment than coal, oil, or gas power plants do, and their safety record is at least as good as that of fossil-fueled power plants. On the other hand, increasingly stringent regulations coupled with the US penchant for building each plant slightly differently has made nuclear power much more expensive than it ought to be. In any event, as I said before, I am neither pro-nor anti-nuke, and really didn't feel strongly either way while in the Navy. I'll also state outright that I've never worked for a commercial nuclear power plant or for any of the nuclear weapons facilities.

That being said, I also have to admit that I never really had any concerns about the levels of radiation I was exposed to while in the Navy. Part of the reason is that, in Nuclear Power School (a six-month school required of all nukes) we had some pretty extensive education about the effects of exposure to radiation. Going through the information we were given, I realized that the most exposure I was allowed to receive in a year was not much more than people in some parts of the world receive from back-ground radiation. My assumption was that radiation is radiation, whether it comes from rocks, cosmic rays, or nuclear reactors, so it just wasn't worth getting upset about the dose I'd receive in the nuclear power program. So this predisposed me to not worry. To be honest, it never occurred to me to question the veracity of the information given to us by the Navy. They had no reason to lie to us, especially not about something that could be easily checked, and they really had a good record of giving us nothing but truthful information about all aspects of nuclear power.

One of the biggest surprises to me was finding out the magnitude of radiation dose from natural sources we receive. All told, we are exposed to about a milliRem daily from things like radon, cosmic rays, and natural radioactivity in the rocks and soil. We even receive radiation from naturally radioactive potassium in our bodies, not to mention from naturally-occurring tritium and carbon 14. All told, background radiation adds up to about 360 milliRem per year.

To that, we can add the dose we got from the reactor. Believe it or not, operating at sea with the reactor running, our exposure went down for everyone except the ELTs. This is because we were underwater, shielded from all sources of radiation except for the potassium in our bodies, the reactor, and our nuclear weapons. Running at a high bell, radiation levels might be five to ten milliRem per hour in the reactor compartment tunnel or at the bulkhead in the Machinery Space. But, more than a meter or so from the bulkhead or anywhere forward of the reactor compartment, rad levels were too low to measure. So we had three watchstanders exposed to these rad levels; AMSUL, AMSLL, and the ELT. And those three watches were asked to minimize their time near the bulkhead when possible.

The highest radiation dose came when we were shut down, because that's when we'd enter the Reactor Compartment for maintenance. But, even then, rad exposure just wasn't that bad. We did a rad survey during the initial RC entry and would post rad levels on a map at the entrance to the RC. Any work to be done was reviewed with the workers to make sure they knew areas to avoid, and they were given strict stay times and dose limits. Anyone approaching their dose limit was ordered out of the RC immediately. And our local exposure limits were far lower than the legal limit of 5 rem per year (the legal limit for radiation workers).

In fact, after eight years in the Navy, including more RC entries than I care to remember, I received less than 1500 millirem. When you consider that I received about 500 mr less background exposure by being at sea, submerged, it's obvious that I was not used as a rad sponge during my time in the Navy.

Something else that was encouraging was some reports I came across about radiation workers. It seems that groups of radiation workers studied showed similar or lower cancer rates than similar populations who were exposed to only background radiation levels. Similarly, the lowest-dosed groups of people near Hiroshima, Nagasaki, Chernobyl, and people in areas of high natural background radiation levels don't seem to have any higher rates of cancer than the general population. All of this made me realize that the radiation I was exposed to from the reactor was not going to kill me or give me cancer. I may get cancer, but if I do, the odds that it will not be the result of my work with radiation, nuclear reactors, or (for a short time) around nuclear weapons.

The other thing I didn't really worry much about was our reactor melting down or blowing up. Commercial reactors are able to melt down, as was shown at Three Mile Island. But they can't blow up. At least, not with a nuclear explosion. It's not physically possible because the uranium isn't highly enriched in the isotope that bombs are made of. And, even at TMI, the containment structures worked as designed and virtually no radioactivity made it into the environment. I'm not sure what the highest dose was, but it was lower than what I'd expect to receive in a year, and that was dose to workers. The public received much less dose; almost too low to measure.

Anyhow, our reactor was designed so that we would really have to work hard to damage the core, so the chances of a core melt were pretty low. We had an emergency cooling system to remove heat from the reactor, so as long as we kept water in the core we had it made. And, to make sure we kept water in the core, we had all sorts of valves to isolate leaking parts of the system, plus a number of ways to add water to keep the core covered if some of the isolation valves leaked by. I think that the best indication as to the difficulty of damaging the reactor is that, when we ran drills that included damage to the reactor, the scenarios were so contrived and unlikely that the first reaction was disbelieving laughter. In fact, there were times that the drill monitors had to intervene to keep us from taking our immediate actions in order to force a situation in which the core might be damaged. In short, this was not something I lost a lot of sleep over. Added to this was the fact that the Navy had a nearly flawless safety record. Our training, drills, and reactor plant design made us the single best-run nuclear power program in the world, something we were justifiably proud of (if I may say so without sounding too self-congratulatory).

Finally, there's the issue of releasing radioactivity to the environment. All nuclear reactors do release some radioactivity during their normal operations, and we were no different. But we did what we could to minimize this. First and foremost, we were strictly prohibited from discharging with 50 miles of any land. The Quartermaster informed the OOD when we passed the 50 mile line and the OOD told the EOOW. All discharges, even outside of 50 miles were filtered to remove the maximum amount of particulate and dissolved radioactivity, and whenever possible, we discharged to our onboard retention tanks (OBRTs) to store the water for radioactive decay before discharging them to the sea or to shore-side facilities. And we had discharge limits that were pretty strict. In fact, all nuclear ships in the Navy, discharging at their annual limits, put less radioactivity into the oceans than is created naturally in just a few minutes by cosmic ray bombardment in the upper atmosphere. In case you're wondering, cosmic rays striking the atmosphere create radioactive tritium and carbon 14 at the rate of tens of thousands of curies daily. By comparison, we put only a few millicuries per year into the oceans. By way of further comparison, patient drink up to a few hundred millicuries of radioactive iodine to help cure thyroid cancer, suffering no increase in cancer risk from this treatment. The bottom line is that the biggest source of radioactivity (with the exception of Chernobyl and the now-banned nuclear weapons testing) is Nature.

The risk of receiving a radiation dose of 100 mrem per year is about one in ten thousand. In other words, you can expect that one person will die for every ten thousand exposed to this level of radiation at work. That makes working with radiation about as risky as working as a secretary and bleeding to death from paper cuts and it's far safer than working as a farmer, miner, or in industrial settings. And, I should add, this is based on the most conservative model for radiation exposure. In other words, the model used for these numbers is more likely to predict more problems than actually exist. Believe it or not, the risk from driving is a lot greater.

The bottom line for me is that I have never worried about the radiation exposure I received, either in the Navy or post-Navy. I never had any reason to believe it was going to hurt me and I still don't believe it will, even with the much greater knowledge of the topic that I now have. I have spent (as of 2001) nearly 20 years working around radiation, radioactivity, nuclear reactors, and some stints on contaminated sites, near nuclear weapons, and on uranium enrichment facilities, and I just have better things to worry about than the piddling amounts of radiation I received.

Appendix D: History of Ships Named Plunger

Excerpted from documents in the US Naval Archives

USS Plunger (SSN 595) was the third ship of the Navy named in commemoration of the first submarine authorized for the US Navy. The first submarine torpedo boat was authorized by the US Congress in the Act of 3 March 1893. This was the original *Plunger* which was contracted for with the Holland Torpedo Boat Company on 13 March 1895. This boat was never accepted and the contract was cancelled in April 1900, the amount previously appropriated toward her construction was credited on a new contract of 19 November 1900. This new contract was for a new *Plunger* (SS 2), payment being made out of the appropriation of 1893 in the amount of $200,000.

The original *Plunger* was built by the Columbian Iron Works of Baltimore, Maryland. This firm was a subcontractor for the J.P. Holland Torpedo Boat Company. Her keel was laid 23 June 1896 but she was never accepted by the Navy. Her designed complement was 1 officer and six men; designed depth 75 feet, surface speed 15 knots, submerged speed at a six hour rate of 8 knots. She was to be armed with two 18-inch torpedo tubes and to carry 5 torpedoes.

The first *Plunger* (SS 2) was built at the Crescent Shipyard, Elizabethport, NJ, subcontractor for the Holland Torpedo Boat Company. Her keel was laid 21 May 1901 and she was launched 1 February 1902 under the sponsorship of Miss Ernestine Wardwell of Baltimore, Maryland. The second submarine of the US Navy, *Plunger*

Boat	SS-1	SS-2	SS-179	SSN-595
Commissioned	1895 (ordered)	1902	1936	1962
Length	85 ¼ feet	63' 10"	300' 7"	278 feet
Beam	11 ½ feet	11' 11"	25' 1"	31 feet
Draft	11 feet	10' 7"	13' 10"	26 feet
Displacement (submerged)	168 tons	123 tons	1997 tons	4400 tons
Crew (officers)	1	1	5	12
Crew (enlisted)	6	6	45	120
Speed (surface)	15 kts	15 kts	19 kts	>20 kts
Speed (submerged)	8 kts	8 kts	9 kts	>20 kts
Depth	75 feet	75 feet	250 feet	>400 feet
Tubes	2	1	6	4 amidships
Weapons	5 torpedoes	5 torpedoes	7 deck guns	12 torpedoes 24 torpedoes and missiles
Power plant	Steam	Diesel-electric	Diesel-electric	Nuclear

(SS 2) was commissioned at the Holland Company dock, New Suffolk, Long Island on 19 September, 1903, LT Charles P. Nelson in command.

Theodore Roosevelt was the first president of the United States to dive in a submarine, and it was *Plunger* who had the honor of satisfying his determination to see this comparatively new naval weapon of defense at work. Though the president was advised by some against taking what they considered a risky venture, he was set on making a dive. When asked, the CO declared that diving in *Plunger* was as safe as riding a trolley car, and on Friday, 25 March 1905, *Plunger* came into Oyster Bay for a rendezvous with a launch from the presidential yacht Slyph. President Roosevelt, dressed in oilskins, high rubber boots, and a visored cap, came on board at 3:30 PM. *Plunger* made a series of dives during the next few hours, dove to the bottom of Long Island Sound, and returned to drop off the President at 6:10 PM. Following this excursion, President Roosevelt was so impressed that he authorized $1 per dive for every submariner in the Navy.

Plunger (SS 2) arrived in the Charlestown Navy Yard on 4 November 1909 under the command of Ensign Chester W. Nimitz, who placed her in reserve. *Plunger* was stricken from the Navy List of Ships on 24 February, 1913, used for target practice, and sold for scrap on 26 January, 1922.

The second *Plunger* (SS 179) was built by the Portsmouth Navy Yard in Portsmouth, New Hampshire. She was launched on 8 July 1936 under the sponsorship of Miss Edith Greenlee and was placed in commission on 19 November 1936. Following her shakedown cruises and a series of port calls, *Plunger* reported to San Diego on 24 November 1937.

On 7 December 1941, on her way into Pearl Harbor, *Plunger* heard of the Japanese attack and had her first encounter with the enemy an hour later when she was strafed from the air. She was quickly dispatched on war patrol, leaving on the 14th. *Plunger*, *Gudgeon*, and *Pollack* became the first three US submarines to invade the waters of the Japanese Empire, about 3400 miles away.

During this patrol, *Plunger* sustained the first depth charge attack by a US submarine, dodging two dozen depth charges before evading the attacking destroyer. On the 18th she sunk her first victim, the 4700 ton *Eizan Maru*. *Plunger* left her patrol area on 20 January, 1942 and returned to Pearl Harbor on 4 February. Eighteen months and five war patrols later, *Plunger* joined *Lapon* and *Permit* in the first wartime penetration of the Sea of Japan.

This mission was particularly hazardous as there were only four entrances into the Sea of Japan, two of which were mined and one of which was in Russian waters. The fourth, the Straits of La Perouse, was frozen for much of the year, was dangerously shallow, and was often subject to thick fogs. Nonetheless, all three boats made the transit and began waging war on the Japanese merchant fleet that had previously operated with impunity in these waters.

Over the course of the war, *Plunger* made a total of 12 war patrols, sinking a total of 16 ships and earning 13 battle stars. She served as a Submarine Reserves training vessel from 1946 until 1956, when she was stricken from the Naval Register of Ships. She was sold for scrap on 22 April, 1957 to the Bethlehem Steel Company.

Appendix E: A mother's view of a dependents' cruise

> **Note:** The recent collision of the USS *Greenville* with the *Ehime Maru*, a Japanese fishing training vessel has focused much attention on the practice of offering rides to civilians on Naval vessels. We conducted two sets of dependents' cruises during my time on *Plunger*; my mother and a friend went with us on one and two other friends on the other. In the civilian world, most of us can take our loved ones to our workplace to show them how we spend our time, but this is not possible on a naval ship. True, visitors can come aboard when the ship is in port, but it's simply not the same thing. Most of the crew were married and had children, and most of them spent nearly three quarters of their time away from home, at sea. Showing families what that at-sea time was like was necessary, if only to help them understand a little better what their husband, father, or son was doing so much of the time. Many of the evolutions we performed were fun, but they were also deadly serious. High speed turns felt like a carnival ride, and helped us avoid torpedoes. Emergency blows were fun, too, and were our only chance of survival if we started to flood.
>
> What follows is my mother's account of the dependents' cruise she went on with us, written shortly afterwards.

According to the Beatles, it should have been yellow. In my case, it was black and I only lived in it for five hours. That was enough for me to have a feel for life on a US Navy nuclear submarine.

Towards the end of May, 1987 my son called and told me that his boat (apparently submarines are called boats, ships are much larger) was having a dependents' cruise in a month. Would I like to go? In spite of my claustrophobia and tendency to get seasick (both of which worried me, given the nature of the upcoming adventure), I decided this was the opportunity of a lifetime that I simply could not pass up. Aside from Disneyworld (which I assumed was a little different) I did not personally know any other civilian who had gone on a submarine ride. I quickly purchased a non-refundable plane ticket to San Diego to I would not chicken out, and told Andy to have some Dramamine ready for me.

Andy met me at the airport on July 1, the day before the cruise, and told me I was scheduled for the first cruise, leaving at 8 AM (and here I thought I was on vacation). He picked me up at 6:30 to be at the pier by 7:30. This barely gave us time for our traditional McDonald's breakfast, something that has preceded many momentous events (Ohio State football games, ski trips, our visit to the Grand Canyon). I was nervous, had not eaten much of my breakfast, and hoped I would behave "admirably" on this mission. At this point, you must understand that I'm basically a surface-of-the-earth type of person. Being either above or below just seems to be defying some kind of natural law.

While waiting for the boat to return from a two-day exercise, my Good Angel of the West appeared in the form of a Chief Petty Officer, asking if I got seasick (Andy's note: MMC/SS Greg Hauser – our M-Div chief). With his help, I received a small pink tablet and an assurance that I would not get sick now. What a promising omen! The next omen was seeing the submarine pull in, looking quite seaworthy. I had thought it would be gray instead of black, and I was also surprised at how little of it was out of the water (like an iceberg).

There were about fifty of us waiting on the pier; wives, sweethearts, children, parents, and friends. We were given a brief preview of events by one of the officers and then crossed over to the submarine to the hatch. The top of the boat was round, and we walked about 50 feet or so to a small, round opening with a ladder going straight down into the boat. The ladder looked like one of those things on the side of a water tank, and watching people descend was like seeing the boat suck them down inside. They just disappeared from sight. When my turn came, I gripped the slippery sides of the ladder, held on for dear life, and cautiously made my way to the bottom, feeling and looking for every single rung. It seemed to take several minutes, although it was probably less than one to make it ten feet down. The crew, of course, scampers up and down, even carrying heavy loads, as if it were child's play, sometimes not even using their hands but, instead, leaning back to rest against the wall (I'm sorry – bulkhead) behind the ladder.

Feeling very proud of myself for making it down without falling, I was sure that nothing else would be as difficult. I was wrong, of course, but I felt satisfied. From the bottom of the ladder, we were assembled in the crew's mess, which was four tables with benches on both sides, each bench seating three people. Obviously, everyone on board does not eat at once! This room also serves as the entertainment center, holding a TV, stereo, and coffee pot. Behind the mess was a tiny galley – smaller than an apartment kitchen, where the cooks prepare food for over 130 men.

In the mess, we were welcomed, given some information about the boat, and given some safety procedures, including the use of a mask in case of a "casualty". It reminded me of an airplane trip, and my mind immediately started imagining the worst; I wondered if it was too late to go ashore. The most important directions, though, were the proper way to flush the toilet. I hadn't expected it to be much different than a regular toilet, and I was wrong again. Turn a valve, let some water in, pull a big heavy lever, push the big heavy lever after everything is flushed, let some more water in – I'm sure I left something out. The considerate toilet flusher leaves a little bit of water in the bowl for the next person. I actually learned to flush properly, but I also decided to limit my intake of fluids!

After this introduction we were free to explore most of the boat. Unfortunately, I could not visit the engineering spaces, where Andy works, because they are off-limits to anyone without a security clearance, but I did see the rest of the boat. I decided to stop in the sonar room, to try to figure out what all the lines meant on the screens. Believe it or not, I ran into a former student of mine. How amazing to find him on this particular boat, with a crew of only 130 or so men! Brad spent some time teaching me – telling me what all the different lines and sounds meant.

My initial impression of the sub was narrow, compact, and utilitarian. There was NO wasted space anywhere onboard; people who design subs should consider a second career designing efficiency apartments. The needs of the boat are the highest priority with personal needs secondary. So storage space is built around the boat's equipment. A small space in front of a pipe becomes a storage space for books, tools, or parts. Aisles contain bunks, and in the torpedo room, skids that do not hold weapons instead hold more bunks (imagine sleeping with a room full of torpedoes – I was afraid to ask who slept in the tubes). To accommodate the perpetual cup of coffee so beloved by sailors, cup holders were scattered liberally through the boat.

It was impossible for me to not be in the way, no matter where I stood. The aisles were about as wide as the aisle on a small passenger plane. Two people could not stand directly opposite each other in the aisles, and had to turn sideways to pass. Everywhere I looked, things were anchored down, fastened into cabinets, or otherwise secured from accidentally falling. Even the cabinet and locker doors latched shut, to keep them from opening accidentally.

After this, I went to the berthing area to see where the men slept. Since some of the crew are on duty at all times, each man does not necessarily have his own "rack", so fewer racks are needed. The sleeping space was tiny, and surrounded by a curtain to give some degree of privacy. Being a concerned and protective mother, I made Andy lay down and turn over, just to prove he could fit (he's 6'3" tall). How he humors me! Luckily, there was nobody else around to see him.

Going up to the control room, I found a space full of screens, dials, knobs, and charts with two periscopes in the middle. Since we had not yet submerged, I looked through the periscope, and the view was exactly the way I had seen it in the movies. This surprised me! I was also surprised to be able to see another submarine not far away, going out to sea. Around me, I could tell the control room was a very busy place – it is in constant communication with the rest of the boat and there was a continual talking, none of which made any sense to me at all.

My next big opportunity was when the Captain asked if anyone wanted to drive the sub. Of course I did! The steering wheel is somewhat smaller than that of a car, and the boat responded quite quickly to the slightest turn of the wheel. The helmsman told me that it responded even more quickly at high speeds. Luckily, I just had to go in a straight line and didn't have to worry about our depth, so I only had to watch two dials. Wisely, the regular driver stayed right next to me, watching the dials intently and making sure I didn't do anything wrong.

When we finally submerged, aside from a slight forward angle, I felt nothing. It was quite smooth and, once underwater, I felt no motion at all. At times I forgot I was underwater and imagined I was in a tunnel or inside Hoover Dam. I was disappointed, though, that there were no windows to look out – perhaps I'll suggest that to the Navy.

After submerging it was time for maneuvers. This involved doing some up and down angles. We were all warned that they were coming and to hold on tightly. The boat dove steeply, leveled off, and then rose sharply at an angle. I saw why everything (including the three drivers) was securely fastened down! I hung on to Andy and to any machinery that I hoped was tightly bolted down, and still had trouble staying on my feet. I survived, though, and decided to take a small break (food, but no liquids).

Soon, it was time to resurface and head home. Prior to surfacing, the area was scanned to make sure no boats were in the immediate area. Once we reached periscope depth, one of both scopes were continuously manned, making 360° observations. Andy had told me I should try to go to the bridge at the top of the submarine once we surfaced. They allowed two dependents up at a time, and they had to come down before the next two could go up. The bridge is small – three people can fit comfortably into it, and others stand on the planes to either side of the "sail" or even up on top of the sail itself, behind the bridge cockpit.

When it was my turn to go up, I took a look at how I would get there. It was another slippery ladder, twice as high as the one into the boat, straight up into a black tunnel. The space between some of the rungs was too large for my short legs, meaning I'd have to step on a slippery hatch rim in order to make it. With sunlight streaming into the darkness, it seemed even farther up [Andy's note – the sail rises about 12 feet above the deck of the boat, so the ladder is nearly 20 feet high]. Climbing up, however, was not the worst part; that was having to face climbing down again. I gave up my spot in line.

However, sitting there, I watched older men, older women, children, and others go up and come back down. They even looked happy! I finally convinced myself that I simply had to make the climb, and sooner rather than later because I knew that Andy wouldn't be in the Navy forever. So I got back into line, to find it seemed to have stopped moving. We were getting closer to shore, and I was afraid that I'd never make it to the front of the line again. Luckily, my turn finally came, but I made the other person go ahead of me so she could encourage me and give directions. I hung on for dear life and slowly made my way up to the top of the boat.

Emerging into the sail I felt on top of the world. The wind was blowing gently, the sun was shining, and we were gliding into the harbor on smooth gentle water. What a feeling and what a view! I could not even feel the boat moving. Since nobody else was in line, I stayed on the bridge the rest of the way in, watching the crew below getting the boat ready for docking and watching the people on shore get bigger.

We finally made it in and tied up, and I had to face reality – it was time to climb back down the ladder, alone. I somehow made it, inching my way down slowly and hanging on tightly again. After that, I certainly did not fear the ladder up and out – that would be a snap!

I am sure that the entire time the dependents were on the boat, we were in the way, and I know that the men would have been ashore if it weren't for us. Yet every single man was kind, courteous, and willing to help in any way possible. I'm guessing, though, that they had some good laughs at our expense once we left.

I stepped ashore – I had made it! I had not gotten sick, I hadn't embarrassed my son, and I had not crashed the boat. Actually, I'd had a grand time, and I now had a much better appreciation and understanding of what Andy does and how he lives on a submarine. It really helps to be able to visualize the boat when he's talking about it and what he does onboard. I also have a great admiration for the men who serve on a submarine. It is a totally different existence than life on land, and I feel fortunate that there are those who will choose to do this voluntarily for the benefit of all of us. No day, no night, no windows, no sun or moon, no rain or snow – they must live at sea as though they are suspended in time and space. Frankly, I'll choose to stay ashore.

Appendix F: Recommended Reading

THERE ARE MANY WORTHY BOOKS about submarines, submarining, and sea-faring. I haven't read a large fraction of them. Of the ones I have read, I recommend these as my personal favorites.

Diesel boats in World War II

Clear the Bridge, Richard H. O'Kane (outstanding book about the WWII boat, Tang, by her skipper)

Silent Victory, Clay Blair (THE history of the WWII submarine war in the Pacific)

The Terrible Hours, Peter Maas (a compelling, true story about rescuing the crew of the diesel boat, *Squalus*

Nuclear submarines

Around the World Submerged, Edward Beach (a former diesel and nuclear submarine skipper - all of his books are good)

Blind Man's Bluff, Sherry Sontag and Christopher Drew (my favorite book about submarines)

Hostile Waters, Peter Huchthausen, Igor Kurdin, and Alan White (Russian boomer off the coast of the US with reactor problems)

Spy Sub, Roger Dunham (a great story and the only other submarine book written from an enlisted man's point of view)

The Silent War, John Craven, another outstanding book about submarine intelligence operations during the Cold War

The Navy Times Book of Submarines: A Political, Social, and Military History, Brayton Harris, Berkeley Books, 1997 (one of the most comprehensive histories of submarines written)

The Hunt for Red October, Tom Clancy (perhaps the best novel written about submarines)

United States Navy Naval Submarine Force Information Book, James Christley (the most comprehensive resource about US boats from the very first until the present)

Seafaring

Two Years Before the Mast, Richard Henry Dana (written nearly 200 years ago, this may well be the single best book ever written about going to sea; parts of it ring true even on a nuclear submarine)

Sailing Alone Around the World, Joshua Slocum (a personal account of the first solo voyage around the world, extremely well-written and engaging)

Any of Patrick O'Brien's novels in the series about Jack Aubrey and Stephen Maclaurin – they are probably the finest series of novels ever written about the sea

Web Pages

www.subshipstore.com
www.navy.mil

Best-selling titles by Kerry B. Collison

Readers are invited to visit our publishing websites at:

http://www.sidharta.com.au

http://www.publisher-guidelines.com/

http://temple-house.com/

Kerry B. Collison's home pages:

http://www.authorsden.com/visit/uthor.asp?AuthorID=2239

http://www.expat.or.id/sponsors/collison.html

http://clubs.yahoo.com/clubs/asianintelligencesresources

email: author@sidharta.com.au

Also from Sid Harta Publishers

OTHER BEST SELLING SID HARTA TITLES CAN BE FOUND AT
http://www.sidharta.com.au
http://Anzac.sidharta.com

✳ ✳ ✳

HAVE YOU WRITTEN A STORY?
http://www.publisher-guidelines.com
for manuscript guideline submissions

✳ ✳ ✳

LOOKING FOR A PUBLISHER?
http://www.temple-house.com

New Releases...